COLLOQUIA MATHEMATICA
SOCIETATIS JÁNOS BOLYAI, 11.

Colloquium on Limit Theorems of Probability and Statistics, Keszthely, Hungary, 1974.

LIMIT THEOREMS OF PROBABILITY THEORY

Edited by:

P. RÉVÉSZ

NORTH HOLLAND PUBLISHING COMPANY
AMSTERDAM-LONDON

ISBN North-Holland: 0 7204 2834 3

Joint edition published by

JÁNOS BOLYAI MATHEMATICAL SOCIETY

and

NORTH-HOLLAND PUBLISHING COMPANY

Amsterdam-London

Technical editors:

P. BÁRTFAI and LIDIA REJTŐ

Printed in Hungary

ÁFÉSZ, VÁC

Sokszorosító üzeme

PREFACE

This volume contains the papers presented at the "Colloquium on Limit Theorems of Probability Theory and Statistics" organized by the Bolyai János Mathematical Society and held in Keszthely from 24 to 29 June, 1974.

Choosing only a special area of Probability and Statistics, we intended to bring together mathematicians who are really interested in, and appreciate and understand the problems of each other. It is, however, quite difficult to define the bounderies of this topic. Indeed, in a sense, it covers nearly all the Theory of Probability and Statistics. In order to illustrate what we had in mind when talking about limit theorems, the following special sessions were organized:

Invariance principle
Limit properties of order statistics
Limit theorems on stochastic approximation
Limit theorems of independent random variables and martingales
Limit theorems for dependent random variables
Limit theorems of abstract valued random variables

We tried to find speakers in only these subjects and, to a large extent, we have succeeded in doing so. However, a separate session was organized to accomodate a number of speakers whose talks, though strictly related to limit theorems, could not be classified under any of the above sections.

As a result of the relatively restricted nature of the Colloquium, there was an excellent scientific and personal contact throughout, and many new friendships were established in these days. The importance of these new contacts is underlined by the fact that of the 78 attendants of the Colloquium 33 came from abroad, representing 13 different countries: Austria, Belgium, Bulgary, Canada, Denmark, GBR, Great Britain, Japan, The Netherlands, Poland, Sovietunion, Sweden, USA.

Excellent scholars, mostly from abroad, were asked to organize the 6 special sessions. The respective chairmen and organizers of these sessions were:

G. Tusnády
M. Csörgő
L. Schmetterer
M. Zolotarev
W. Philipp
H. Heyer

These chairmen had complete freedom as to how to organize their sessions. Some of them gave expository talks, others invited a number of excellent speakers but, whatever it was they decided to do, all did a lot for the succes of the Colloquium. Our sincere thanks and appreciation to go herewith to them.

We also wish to express our special thanks to Professor L. Schmetterer for his warm words at the Closing Banquet of the Colloquium. He said: "This was the first Meeting in Probability Theory in Hungary after the death of Professor Rényi. If Rényi could have seen this Meeting he would have been very proud of his School, which more than proved its strength after the serious loss of its leader."

We, the Organizing Committee, could not have hoped to achieve more than that.

P. Révész (Chairman)
Mrs. L. Rejtő (Secretary)

CONTENTS

SCIENTIFIC PROGRAM

June 24. 1974

3.00 p.m. Opening ceremony

3.30 p.m. J. Komlós – P. Major – G. Tusnády: An approximation of partial sums of independent RV's and the sample DF

Session of INVARIANCE PRINCIPLE
Chairman: G. Tusnády

5.00 p.m. J. Mijnheer: Functional law of the iterated logarithm for completely asymmetric stable processes

5.30 p.m. D. Szász: On a random invariance principle

6.00 p.m. H. Walk: An invariance principle for a non-randomized thinning of a renewal process

June 25. 1974

Session of LIMIT PROPERTIES OF ORDER STATISTICS
Chairman: M. Csörgő

9.00 a.m. M. Csörgő – P. Révész: Some notes on the empirical distribution function and the quantile processes

9.50 a.m. E. Csáki: Some notes on the law of the iterated logarithm for empirical distribution function

10.30 a.m. A.A. Balkema – L. de Haan: Limit distributions for the sequences of order statistics

11.00 a.m. K. Sarkadi: On the convergence of the expectation of the empirical quantile

11.30 a.m. W. Philipp: A conjecture of Erdős and Gaal on uniform distribution mod 1 of lacunary sequences

4.00 p.m. P. Gaenssler: Around the Glivenko – Cantelli theorem

4.30 p.m. S. Csörgő: Some remarks on the empirical process and the asymptotic expansion of the von Mieses statistic

5.15 p.m. B. Gyires: On limit distribution theorem of linear order statistics

5.45 p.m. R.-D. Reiss: The joint asymptotic normality of several order statistics

June 26. 1974

Session of LIMIT THOEREMS IN STOCHASTIC APPROXIMATION
Chairman: L. Schmetterer

9.00 a.m. L. Schmetterer: Some relations between the theory of summability and the theory of stochastic approximation

9.50 a.m. M.B. Nevel'šon: On asymptotically optimal recursive estimate of a functional of an unknown distribution function

Session of LIMIT THEOREMS OF INDEPENDENT RANDOM VARIABLES AND MARTINGALES
Chairman: M. Zolotarev

10.30 a.m. P. Bártfai: On the multivariate Chernoff theorem

11.00 a.m. A. Gut: Weak convergence for first passage time processes

11.35 a.m. J.L. Teugels – N. Veraverbeke: On the approach to the limit of successive maxima of partial sums

12.05 a.m. W. Vervaat: Strassen's iterated logarithm law for i.i.d. Hilbert space valued random variables

Chairman: V. Statulevicius

10.30 a.m.	Yu. Beljaev: Probability methods for detection of effects
11.10 a.m.	J. Tomkó: A limit theorem for rarefying multivariate point processes
11.50 a.m.	B.N. Dimitrov: A limit theorem for nonnegative random variables
12.10 a.m.	T. Nemetz: On a theorem of S. Kakutani

Juni 27. 1974

Session of LIMIT THOEREMS FOR DEPENDENT RANDOM VARIABLES

Chairman: W. Philipp

9.00 a.m.	S. Takahashi: Probability limit thoerems for trigonometric series
9.30 a.m.	H. Oodaira: Some functional laws of the iterated logarithm for dependent random variables
10.00 a.m.	W. Philipp: Almost sure invariance principles for sums of dependent random variables, I
11.00 a.m.	W.F. Stout: Almost sure invariance principles for sums of dependent random variables, II
11.40 a.m.	I. Berkes: Some result for lacunary series
4.00 p.m.	G. Halász: Two problems on random functions
4.30 p.m.	V. Statulevicius: On limit theorems for dependent random variables under different conditions of regularity
5.00 p.m.	G.J. Székely: On polynomials of independent random variables
5.30 p.m.	V. Zolotarev: New types of mixing conditions for sequences of dependent random variables
6.10 p.m.	A. Szép: Moment inequalities and almost everywhere convergence

Chairman: Yu. Beljaev

4.00 p.m. B.S. Koroljuk – A. Turbin: Some methods of linear operators perturbed on spectra and its application to limit theorems in the theory of probability

4.40 p.m. I.A. Ibragimov – R.Z. Has'minskii: On the properties of statistical estimates which are valid with probability 1

5.20 p.m. M. Arató: Limit thoerems in optimal CPU scheduling

Juni 28. 1974

Session of LIMIT THEOREMS OF ABSTRACT VALUED RANDOM VARIABLES

Chairman: H. Heyer

9.00 a.m. H. Heyer: Gauss distribution and central limit theorem for locally compact groups

10.30 a.m. J. Klasa: Limit thoerems and Bohr compactification

11.00 a.m. V.M. Zolotarev: Some properties of metrics in spaces of probability measures and applications in limit theorems

11.40 a.m. T. Byczkowski: The notion of variance on compact semigroups

LIST OF PARTICIPANTS

ARATÓ, M., Res. Inst. of Comp. and Automat. Sci., Budapest XI, Kende u. 13-17, Hungary

BÁRTFAI, P., Math. Inst. Hung. Acad. Sci., Budapest V, Reáltanoda u. 13-15, Hungary

BELIAEV, I.K., Moskovskii Univ., Moscow V-234, USSR

BERKES, I., Math. Inst. Hung. Acad. Sci., Budapest V, Reáltanoda u. 13-15, Hungary

BINGHAM, N.H., Westfield College, Kidderpove Avenue, London N.W. 3, GB

BOGNÁR, KATALIN, Univ. Eötvös, Math. Inst., Budapest VIII, Múzeum krt. 6-8, Hungary

BYCZKOWSKI, L., Math. Inst. Polish Acad. Sci., Ul. Kopernika 57, Wroclaw, Poland

CSÁKI, E., Math. Inst. Hung. Acad. Sci., Budapest V, Reáltanoda u. 13-15, Hungary

CSÁKI, P., Res. Inst. of Comp. and Automat. Sci., Budapest I, Uri u. 49, Hungary

CSÖRGŐ, M., Dept. Math., Carleton Univ., Colonel by Drive, Ottawa K1S 5B6, Canada

CSÖRGŐ, S., Univ. A. József, Szeged, Aradi vértanuk tere 1, Hungary

DIMITROV, B.N., Inst. Math. Mech., Sofia, Bulgary

ENGER, J., Uppsala Univ., Dept. Math., Sysslomansgatan 8, 75223 Uppsala, Sweden

FÖLDES, ANTÓNIA, Math. Inst. Hung. Acad. Sci., Budapest V, Reáltanoda u. 13-15, Hungary

FRITZ, J., Math. Inst. Hung. Acad. Sci., Budapest V, Reáltanoda u. 13-15, Hungary

GAENSSLER, P., Ruhr-Univ. Bochum, Math. Inst., Buscheystr., 463 Bochum, GBR

GULYÁS, O., National Meteorological Institute, Budapest II, Kitaibel Pál u. 1, Hungary

GUT, A., Uppsala Univ., Dept. of Math., Sysslomansgatan 8, 75223 Uppsala, Sweden

GYIRES, B., Kossuth L. University, Debrecen 10, Hungary

GYŐRFI, L., Res. Inst. Telecommunication, Budapest II, Gábor Áron u. 65, Hungary

de HAAN, L., School of Economics, Burgemeester Oudlaan 50, Rotterdam 3016, The Netherlands

HALÁSZ, G., Math. Inst. Hung. Acad. Sci., Budapest V, Reáltanoda u. 13-15, Hungary

HALÁSZ, SZILVIA, 1121 Budapest, Költő u. 2-4/b, Hungary

HASMINSKII, R., Z., Inst. Problem Pered. Inform. A.N. SSSR, ul. Aviamotornaia 8, k.2, Moscow, USSR

HEYER, H., Math. Inst. Univ. Tübingen, Auf der Morgenstelle 10, 74 Tübingen, GBR

HORÁNYI, ANNA, National Bureau for Planning, Budapest V, Arany János u. 6, Hungary

HORVÁTH-GAUDI, I., Res. Inst. of Comp. and Automat. Sci., Budapest XI, Kende u. 13-17, Hungary

KLASA, JACQUELINE, Univ. Ottawa, Dept. Math., 58 5 King Edward Ave., Ottawa K1N 6N5, Canada

KOMLÓS, J., Math. Inst. Hung. Acad. Sci., Budapest V, Reáltanoda u. 13-15, Hungary

KOROLJUK, V.S., Inst. Mat. A.N. SSSR, pl. Kalininia 6. Kiev, USSR

LUKÁCS, P., Res. Inst. of Comp. and Automat. Sci., Budapest XI, Kende u. 13-17, Hungary

MAJOR, P., Math. Inst. Hung. Acad. Sci., Budapest V, Reáltanoda u. 13-15, Hungary

MAROSI, JUDIT, Res. Inst. of Comp. and Automat. Sci., Budapest I, Uri u. 49, Hungary

MIJNHEER, J., Univ. Leiden, P.O.B. 20 60, Leiden, The Netherlands

MÓRICZ, F., Univ. A. József, Szeged, Aradi vértanuk tere 1, Hungary

NAGY, ROZÁLIA, Univ. Kossuth Lajos, Debrecen 10, Hungary

NEMETZ, T., Math. Inst. Hung. Acad. Sci., Budapest V, Reáltanoda u. 13-15, Hungary

NEVELSON, M.B., Inst. Problem Pered. Inform. A.N. SSSR., ul. Aviamotornaia 8, k.2. Moscow, USSR

OODAIRA, H., Yokohama Nat. Univ., Dept. Appl. Math., Yokohama, Japan

PALÁSTI, ILONA, Math. Inst. Hung. Acad. Sci., Budapest V, Reáltanoda u. 13-15, Hungary

PFANZAGL, J., Math. Inst. Univ. Köln, Weyertal 86, 5 Köln 41, GBR

PHILIPP, W., Dept. Math., Univ. Illinois, Urbana, IL 61801, USA

POLLARD, D.B., Mat. Inst., Universitetsparken 5, 2100 Copenhagen Ø, Denmark

REISS, D.-R., Math. Inst. Univ. Köln, Weyertal 86-90, 5 Köln 41, GBR

REJTŐ, LIDIA, Math. Inst. Hung. Acad. Sci., Budapest V, Reáltanoda u. 13-15, Hungary

RÉVÉSZ, KLÁRA, Telecommunic. Inst. Hung. Radio, Budapest V, Akadémia u. 17, Hungary

RÉVÉSZ, P., Math. Inst. Hung. Acad. Sci., Budapest V, Reáltanoda u. 13-15, Hungary

ROTZEN, H.L., Dept. Math., Stat. Univ. Lund, Box 725, S-22007 Lund, Sweden

RUDA, M., Res. Inst. of Comp. and Automat. Sci., Budapest I, Uri u. 49, Hungary

SARKADI, K., Math. Inst. Hung. Acad. Sci., Budapest V, Reáltanoda u. 13-15, Hungary.

SCHMETTERER, L., Math. Inst. Univ., Strudlhofgasse 4, Wien IX, Austria

STATULEVICIUS, V.A., Inst. Fiz. Mat. A.N. Lit. SSR, ul. K. Pozelos 52, Vilnius, USSR

STOUT, W.F., The Univ. of North Carolina at Chapel Hill, Dept. Stat., Chapel Hill NC 27514, USA

SULYOK, M., Math. Inst. Hung. Acad. Sci., Budapest V, Reáltanoda u. 13-15, Hungary

SZÁDECZKY KARDOSS, G., Budapest V, Münnich Ferenc u. 20. Hungary

SZÁNTÓ, GY., Budapest XVI, Varga J. u. S/5.b, Hungary

SZÁSZ, D., Math. Inst. Hung. Acad. Sci., Budapest V, Reáltanoda u. 13-15, Hungary

SZEIDL, L., Res. Inst. of Comp. and Automat. Sci., Budapest XI, Kende u. 13-17, Hungary

SZÉKELY, G., Math. Inst. Hung. Acad. Sci., Budapest V, Reáltanoda u. 13-15, Hungary

SZÉKELY, J.G., Univ. Eötvös, Math. Inst., Budapest VIII, Múzeum-krt. 6-8, Hungary

SZÉP, A., Math. Inst. Hung. Acad. Sci., Budapest V, Reáltanoda u. 13-15, Hungary

SZILLÉRI, ÉVA, Res. Inst. Telecommunication, Budapest II, Gábor Áron u. 65, Hungary

SZLANKA, I., Budapest II, Budai László u. 4, Hungary

TAKAHASHI, S., Dept. Math. Kanazawa Univ, Marunouchi 1-1, Kanazawa, Japan

TEUGELS, L., Wiskundig Inst. KU. L., Celestijnenlaan 200B, 3030 Heverlee, Belgium

TOMKINS, R.J., Univ. Saskatchewan, Regina Sask., Canada

TOMKÓ, J., Res. Inst. of Comp. and Automat. Sci., Budapest XI, Kende u. 13-17, Hungary

TØPSØE, F., Mat. Inst., Universitetsparken 5, 2100 Copenhagen Ø, Denmark

TÓTH, BEÁTA, Res. Inst. of Comp. and Automat. Sci., Budapest I, Uri u. 49, Hungary

TÓTH, J., Group for Computing of Semmelweiss Medical Univ., Budapest VIII, Üllői út 22, Hungary

TUSNÁDY, G., Math. Inst. Hung. Acad. Sci., Budapest V, Reáltanoda u. 13-15, Hungary

VERVAAT, W., Inst. Appl. Math., Univ. Amsterdam, Roeterstraat 15, Amsterdam, The Netherlands

VETIER, A., Technical University, Budapest XI, Budafoki út 4, Hungary

WALK, H., Univ. Stuttgart, Math. Inst., A. 7 Stuttgart N, Herdweg 23, GBR

WEFELMEYER, W., Math. Inst., Univ. Köln, Weyerthal 86, 5 Köln 41, GBR

ZIELINSKI, R., Inst. Math. Polish Acad. Sci., Sniadeckich 8, 00-950, Warsaw, Poland

ZIERMANN, MARGIT, National Bureau for Planning, Budapest V, Arany János u. 6, Hungary

ZOLOTAREV, V.M., Mat. Inst. A.N. SSSR, ul. Vavilova 40, Moscow V-333, USSR

COLLOQUIA MATHEMATICA SOCIETATIS JÁNOS BOLYAI
11. LIMIT THEOREMS OF PROBABILITY THEORY, KESZTHELY (HUNGARY), 1974.

LIMIT LAWS FOR ORDER STATISTICS

A.A. BALKEMA – L. de HAAN

Suppose $X_1, X_2, \ldots$ are independent, identically distributed (i.i.d.) real-valued random variables with common distribution function F. Let $X_{k,n}$ be the kth order statistics among $X_1, \ldots, X_n$ $(1 \leqslant k \leqslant n$, $n = 1, 2, 3, \ldots)$. Now let $k = k(n)$ be a sequence of integers $(1 \leqslant k(n) \leqslant n)$. What are the possible limit distributions of $X_{k(n),n}$ as $n \to \infty$, i.e. for which distribution functions F is it possible to select real constants $a_n > 0$ and b_n such that

$$(1) \qquad \frac{X_{k(n),n} - b_n}{a_n} \to V$$

in distribution as $n \to \infty$ where V is not constant?

For the uniform distribution on $(0, 1)$ the answer has been given by Smirnov [4]. Let $U_1, U_2, \ldots$ be i.i.d. random variables, uniformly distributed and let $U_{k,n}$ be the kth order statistics among $U_1, \ldots, U_n$. Take $k = k(n)$, $n \to \infty$. If $k(n)$ is constant then $nU_{k,n} \overset{\mathcal{D}}{\to} \sum_{i=1}^{k} Y_i$, where

$\xrightarrow{\mathcal{D}}$ means convergence in distribution and Y_i are i.i.d. exponential $(i = 1, \ldots, k)$.

Also if $n - k(n)$ is constant then $n(U_{k,n} - 1) \xrightarrow{\mathcal{D}} \sum_{i=1}^{n-k} Y_i$. If $k(n) \to \infty$ and $n - k(n) \to \infty$ then

$$\frac{U_{k,n} - \frac{k}{n}}{\sqrt{\frac{k}{n}\left(1 - \frac{k}{n}\right)\frac{1}{n}}} \xrightarrow{\mathcal{D}} U$$

a random variable with the standard normal distribution. In the sequel we shall write μ_n for $\frac{k(n)}{n}$ and σ_n for $\sqrt{\frac{\mu_n(1 - \mu_n)}{n}}$. From now on we restrict ourselves to the non-extreme-value case, i.e. we require

(2) $\qquad k(n) \to \infty \quad$ and $\quad n - k(n) \to \infty \quad$ as $\quad n \to \infty$.

Now let F be an arbitrary distribution function. Then it is well known that the X_n are distributed like $f(U_n)$ where f is an inverse function to F. Hence the X_{k,n_2} are distributed like $f(U_{k,n})$ and since $U_{k,n}$ is asymptotically normal $N(\mu_n, \sigma_n)$ for our purposes we may replace $U_{k,n}$ by $\sigma_n U + \mu_n$ and we find that (1) holds with V distributed like $\varphi(U)$ if and only if

$$\frac{f(\sigma_n y + \mu_n) - b_n}{a_n} \to \varphi(y)$$

weakly on R (Smirnov [4], part I, Lemma 2).

This reduces the original problem to a problem of real analysis. It turns out that every random variable can occur as a limit in (1). In fact we can prove a stronger result.

Theorem 1. *There exists a distribution function F with the following property: for each distribution function G and each $p \in [0, 1]$, there is a sequence of integers $k(n)$ satisfying* (2) *such that* $\lim_{n \to \infty} \frac{k(n)}{n} = p$ *and such that the distribution of $X_{k(n),n}$ properly normed converges* *weakly to* G.

From this it follows that we need some regularity condition on the sequence $k(n)$ in order to obtain a non-trivial theory. We call a sequence of integers $k(n)$ with $1 \leqslant k(n) \leqslant n$ *regular* if it satisfies (2) and

(3) $$k(n+1) - k(n) = o(\min(\sqrt{k(n)}, \sqrt{n - k(n)})) .$$

The following results are known. Smirnov [4] requires that there exists a number $p \in (0, 1)$ such that

(4) $$t = \lim_{n \to \infty} \sqrt{n}\left(\frac{k(n)}{n} - p\right)$$

exists and is finite. This condition implies that $k(n)$ is regular. The possible limit random variables under (4) are given by $\varphi(U)$ with

(5) $$\varphi(x) = \begin{cases} b + a_1(x - x_0)^\rho & x \geqslant x_0 \\ b - a_2(x_0 - x)^\rho & x < x_0 . \end{cases}$$

Here $b \in R$; $a_1 + a_2 > 0$; $\rho, a_1, a_2 \geqslant 0$ and $x_0 = \dfrac{t}{\sqrt{p(1-p)}}$.

Remark. The class (5) includes the normal limit distribution ($\rho = 1$, $a_1 = a_2$).

Chibisov [3] requires that $\dfrac{k(n)}{n} \to 0$ like $n^{\alpha - 1}$ with $0 < \alpha < 1$ in such a way that $\sqrt{k(n+r)} - \sqrt{k(n)} \to \alpha lc$ whenever $r = r(n) \sim cn^{1 - \frac{\alpha}{2}}$ as $n \to \infty$. This condition implies that $k(n)$ is regular. The possible limit random variables in Chibisov's case are $\varphi(U)$ with

$$\varphi(x) = b + ax$$

(6) $$\varphi(x) = b + ae^{\lambda x}$$

(7) $$\varphi(x) = b - ae^{-\lambda x}$$

Here $b \in R$; $a, \lambda > 0$. Smirnov and Chibisov give a complete characterization of the domains of attraction of the different limit distributions. Additional results can be found in Smirnov [5], [6] and Cheng [2].

We can prove the following

Theorem 2. *If* (1) *holds and* $k(n)$ *is regular then* $V = \varphi(U)$ *in distribution with* U *normal* $N(0, 1)$ *and* φ *one of the functions in* (5), (6) *or* (7).

The proof of this theorem is a straightforward application of results in Balkema [1]. Next we turn to the domain of attraction problem in this general situation. A complete answer can be given in case the limiting distribution is not normal. We assume throughout that the sequence $k(n)$ is regular.

Theorem 3. *If the limit random variable* V *has the form* $\varphi(U)$ *with* φ *as in* (5) *and* V *is not normal, then there exists* $p \in (0, 1)$ *and* t *such that* (4) *holds; hence Smirnov's characterization of the domains of attraction applies.*

An analogue of (4) in case of a lognormal limit distribution (6) and (7) is the following.

Theorem 4. *If the limit random variable* V *has the form* $\varphi(U)$ *with* φ *as in* (6) *or* (7), *then* $\frac{k(n)}{n} \to p+$ *or* $p-$ *as* $n \to \infty$ *with* $p \in [0, 1]$. *There exists a positive function* Ψ *such that* $\Psi(p+) = \Psi'(p+) = 0$ *(or* $\Psi(p-) = \Psi'(p-) = 0$, *respectively),* $\frac{\Psi(x)}{x(1-x)}$ *monotone and such that*

$$\frac{\Psi\left(\frac{k(n)}{n}\right)}{\sqrt{\frac{k(n)}{n}\left(1 - \frac{k(n)}{n}\right)}} \sim \frac{1}{\sqrt{n}} \quad \text{as} \quad n \to \infty .$$

The following theorem gives a characterization of the domain of attraction of a lognormal distribution. The results are different for $\lambda > 0$ and $\lambda < 0$ and for $p = 0$, $0 < p < 1$, $p = 1$. As an example we pick the case $\lambda > 0$ and $p = 0$.

Theorem 5. *If the limit random variable* V *has the form* $V = b + ae^{\lambda U}$ *with* $a, \lambda > 0$ *and* $\frac{k(n)}{n} \to 0$ *as* $n \to \infty$, *then* F *is con-*

tinuous at its lower endpoint $x_0 = \inf\{x: F(x) > 0\}$, x_0 *is finite and* F *satisfies*

$$(8) \qquad \lim_{t \downarrow 0} \frac{F(x_0 + tx) - F(x_0 + t)}{F(x_0 + te) - F(x_0 + t)} = \log x$$

for all positive x; *moreover the function* $\rho(t) = \sqrt{F(x_0 + te)} - \sqrt{F(x_0 + t)}$ *is asymptotic to a non-decreasing functions as* $t \downarrow 0$. *Conversely if* x_0 *is finite,* F *is continuous at* x_0, F *satisfies* (8) *and* ρ *is asymptotic to a non-decreasing function then* (1) *holds with* $V = b + ae^{\lambda U}$ *for some regular sequence* $k(n)$.

A complete version of this paper with full proofs will appear elsewhere. That version also includes a number of results not mentioned here, e.g. concerning the domain of attraction of the normal distribution. However, the problems related to the normal limit distribution have only be partly solved to date.

REFERENCES

[1] A.A. Balkema, Monotone Transformations and Limit Distributions, Math. Centrum (Amsterdam).

[2] B. Cheng, The Limiting Distributions of Order Statistics, *Acta Math. Sinica,* 14 (1964), 694-714 (translation in *Chinese Mathematics,* 6 (1965), 84-104).

[3] D.M. Chibisov, On Limit Distributions for Order Statistics, *Theory Prob. and Its Applications,* 2 (1964), 142-148 (English translation).

[4] N.V. Smirnov, Limit Distributions for the Terms of a Variational Series, *Amer. Math. Soc. Transl.*, Ser. 1, no. 67 (Original published in 1949).

[5] N.V. Smirnov, Convergence of Distributions of Order Statistics to the Normal Distribution, *Izv. Akad. Nauk. Uz SSR,* 10 (1966), 24-32 (in Russian).

[6] N. V. Smirnov, Some Remarks on Limit Laws for Order Statistics, *Theory Prob. and Its Applications,* 12 (1967), 337-339 (English translation).

COLLOQUIA MATHEMATICA SOCIETATIS JÁNOS BOLYAI
11. LIMIT THEOREMS OF PROBABILITY THEORY, KESZTHELY (HUNGARY), 1974.

ON THE ASYMPTOTIC BEHAVIOUR OF $\sum f(n_k x)$

I. BERKES

1. INTRODUCTION

Let $f(x)$ $(-\infty < x < \infty)$ be a measurable function such that

$$(1.1) \qquad f(x+1) = f(x), \quad \int_0^1 f(x)\,dx = 0, \quad \|f\|^2 = \int_0^1 f^2(x)\,dx < +\infty .$$

The asymptotic properties of the sequence $f(n_k x)$ for rapidly increasing sequences n_k of integers have been investigated by many authors. In particular, it has been proved (see [8]) that for any fixed f satisfying (1.1) there exists a sequence n_k such that the sequence $f(n_k x)$ imitates the properties of independent random variables in a very strong sense. If f satisfies certain smoothness conditions, one can also give estimates for the rate of growth of the sequence n_k implying this "independent-like" behaviour. For instance, if f satisfies the Lipschitz condition then $\frac{n_{k+1}}{n_k} \to \infty$ guarantees that $f(n_k x)$ obeys the central limit theorem and the law of iterated logarithm (see [10], [21]). Here $\frac{n_{k+1}}{n_k} \to \infty$ cannot be replaced by the weaker condition

$$(1.2) \qquad \frac{n_{k+1}}{n_k} \geqslant q > 1 \qquad (k = 1, 2, \ldots)$$

even for very smooth functions f: a simple example shows that for any given q (arbitrary large) there exists a trigonometric polynomial f and a sequence n_k satisfying (1.2) such that the sequence $f(n_k x)$ fails to satisfy the central limit theorem. A deeper examination of the problem shows that in the case when only (1.2) is assumed, the asymptotic behaviour of $f(n_k x)$ is strongly influenced by the arithmetical properties of the sequence n_k. For instance, the independent-like behaviour holds if $n_k = a^k$ ($a \geqslant 2$ is integer) but can fail if $n_k = a^k - 1$. Similarly, we have the independent-like behaviour if $\frac{n_{k+1}}{n_k} \to \alpha$ where α^r is irrational for every integer $r \geqslant 1$. This phenomenon has been investigated profoundly by Gapoškin (see [9] and also [7]) who gave a necessary and sufficient condition at which the central limit theorem holds for $f(n_k x)$.

A sequence $m_1 < m_2 < \ldots$ of positive integers satisfies condition B_2 if the number of solutions of $m_k \pm m_l = \nu$ $(k > l)$ does not exceed a constant C for any $\nu > 0$.

Gapoškin's theorem states that if n_k satisfies (1.2) then the sequence $f(n_k x)$ obeys the central limit thoerem for all sufficiently smooth functions f (satisfying (1.1)) if and only if, for any $m \geqslant 1$, the set-theoretic union of the sequences $\{n_k\}, \{2n_k\}, \ldots, \{mn_k\}$ satisfies condition B_2.

The purpose of the present paper is to investigate the asymptotic properties of the sequence $f(n_k x)$ when only (1.2) is assumed. Though the central limit theorem does not necessarily hold for such sequences, we shall formulate positive results without any arithmetical restrictions on n_k.

Let us remark that the validity of the central limit theorem and the law of the iterated logarithm for the sequence $f(n_k x)$ mean that the asymptotic distribution and asymptotic order of magnitude of $\sum_{k=1}^{N} f(n_k x)$, $N \to \infty$ are the same as those of $\zeta(N)$, $N \to \infty$ where ζ is a standard Wiener-process. Set

$$\nu_{M,N}^{i,k} = 2^k \int_{i2^{-k}}^{(i+1)2^{-k}} \Big(\sum_{j=M+1}^{M+N} f(n_j x) \Big)^2 \, dx \, .$$

The main result of our paper states that if f is smooth enough, the sequence n_k satisfies (1.2) and $C_1 N \leqslant \nu_{M,N}^{i,k} \leqslant C_2 N$ holds for certain values of M, N, i, k (C_1, C_2 are positive constants) then the asymptotic behaviour of $\sum_{k=1}^{N} f(n_k x)$, $N \to \infty$ is like to that of $\zeta(\tau_N)$, $N \to \infty$. Here ζ is a standard Wiener-process and τ_N is a sequence of random variables, closely related to the quantities $\nu_{M,N}^{i,k}$. Hence the asymptotic behaviour of $\sum_{k=1}^{N} f(n_k x)$ is closely connected to that of the $\nu_{M,N}^{i,k}$'s. Using this fact, we can derive many limit theorems for the sequence $f(n_k x)$ both in the case when the sequence possesses an independent-like behaviour and in the case when this behaviour does not hold.

As a first application let us consider the case when the sequence n_k satisfies a certain arithmetical condition of Gapoškin type. Then, it can easily be seen that the quantities $\nu_{M,N}^{i,k}$ are asymptotically independent of i, k and thus τ_N is asymptotically constant. Hence, in this case the asymptotic behaviour of $\sum_{k=1}^{N} f(n_k x)$ is like to that of $\zeta(a_N)$ for a certain numerical sequence a_N. Donsker's invariance principle, Strassen's law of the iterated logarithm and Kolmogorov – Erdős – Petrovski type upper and lower class criteria for the sequence $f(n_k x)$ are typical corollaries of this fact. These results unify and extend several limit theorems obtained earlier in the literature.

As a second application we show that though the central limit theorem and the law of the iterated logarithm do not necessarily hold under condition (1.2), they are "nearly" satisfied if q is large. More exactly, if f is smooth enough and (1.2) holds then we have*

$$\overline{\lim_{N\to\infty}} \sup_{-\infty < t < +\infty} \Big| \mathsf{P}\Big(\sum_{k=1}^{N} f(n_k x) < \sigma t \sqrt{N} \Big) - \Phi(t) \Big| \leqslant \epsilon(q)$$

*In probabilistic statements concerning the sequence $f(n_k x)$ the probability space is the interval $[0, 1)$ with Lebesgue measure.

where $\sigma = \|f\|$ and $\epsilon(q) \to 0$ if $q \to \infty$. Similarly,

$$1 - \epsilon(q) \leqslant \overline{\lim_{N\to\infty}} \frac{1}{\sqrt{2\sigma^2 N \log\log N}} \sum_{k=1}^{N} f(n_k x) \leqslant 1 + \epsilon(q) \qquad \text{a.e.}$$

The functional versions of these results are also valid.

Thirdly, our results lead to interesting consequences even in the classical case $f(x) = \cos 2\pi x$ when we get an a.s. invariance principle under the mere condition (1.2).

It is an interesting fact that our results hold without the assumption that n_k are integers. It seems that for non-integral n_k even the central limit theorems and the laws of iterated logarithm implied by our results are new. We get, e.g., the interesting result that the sequence $f(q^k x)$ obeys the central limit theorem (in the sense of the footnote above) for any real $q > 1$ (for a related result see [19]).

The main results of our paper are contained in Section 2. In Sections 3-5 we give some applications of these theorems (which were already mentioned above). For the proofs we refer to [1]; the present paper is only a statement of results. The method of [1] was also used in [3] where we proved some a.s. invariance principles for mixing processes. Independently and at the same time, Philipp and Stout used a similar approach to get a.s. invariance principles for many classes of weakly dependent random variables; see their nice and exhaustive paper [15] or, for a shorter account, [16].

2. MAIN RESULTS

Before formulating our theorems we make several preliminary remarks.

Let $X_1, X_2, \ldots$ be a sequence of independent random variables on the probability space $(\Omega, \mathscr{F}, \mathrm{P})$ and put $S_n = \sum_{i=1}^{n} X_i$ $(S_0 = 0)$. The investigation of the asymptotic properties of the sequence S_n is a classical problem of probability theory. In [17], [18] Strassen developed a new and powerful method for approaching this problem. Namely, he proved that in certain cases it is possible to construct a Wiener-process $\zeta(t)$ such that the sequences S_n and $\zeta(n)$ are "near" to each other with probability one. Such an approximation theorem was called by him an "almost sure invariance principle" because a theorem of this type enables us to carry over many asymptotic properties of the Wiener-process in an unchanged form for the partial sums S_n. For instance, it is easy to see that if $S_n = \zeta(n) + o(n^{\frac{1}{2}-\eta})$ almost surely with a suitable Wiener-process $\zeta(t)$ and a constant $\eta > 0$ then the sequence $X_1, X_2, \ldots$ obeys not only the central limit theorem and the law of the iterated logarithm but also a larger class of stronger limit theorems including Donsker's invariance principle, the functional form of the law of the iterated logarithm, the Kolmogorov – Erdős – Petrovski integral test for functions of upper and lower classes etc. A typical result of Strassen states that if $X_1, X_2, \ldots$ are independent, identically distributed with $\mathsf{E}X_1 = 0$, $\mathsf{E}X_1^2 = 1$, $\mathsf{E}|X_1|^{2+\delta} < \infty$ $(\delta > 0)$ then there exists a new probability space $(\Omega', \mathcal{F}', \mathsf{P}')$, a sequence $X_1', X_2', \ldots$ of i.i.d. random variables and a Wiener-process $\zeta'(t)$ (all defined on $(\Omega', \mathcal{F}', \mathsf{P}')$) such that X_1 and X_1' have the same distribution and putting $S_n' = \sum_{i=1}^{n} X_i'$ we have $S_n' = \zeta'(n) + o(n^{\frac{1}{2}-\eta})$ for $n \to \infty$ with probability one where η is a positive constant depending on δ. The fact that here we approximate not the partial sums of the sequence $X_1, X_2, \ldots$ but a "copy" of it, makes no trouble in applications since if a sequence $Y_1, Y_2, \ldots$ (of arbitrary random variables) obeys, e.g., the law of the iterated logarithm then the same holds for every sequence $Y_1', Y_2', \ldots$ having the same finite dimensional distributions. Strassen also proved that similar results hold in the case when $X_1, X_2, \ldots$ is a martingale difference sequence. In the latter case, however, the approximation theorem has the slightly modified form $S_n = \zeta(\tau_n) + o(n^{\frac{1}{2}-\eta})$ a.s. where ζ is a Wiener-process and τ_n is a certain increasing sequence of random variables such that $\tau_n \to \infty$ a.s. In the present paper we shall formulate results of this type for the sequence $f(n_k x)$ which can be considered as a sequence of (dependent) random variables on the probability space $(\Omega_0, \mathcal{F}_0, \mathsf{P}_0)$ where $\Omega_0 = [0, 1)$, $\mathcal{F}_0$ is the class of measurable subsets of $[0, 1)$ and P_0 is the Lebesgue measure on $\mathcal{F}_0$.

Throughout our paper we shall assume the standard condition

(2.1) $\quad |f(x)| \leqslant M \quad$ and $\quad \|f - s_n\| \leqslant An^{-\alpha} \qquad (\alpha > 0,\ n = 1, 2, \ldots)$

where s_n denotes the n'th partial sum of the Fourier-series of f. The second relation of (2.1) can also be written as

(2.2) $$\frac{1}{2} \sum_{k=n+1}^{\infty} (a_k^2 + b_k^2) \leqslant A^2 n^{-2\alpha}$$

where

$$f \sim a_0 + \sum_{k=1}^{\infty} (a_k \cos 2\pi kx + b_k \sin 2\pi kx)$$

is the Fourier-expansion of f. Condition (2.1) holds e.g., if f satisfies the Lipschitz condition with exponent α (see [23] p. 241, formula (3.3)) or it is of bounded variation. (In the latter case we have $a_k = O\left(\frac{1}{k}\right)$, $b_k = O\left(\frac{1}{k}\right)$, hence (2.2) is valid with $\alpha = \frac{1}{2}$.)

Definition 1. Let $Y_1, Y_2, \ldots$ and $Z_1, Z_2, \ldots$ be two sequences of random variables defined on possibly different probability spaces. The two sequences will be called equivalent if their finite dimensional distributions coincide.

Definition 2. Let $Y_1, Y_2, \ldots$ and $Z_1, Z_2, \ldots$ be sequences of random variables on the probability spaces $(\Omega, \mathscr{F}, \mathrm{P})$ and $(\tilde{\Omega}, \tilde{\mathscr{F}}, \tilde{\mathrm{P}})$, respectively. We say that the two sequences are quasi-equivalent if there exist sequences $\hat{Y}_1, \hat{Y}_2, \ldots$ and $\hat{Z}_1, \hat{Z}_2, \ldots$ (defined on $(\Omega, \mathscr{F}, \mathrm{P})$ and $(\tilde{\Omega}, \tilde{\mathscr{F}}, \tilde{\mathrm{P}})$, respectively) such that $\sum_{k=1}^{\infty} |Y_k - \hat{Y}_k| < \infty$ a.s., $\sum_{k=1}^{\infty} |Z_k - \hat{Z}_k| < \infty$ a.s. and the sequences $\hat{Y}_1, \hat{Y}_2, \ldots$ and $\hat{Z}_1, \hat{Z}_2, \ldots$ are equivalent.

Now we can formulate our results.

Theorem (2.1). *Let us assume that*

(a) $f(x)$ *satisfies* (1.1) *and* (2.1),

(b) *the sequence* n_k *of positive numbers satisfies* (1.2),

(c) *there exist constants* $\sigma_2 > \sigma_1 > 0$ *such that for* $k \geq 1$, $0 \leq i \leq 2^k - 1$ *we have*

$$(2.3) \qquad \sigma_1 N \leq 2^k \int_{\frac{i}{2^k}}^{\frac{i+1}{2^k}} \Big(\sum_{j=M+1}^{M+N} f(n_j x) \Big)^2 dx \leq \sigma_2 N$$

provided that M, N *and* $\frac{n_M}{N 2^k}$ *are large enough.*

Then there exist a probability space $(\Omega, \mathscr{F}, \mathsf{P})$ *and a sequence* $X_1, X_2, \ldots$ *of random variables (defined on* $(\Omega, \mathscr{F}, \mathsf{P})$*) such that the sequences* $\{f(n_k x)\}$ *and* $\{X_k\}$ *are quasi-equivalent and*

$$(2.4) \qquad X_1 + \ldots + X_n = \zeta(\tau_n) + o(n^{\frac{1}{2} - \eta}) \qquad a.s. \text{ as } \quad n \to \infty$$

where $\eta > 0$ *is an absolute constant,* $\zeta(t)$ *is a Wiener-process on* $(\Omega, \mathscr{F}, \mathsf{P})$ *and* τ_n *is a strictly increasing sequence of positive random variables (defined on* $(\Omega, \mathscr{F}, \mathsf{P})$ *as well) such that* $\tau_n - \tau_{n-1} = O(1)$ *a.s. as* $n \to \infty$ *and*

$$(2.5) \qquad \sigma_1 \leq \liminf_{n\to\infty} \frac{\tau_n}{n} \leq \limsup_{n\to\infty} \frac{\tau_n}{n} \leq \sigma_2 \qquad a.s.$$

In applications we shall need also the following, somewhat more general form of Theorem (2.1).

Theorem (2.2). *Let us replace condition* (c) *of Theorem* (2.1) *by the following one:*

(c*) *there exist constants* $\sigma_2 > \sigma_1 > 0$ *such that for* $k \geq 1$, $0 \leq i \leq 2^k - 1$ *we have*

$$(2.6) \qquad \sigma_1 a_{M,N} \leq 2^k \int_{\frac{i}{2^k}}^{\frac{i+1}{2^k}} \Big(\sum_{j=M+1}^{M+N} f(n_j x) \Big)^2 dx \leq \sigma_2 a_{M,N}$$

provided that M, N *and* $\frac{n_M}{N2^k}$ *are large enough. Here* $a_{M,N}$ $(M \geq 0,$ $N \geq 1)$ *are positive numbers such that* $A_1 N \leq a_{M,N} \leq A_2 N$ $(M \geq M_0,$ $N \geq N_0)$ *with positive constants* A_1, A_2.

Then the conclusion of Theorem (2.1) *remains valid but instead of* (2.5) *we have now*

$$(2.7) \qquad \sigma_1 \leq \liminf_{n\to\infty} \frac{\tau_n}{b_n} \leq \limsup_{n\to\infty} \frac{\tau_n}{b_n} \leq \sigma_2 \qquad a.s.$$

where b_n *is a strictly increasing numerical sequence such that** $b_n \asymp n$.

The next theorem states, that replacing (2.3) by a stronger assumption, we have (2.4) with $\tau_n = \sigma n$.

Theorem (2.3). *Let us assume that*

(a) $f(x)$ *satisfies* (1.1) *and* (2.1),

(b) *the sequence* n_k *of positive numbers satisfies* (1.2),

(c) *there exists a constant* $\sigma > 0$ *such that for* $k \geq 1$, $0 \leq i \leq$ $\leq 2^k - 1$, $M \geq M_0$, $N \geq N_0$ *we have*

$$(2.8) \qquad 2^k \int_{\frac{i}{2^k}}^{\frac{i+1}{2^k}} \Big(\sum_{j=M+1}^{M+N} f(n_j x)\Big)^2 dx = \sigma N + O\Big(\frac{N2^k}{n_M}\Big)$$

where the constant in O *depends only on* $f(x)$ *and* q.

Then there exist a probability space $(\Omega, \mathscr{F}, \mathrm{P})$ *and a sequence* $X_1, X_2, \ldots$ *of random variables (defined on* $(\Omega, \mathscr{F}, \mathrm{P})$*) such that the sequences* $\{f(n_k x)\}$ *and* $\{X_k\}$ *are quasi-equivalent and*

$$(2.9) \qquad X_1 + \ldots + X_n = \zeta(\sigma n) + o(n^{\frac{1}{2} - \eta}) \qquad a.s. \quad as \qquad n \to \infty$$

*The symbols $a_n \sim b_n$ and $a_n \asymp b_n$ mean $\lim_{n\to\infty} \frac{a_n}{b_n} = 1$ and $0 < \liminf_{n\to\infty} \frac{a_n}{b_n} \leq$ $\leq \limsup_{n\to\infty} \frac{a_n}{b_n} < \infty$, respectively.

where $\zeta(t)$ *is a Wiener-process on* $(\Omega, \mathcal{F}, \mathrm{P})$ *and* $\eta > 0$ *is an absolute constant.*

Remarks.

1. Conditions (c) of Theorem (2.1) and Theorem (2.3) have the same nature: both require an estimate for the quantity

$$2^k \int_{\frac{i}{2^k}}^{\frac{i+1}{2^k}} \Big(\sum_{j=M+1}^{M+N} f(n_j x)\Big)^2 \, dx$$

provided that M, N and $\frac{n_M}{N2^k}$ are large enough. These conditions can slightly be weakened. In Theorem (2.1) it is sufficient to require that (2.3) holds if M, N and $\frac{n_M}{N^\gamma 2^k}$ are large enough where $\gamma > 0$ is a fixed constant. Similarly, the remainder term $O\Big(\frac{N2^k}{n_M}\Big)$ in (2.8) (and also in (2.10) below) can be replaced by $O\Big(\frac{N^\gamma 2^k}{n_M}\Big)$. The proofs of Theorems (2.1)-(2.3) (which are given in [1]) apply also under these conditions without change.

2. If the sequence $f(n_k x)$ satisfies condition (c) of Theorem (2.1) with some pairs (σ_1, σ_2) then we can choose a universal $\{X_n\}$, $\{\tau_n\}$ and ζ satisfying (2.4), (2.5) (and $\tau_n - \tau_{n-1} = O(1)$ a.s.) with all pairs (σ_1, σ_2). A similar remark holds for Theorem (2.2).

3. The proofs of our theorems yield an explicit estimate for the absolute constant η in (2.4) and (2.9). Actually, in [1] it is shown that (2.4) and (2.9) are valid with any constant $0 < \eta < \frac{1}{40}$. We could get slightly better estimates by more precise calculations and by some simple modifications of the argument but to find the best constant seems to be very difficult. In view of a recent result of Komlós, Major and Tusnády (see [12]) it is even possible that the remainder term $o(n^{\frac{1}{2}-\eta})$ in (2.4) and (2.9) can be replaced by $o(n^\epsilon)$ for any $\epsilon > 0$.

4. For the sequence b_n in Theorem (2.2) we have

$$A_1 \leqslant \liminf_{n\to\infty} \frac{b_n}{n} \leqslant \limsup_{n\to\infty} \frac{b_n}{n} \leqslant A_2 .$$

5. Let us replace condition (2.8) by

$$2^k \int_{\frac{i}{2^k}}^{\frac{i+1}{2^k}} \Big(\sum_{j=M+1}^{M+N} f(n_j x)\Big)^2 dx = a_{M,N} + O\Big(\frac{N2^k}{n_M}\Big) \tag{2.10}$$

where $a_{M,N}$ $(M \geqslant 0,\ N \geqslant 1)$ are positive numbers such that $A_1 N \leqslant$ $\leqslant a_{M,N} \leqslant A_2 N$ $(M \geqslant M_0,\ N \geqslant N_0)$ with positive constants A_1, A_2. Then the conclusion of Theorem (2.3) remains valid with the modification that $\zeta(\sigma n)$ in (2.9) is to be replaced by $\zeta(b_n)$ where b_n is a strictly increasing numerical sequence such that $b_n \asymp n$. (Actually $A_1 \leqslant \liminf_{n\to\infty} \frac{b_n}{n} \leqslant$ $\leqslant \limsup_{n\to\infty} \frac{b_n}{n} \leqslant A_2$.)

6. Theorem (2.1) remains valid if (2.3) is replaced by

$$\sigma_1 N \leqslant a^k \int_{\frac{i}{a^k}}^{\frac{i+1}{a^k}} \Big(\sum_{j=M+1}^{M+N} f(n_j x)\Big)^2 dx \leqslant \sigma_2 N$$

for a fixed integer $a \geqslant 2$. A similar remark applies to Theorems (2.2) and (2.3).

3. THE ASYMPTOTICALLY INDEPENDENT CASE

A sequence $n_1 < n_2 < \ldots < n_k < \ldots$ of positive numbers will be said an element of the class Λ^*, if $n_k \to \infty$ and, for every $m \geqslant 1$, the set-theoretic union of the sequences $\{n_k\}, \{2n_k\}, \ldots, \{mn_k\}$ (considered as a new sequence) satisfies the Hadamard gap condition. The purpose of the present section is to investigate the properties of the sequence $f(n_k x)$ provided that $\{n_k\} \in \Lambda^*$. We shall prove that in this case the random variables τ_n occuring in Theorem (2.2) become asymptotically constant and thus the asymptotic behaviour of $\sum_{k=1}^{N} f(n_k x)$ as $N \to \infty$ is like to that of $\zeta(b_N)$ with a certain numerical sequence $b_N \asymp N$. Donsker's invariance principle, Strassen's law of the iterated logarithm, Kolmogorov – Erdős – Petrovski type upper and lower class tests etc. for the sequence $f(n_k x)$ are typical corollaries of this fact. These results unify and extend several limit theorems obtained earlier in the literature by different methods. For instance, Corollary 2 of Theorem (3.1), if we specialize it to the ordinary law of the iterated logarithm and integral n_k, implies the theorem of [21], it yields some laws of the iterated logarithm similar to those stated in [7], Chap. 2 §4 without proof, etc. For non-integral n_k even the central limit theorems implied by our results seem to be new. (A theorem of this type was mentioned in the Introduction.)

The class Λ^* was introduced (for integral n_k) by Gapoškin. The following lemma is due to him as well.

Lemma (3.1). *The sequence* $\{n_k\}$ *of positive numbers belongs to class* Λ^* *if and only if there exist no subsequences* n_{k_i}, n_{s_i} *and rational number* $r \neq 0$ *such that*

$$\lim_{i\to\infty} \frac{n_{k_i}}{n_{s_i}} = r\,, \qquad \frac{n_{k_i}}{n_{s_i}} \neq r \qquad (i = 1, 2, \ldots)\,.$$

Lemma (3.1) shows that the sequence $\{n_k\}$ belongs to class Λ^* in each of the following cases:

1. $n_k = q^k$ ($q > 1$ is arbitrary real number).
2. $\dfrac{n_{k+1}}{n_k}$ is integer for any $k \geqslant 1$.
3. $\lim_{k\to\infty} \dfrac{n_{k+1}}{n_k} = \infty$.
4. $\lim_{k\to\infty} \dfrac{n_{k+1}}{n_k} = \alpha$ where α^r is irrational for $r = 1, 2, \ldots$.

We formulate now the main result of this Section.

Theorem (3.1). *Let us assume that*

(a) $f(x)$ *satisfies* (1.1) *and* (2.1),

(b) *the sequence* $\{n_k\}$ *of positive numbers belongs to class* Λ^*,

(c) *there exists a positive constant* C_1 *such that*

$$\int_0^1 \Big(\sum_{j=M+1}^{M+N} f(n_j x) \Big)^2 dx \geq C_1 N$$

for $M \geq 0$, $N \geq N_0$.

Then there exists a probability space $(\Omega, \mathscr{F}, \mathrm{P})$ *and a sequence* $X_1, X_2, \ldots$ *of random variables (defined on* $(\Omega, \mathscr{F}, \mathrm{P})$*) such that the sequences* $\{f(n_k x)\}$ *and* $\{X_k\}$ *are quasi-equivalent and*

$$X_1 + \ldots + X_n = \zeta(\tau_n) + o(n^{\frac{1}{2} - \eta}) \qquad \text{a.s. as} \qquad n \to \infty$$

where $\eta > 0$ *is an absolute constant,* ζ *is a Wiener-process on* $(\Omega, \mathscr{F}, \mathrm{P})$ *and* τ_n *is a strictly increasing sequence of random variables (also on* $(\Omega, \mathscr{F}, \mathrm{P})$*) such that* $\tau_n - \tau_{n-1} = O(1)$ *a.s. as* $n \to \infty$ *and*

$$\lim_{n \to \infty} \frac{\tau_n}{b_n} = 1 \qquad \text{a.s.}$$

with a strictly increasing positive numerical sequence $b_n = n$.

Corollary 1. *Let us assume that the conditions of Theorem* (3.1) *are satisfied and put* $S_N = \sum_{k=1}^{N} f(n_k x)$. *Then there exists a strictly increasing positive numerical sequence* $b_n \asymp n$ *such that**

$$\varphi_n \xrightarrow{\mathscr{D}} \zeta$$

where $\zeta(t)$ *is the Wiener-process in* $[0, 1]$ *and* $\varphi_n(t)$ $(0 \leq t \leq 1)$ *is the random function defined by***

*The symbol $\xrightarrow{\mathscr{D}}$ means weak convergence of continuous processes, for definition and properties see [5].

**We put $b_0 = 0$.

$$\varphi_n(t) = \begin{cases} \dfrac{S_k}{\sqrt{b_n}} & \text{for} \quad t = \dfrac{b_k}{b_n} \quad (k = 0, 1, \ldots, n), \\ \text{linear for} & t \in \left[\dfrac{b_k}{b_n}, \dfrac{b_{k+1}}{b_n}\right] \quad (k = 0, 1, \ldots, n-1). \end{cases}$$

To formulate Corollary 2 let K denote Strassen's set of functions

$$K = \Big\{x(t)\colon x(t) \text{ is absolutely continuous in } [0, 1], \\ x(0) = 0 \text{ and } \int_0^1 \dot{x}(t)^2\, dt \leqslant 1\Big\}. \tag{3.1}$$

Corollary 2. *Let us assume that the conditions of Theorem* (3.1) *are satisfied and put* $S_N = \sum_{k=1}^{N} f(n_k x)$. *Then there exists a strictly increasing positive numerical sequence* $b_n \asymp n$ *such that if* $\psi_n(t)$ $(0 \leqslant t \leqslant 1)$ *denotes the random function defined by*

$$\psi_n(t) = \begin{cases} \dfrac{S_k}{\sqrt{2b_n \log\log b_n}} & \text{for} \quad t = \dfrac{b_k}{b_n} \quad (k = 0, 1, \ldots, n) \\ \text{linear for} & t \in \left[\dfrac{b_k}{b_n}, \dfrac{b_{k+1}}{b_n}\right] \quad (k = 0, 1, \ldots, n-1) \end{cases}$$

then $\psi_n(t)$ *is relatively compact in* $C[0, 1]$ *with probability one and its derived set coincides with* K.

In particular,

$$\overline{\lim_{n \to \infty}} \frac{S_N}{\sqrt{2b_N \log\log b_N}} = 1 \quad a.e.$$

Corollaries 1 and 2 establish Donsker's invariance principle and Strassen's functional version of the law of the iterated logarithm for the sequence $f(n_k x)$.

Remark 1. Condition (b) of Theorem (3.1) requires that, for any $m \geqslant 1$, the set-theoretic union of the sequences $\{n_k\}, \{2n_k\}, \ldots, \{mn_k\}$ satisfies the Hadamard gap condition. If $f(x)$ happens to be a trigonometric polynomial of order L:

$$f(x) = \sum_{k=1}^{L} (a_k \cos 2\pi kx + b_k \sin 2\pi kx)$$

then it suffices to require this condition only for $m = L$.

Remark 2. For the sequences τ_n and b_n in Theorem (3.1) we stated $\lim_{n\to\infty} \frac{\tau_n}{b_n} = 1$ a.s. and $b_n \asymp n$. For certain special sequences $\{n_k\} \in \Lambda^*$ we can say more about τ_n and b_n. We mention two such cases.

(a) If $\frac{n_{k+1}}{n_k} \to \infty$ then we have $b_n \sim \|f\|^2 n$.

(b) If $n_k = a^k$ ($a \geqslant 2$ is integer) and $\sigma^2 \neq 0$ where*

$$\sigma^2 = \|f\|^2 + 2 \sum_{k=1}^{\infty} \int_0^1 f(x) f(a^k x)\, dx\,,$$

then we have $b_n \sim \sigma^2 n$ and moreover, we can choose $\tau_n = b_n$. From this fact it follows (see [18] pp. 337-338) that in this case the sequence $f(n_k x)$ obeys the Kolmogorov – Erdős – Petrovski integral test in the following form: Let $\varphi(t) > 0$ be an increasing function. Then the set of those $x \in [0, 1)$ for which the relation

$$\sum_{k=1}^{N} f(n_k x) > b_N^{\frac{1}{2}} \varphi(b_N)$$

holds for infinitely many N has Lebesgue-measure 0 or 1 according to the convergence or divergence of the integral

$$\int_1^{\infty} t^{-1} \varphi(t) \exp\left\{-\frac{1}{2}\varphi^2(t)\right\} dt\,.$$

Corollaries 1 and 2 follow from Theorem (3.1) in a standard way. On the other hand, Theorem (3.1) is an immediate consequence** of Theorem (2.2) and the following lemma which is not difficult to obtain.

*The series is absolutely convergent by a result of [11].

**See also Lemma (4.1) and Remark 2 after Theorem (2.3).

Lemma (3.2). *Let us suppose that the conditions of Theorem* (3.1) *are fulfilled and put*

$$a_{M,N} = \int_0^1 \Big(\sum_{j=M+1}^{M+N} f(n_j x) \Big)^2 dx \qquad (M \geq 0,\ N \geq 1)\,.$$

Then for any $0 < \epsilon < 1$ *there exists an* $\omega_0 = \omega_0(\epsilon)$ *such that for any* $M \geq 0,\ k \geq 1,\ 0 \leq i \leq 2^k - 1$ *we have*

$$(1-\epsilon)a_{M,N} < 2^k \int_{\frac{i}{2^k}}^{\frac{i+1}{2^k}} \Big(\sum_{j=M+1}^{M+N} f(n_j x) \Big)^2 dx < (1+\epsilon)a_{M,N}$$

provided that $N \geq N_0,\ \dfrac{n_M}{N2^k} \geq \omega_0$.

4. SOME ϵ-LIMIT THEOREMS

It is well known that the lacunarity condition

$$\frac{n_{k+1}}{n_k} \geq q > 1 \qquad (k = 1, 2, \ldots)$$

does not imply the central limit theorem and the law of the iterated logarithm for the sequence $f(n_k x)$ even if q is large and f satisfies strong smoothness conditions. This is shown, e.g., by an example of Erdős and Fortet (see [10])

(4.1) $\qquad f(x) = \cos 2\pi x + \cos 2\pi m x\,, \qquad n_k = m^k - 1\,.$

In this case we have*

$$\lim_{N\to\infty} \mathsf{P}\Big(\frac{1}{\sqrt{N}} \sum_{k=1}^{N} f(n_k x) < t \Big) = \frac{1}{\sqrt{2\pi}} \int_0^1 \int_{-\infty}^{\frac{t}{\sqrt{2}\,|\cos (m-1)\pi s\,|}} e^{-\frac{u^2}{2}}\, du\, ds$$

and

$^*\frac{t}{0}$ denotes $+\infty$, 0 and $-\infty$ according as $t > 0$, $t = 0$ and $t < 0$.

$$\overline{\lim_{N\to\infty}} \frac{1}{\sqrt{2N \log\log N}} \sum_{k=1}^{N} f(n_k x) = \sqrt{2} \cos(m-1)\pi x \qquad \text{a.e.}$$

Let us note, however, that for the function f in (4.1) the sequence $f(n_k x)$ satisfies both the central limit theorem and the law of iterated logarithm provided that $\{n_k\}$ satsifies

$$\frac{n_{k+1}}{n_k} > 2m \qquad (k = 1, 2, \ldots).$$

(For integral n_k this follows, e.g., from the results of [4], [13], the extension for non-integral n_k is also easy.) This gives us some hope that even if $f(n_k x)$ does not imitate the behaviour of independent random variables for a given f and q, the situation becomes better if we increase q (by keeping f fixed). In this section we shall see that this is really valid. As a matter of fact, it is not true that for any f (satisfying certain smoothness conditions) there exists a q_0 such that the sequence $f(n_k x)$ obeys the central limit theorem and the law of the iterated logarithm if $q \geqslant q_0$. We shall show, however, that the "deviation" from central limit and iterated logarithm behaviour of the sequence $f(n_k x)$ tends to 0 if $q \to \infty$ (and f is being kept fixed). The same holds for Donsker's invariance principle and Strassen's version of the law of iterated logarithm.

Theorem (4.1). *Let $f(x)$ satisfy (1.1) and (2.1). Then for any given $\epsilon > 0$ there exists a $q_0 = q_0(\epsilon, f)$ such that if $\{n_k\}$ satisfies (1.2) with $q \geqslant q_0$ then the following two statements hold (we put $S_N = \sum_{k=1}^{N} f(n_k x)$)*

$$\text{(a)} \quad \overline{\lim_{N\to\infty}} \sup_t \left| \mathsf{P}\left(\frac{S_N}{\sigma\sqrt{N}} < t\right) - \Phi(t) \right| \leqslant \epsilon$$

$$\text{(b)} \quad 1 - \epsilon \leqslant \overline{\lim_{N\to\infty}} \frac{S_N}{\sqrt{2\sigma^2 N \log\log N}} \leqslant 1 + \epsilon \qquad \textit{a.e.}$$

where $\sigma = \|f\| \neq 0$ ($\Phi(t)$ denotes the distribution function of the standard normal distribution).

The functional version of Theorem (4.1) can also be formulated. It is not evident, however, what to call the "functional version" of Theorem (4.1) i.e. how to define the notions "the sequence $f(n_k x)$ satisfies Donsker's invariance principle with accuracy ϵ" and "the sequence $f(n_k x)$ satisfies Strassen's law of the iterated logarithm with accuracy ϵ". The following definitions are quite natural but not the only possible ones.

Definition 1. Let $Y_1, Y_2, \ldots$ be a sequence of random variables, $S_n = \sum_{i=1}^{n} Y_i$ $(S_0 = 0)$ and define the random function $\varphi_n(t)$ $(0 \leq t \leq 1)$ as follows

$$\varphi_n(t) = \begin{cases} \frac{S_k}{\sqrt{n}} & \text{for} \quad t = \frac{k}{n} \quad (k = 0, 1, \ldots, n) \\ \text{linear for} & t \in \left[\frac{k}{n}, \frac{k+1}{n}\right] \quad (k = 0, 1, \ldots, n-1) . \end{cases}$$

Let $\epsilon > 0$ be fixed. We say that the sequence Y_k obeys Donsker's invariance principle with accuracy ϵ if

$$\overline{\lim_{n \to \infty}} \; \rho(\varphi_n, \zeta) \leq \epsilon$$

where $\zeta(t)$ $(0 \leq t \leq 1)$ is the Wiener-process and ρ is the Prohorov-distance*.

Definition 2. Let $Y_1, Y_2, \ldots$ be a sequence of random variables, $S_n = \sum_{i=1}^{n} Y_i$ $(S_0 = 0)$ and define the random function $\psi_n(t)$ $(0 \leq t \leq 1)$ as follows

$$\psi_n(t) = \begin{cases} \frac{S_k}{\sqrt{2n \log \log n}} & \text{for} \quad t = \frac{k}{n} \quad (k = 0, 1, \ldots, n) \\ \text{linear for} & t \in \left[\frac{k}{n}, \frac{k+1}{n}\right] \quad (k = 0, 1, \ldots, n-1) . \end{cases}$$

Let $\epsilon > 0$ be fixed and let K denote the set of functions defined by (3.1).

*For the definition of the Prohorov metric see [5].

We say that the sequence Y_k obeys Strassen's law of the iterated logarithm with accuracy ϵ if

(a) $\overline{\lim_{n\to\infty}}\ d(\psi_n, K) \leqslant \epsilon$ a.s.*,

(b) for any $x(t) \in K$ we have $\underline{\lim_{n\to\infty}}\ d(\psi_n, x) \leqslant \epsilon$ a.s.

Theorem (4.2). *Let $f(x)$ satisfy* (1.1) *and* (2.1) *and assume, for simplicity, that* $\|f\| = 1$. *Then for any given $\epsilon > 0$ there exists a $q_0 = q_0(\epsilon, f)$ such that if $\{n_k\}$ satisfies* (1.2) *with $q \geqslant q_0$, then the sequence $f(n_k x)$ obeys both Donsker's invariance principle and Strassen's law of the iterated logarithm with accuracy ϵ.*

Remark. The example of Erdős and Fortet, mentioned above, shows that q_0 in Theorems (4.1) and (4.2) strongly depends on f.

It is easy to see that Theorem (4.2) implies Theorem (4.1). On the other hand, Theorem (4.2) follows immediately from the following general theorem which is the main result of this Section.

Theorem (4.3). *Let $f(x)$ satisfy* (1.1) *and* (2.1) *and assume, for the sake of simplicity, that* $\|f\| = 1$. *Then for any given $\epsilon > 0$ there exists a $q_0 = q_0(\epsilon, f)$ such that if $\{n_k\}$ satisfies* (1.2) *with $q \geqslant q_0$ then for the sequence $f(n_k x)$ we have the following result:*

There exists a new probability space $(\Omega, \mathscr{F}, \mathrm{P})$ and a sequence $X_1, X_2, \ldots$ of random variables (defined on $(\Omega, \mathscr{F}, \mathrm{P})$) such that the sequences $\{f(n_k x)\}$ and $\{X_k\}$ are quasi-equivalent and

$$X_1 + \ldots + X_n = \zeta(\tau_n) + o(n^{\frac{1}{2} - \eta}) \qquad \text{a.s. as} \qquad n \to \infty$$

where $\eta > 0$ is an absolute constant, ζ is a Wiener-process on $(\Omega, \mathscr{F}, \mathrm{P})$ and τ_n is a positive, strictly increasing sequence of random variables (also on $(\Omega, \mathscr{F}, \mathrm{P})$) such that $\tau_n - \tau_{n-1} = O(1)$ a.s. as $n \to \infty$ and

$$1 - \epsilon \leqslant \liminf_{n\to\infty} \frac{\tau_n}{n} \leqslant \limsup_{n\to\infty} \frac{\tau_n}{n} \leqslant 1 + \epsilon \qquad \text{a.s.}$$

*d denotes the $C[0, 1]$ metric.

Theorem (4.3) is easy to obtain from Theorem (2.1) and the following lemma which is a consequence of the results of [11].

Lemma (4.1). *Let* $f(x)$ *satisfy* (1.1) *and the second relation of* (2.1) *with* $A > 1$ *and* $0 < \alpha \leq 1$. *Let* $1 \leq m_1 < m_2 < \ldots < m_n$ *be arbitrary real numbers such that* $\frac{m_{k+1}}{m_k} \geq q > 1$ *for* $1 \leq k \leq n-1$. *Then for any real* a *we have*

$$\int_a^{a+1} (f(m_1 x) + \ldots + f(m_n x))^2 \, dx = n \| f \|^2 + T$$

where

$$|T| \leq \frac{4q}{q-1} \| f \|^2 +$$

$$+ C_1 A \left(\frac{1}{q^{\frac{1}{2}} - 1} + \frac{1}{q^\alpha - 1} + \frac{\| f \|}{\log q} \right) (\| f \|^2 + \| f \|) n$$

with an absolute constant C_1.

Remark 1. Theorems (4.1) and (4.2) show that if $f(x)$ and $\{n_k\}$ satisfy (1.1), (2.1) and $\frac{n_{k+1}}{n_k} \to \infty$ then the sequence $f(n_k x)$ satisfies the central limit theorem, the law of iterated logarithm and the functional versions of these theorems exactly (i.e. with $\epsilon = 0$). Similarly, in this case the conclusion of Theorem (4.3) holds with $\epsilon = 0$. These facts can be obtained also from the results of the preceding section (see Remark 2 after Theorem (3.1)).

Remark 2. Theorem (4.1) evidently implies the following corollary which extends some results of [14], [20].

Let $f(x)$ *satisfy* (1.1) *and* (2.1) *and let* $\{n_k\}$ *be a sequence of positive numbers satisfying* (1.2). *Then we have*

$$\overline{\lim_{N \to \infty}} \frac{1}{\sqrt{2N \log \log N}} \sum_{k=1}^{N} f(n_k x) \leq C \qquad a.e.$$

where C *is a constant depending on* $f(x)$ *and* q.

5. THE TRIGONOMETRIC CASE

In this section we shall investigate what form of the a.s. invariance principle can be stated in the classical case $f(x) = \cos 2\pi x$. We know that under quite general conditions the asymptotic behaviour of $\sum_{k=1}^{N} f(n_k x)$ as $N \to \infty$ is like to that of $\zeta(\tau_N)$ as $N \to \infty$ where ζ is a Wiener-process and τ_N is a certain sequence of random variables. In Section 3 we have showed that if $\{n_k\} \in \Lambda^*$ (which is a stronger assumption than the Hadamard gap condition) then τ_N are asymptotically constant: $\tau_N \sim b_N$ with a certain numerical sequence $b_N \asymp N$. The example of Erdős and Fortet (see Sec. 4) shows that this is not necessarily valid if we assume only the Hadamard gap condition for $\{n_k\}$. (In fact, in this case even the central limit theorem can fail to hold.) In the sequel we shall show that the case $f(x) = \cos 2\pi x$ is exceptional, namely, in this case the Hadamard gap condition is sufficient to imply the a.s. invariance principle for the sequence $f(n_k x)$ with asymptotically constant τ_N (even with constant τ_N). A result of this type follows at once from Remark 1 after Theorem (3.1). Indeed, $f(x) = \cos 2\pi x$ is a trigonometric polynomial of order 1 and thus for this function f the statement of Theorem (3.1) holds assuming only the Hadamard gap condition for $\{n_k\}$ (instead of $\{n_k\} \in \Lambda^*$). The following theorem (which is an easy consequence of Theorem (2.3)) shows a little more, namely that in the case $f(x) = \cos 2\pi x$ the random variables τ_N can actually be chosen constant.

Theorem (5.1). *Let $\{n_k\}$ be a sequence of positive numbers satisfying (1.2). Then there exists a probability space $(\Omega, \mathcal{F}, \mathsf{P})$ and a sequence $X_1, X_2, \ldots$ of random variables (defined on $(\Omega, \mathcal{F}, \mathsf{P})$) such that the sequences $\{\cos 2\pi n_k x\}$ and $\{X_k\}$ are quasi-equivalent and*

$$X_1 + \ldots + X_n = \zeta\left(\frac{n}{2}\right) + o(n^{\frac{1}{2}-\eta}) \qquad \textit{a.s. as} \qquad n \to \infty$$

where ζ is a Wiener-process on $(\Omega, \mathcal{F}, \mathsf{P})$ and $\eta > 0$ is an absolute constant.

Theorem (5.1) is not the best result in this field. We can state a better result under the same conditions and, on the other hand, we can weaken the assumption that $\{n_k\}$ satisfies the Hadamard gap condition. As to the first line of generalization, we mention the following result of Philipp and Stout giving an a.s. invariance principle for lacunary trigonometric sums with weights.

Theorem (see [15]). *Let $\{n_k\}$ be a sequence of positive numbers satisfying (1.2). Let further $\{a_k\}$ be a sequence of real numbers such that, putting $A_N^2 = \frac{1}{2}\sum_{k=1}^{N} a_k^2$, we have $A_N \to \infty$ and $a_N = O(A_N^{1-\delta})$ with a constant $0 < \delta \leqslant 1$. Then there exists a probability space $(\Omega, \mathcal{F}, \mathrm{P})$ and a sequence $X_1, X_2, \ldots$ of random variables on $(\Omega, \mathcal{F}, \mathrm{P})$ such that the sequences $\{X_k\}$ and $\{a_k \cos 2\pi n_k x\}$ are quasi-equivalent and*

$$X_1 + \ldots + X_n = \zeta(A_n^2) + o(A_n^{1-c\delta}) \qquad \text{a.s. as} \qquad n \to \infty$$

where ζ is a Wiener-process on $(\Omega, \mathcal{F}, \mathrm{P})$ and $c > 0$ is an absolute constant.

The other line of generalization is motivated by a remarkable theorem of Erdős (see [6]). Erdős' theorem states that the sequence $\cos 2\pi n_k x$ satisfies the central limit theorem provided that $\{n_k\}$ is a sequence of integers satisfying

$$(5.1) \qquad \frac{n_{k+1}}{n_k} \geqslant 1 + \frac{c_k}{\sqrt{k}}, \qquad c_k \to \infty .$$

Erdős also remarks that this theorem is best possible i.e. for any fixed $c > 0$ there is a sequence $\{n_k\}$ of integers which satisfies $\frac{n_{k+1}}{n_k} \geqslant 1 + \frac{c}{\sqrt{k}}$ and the sequence $\cos 2\pi n_k x$ does not obey the central limit theorem. (For some other results related to Erdős' theorem see [22] and the bibliography given there.) In view of Erdős' theorem one can expect that if $\{n_k\}$ satisfies (5.1) then the sequence $\cos 2\pi n_k x$ obeys an almost sure invariance principle with constant τ_N. In this direction we have proved the following theorem.

Theorem (see [2]). *Let $\{n_k\}$ be a sequence of integers satisfying*

$$(5.2) \qquad \frac{n_{k+1}}{n_k} \geqslant 1 + \frac{1}{k^\alpha} \qquad \left(\alpha < \frac{1}{2}\right).$$

Then we have the conclusion of Theorem (5.1) *(with the minor modification that now the constant* $\eta > 0$ *can depend on* α*).*

By the remarks above the last theorem is not valid for $\alpha = \frac{1}{2}$. It is very likely that the theorem remains valid if (5.2) is replaced by (5.1).

REFERENCES

[1] I. Berkes, On the asymptotic behaviour of $\sum f(n_k x)$, I-II, *Z. Wahrscheinlichkeitstheorie verw. Geb.*, (to appear).

[2] I. Berkes, An almost sure invariance principle for lacunary trigonometric series, *Acta Math. Acad. Sci. Hung.*, (to appear).

[3] I. Berkes, Almost sure invariance principles for mixing processes, *Annals of Probab.*, (to appear).

[4] I. Berkes, On Strassen's version of the loglog law for multiplicative systems, *Studia Sci. Math. Hung.*, 8 (1973), 425-431.

[5] P. Billingsley, *Convergence of probability measures,* Wiley, New York, 1968.

[6] P. Erdős, On trigonometric sums with gaps, *Magyar Tud. Akad. Mat. Kut. Int. Közl.*, 7 (1962), 37-42.

[7] V.F. Gapoškin, Lacunary series and independent functions, (in Russian), *Uspehi Mat. Nauk,* 21 (1966), 3-82; English translation: *Russian Math. Surveys,* 21 (1966), 3-82.

[8] V.F. Gapoškin, On some sequences of almost independent functions, (in Russian), *Sibirsk Math. Journ.*, 9 (1968), 264-279.

[9] V.F. Gapoškin, On the central limit theorem for some weakly dependent sequences, (in Russian), *Teorija Verojatn. i Primenen.*, 15 (1970), 666-684; English translation: *Theory Prob. and Appl.*, 15 (1970), 649-666.

[10] M. Kac, Probability methods in some problems of analysis and number theory, *Bull. Amer. Math. Soc.*, 55 (1949), 641-665.

[11] M. Kac – R. Salem – A. Zygmund, A gap theorem, *Trans. Amer. Math. Soc.*, 63 (1948), 235-243.

[12] J. Komlós – P. Major – G. Tusnády, An approximation of partial sums of independent RV's and the sample DF, I-II, *Z. Wahrscheinlichkeitstheorie verw. Geb.*, (to appear).

[13] D.L. McLeish, An invariance principle for strongly multiplicative systems, *Acta Math. Acad. Sci. Hung.*, (to appear).

[14] W. Philipp, Limit theorems for lacunary series and uniform distribution mod 1, *Acta Arithmetica,* (to appear).

[15] W. Philipp – W.F. Stout, Almost sure invariance principles for sums of weakly dependent random variables, *Mem. Amer. Math. Soc.*, (to appear).

[16] W. Philipp – W.F. Stout, Asymptotic fluctuation behaviour of sums of weakly dependent random variables, (in this volume).

[17] V. Strassen, An invariance principle for the law of the iterated logarithm, *Z. Wahrscheinlichkeitstheorie verw. Geb.*, 3 (1964), 211-226.

[18] V. Strassen, Almost sure behaviour of sums of independent random variables and martingales, *Proc. Fifth Berkeley Symp. Math. Statist. Probab.*, Vol. II (part I), 315-343.

[19] S. Takahashi, On the distribution of values of the type $\sum f(q^k t)$, *Tohoku Math. Journ.*, 14 (1962), 233-243.

[20] S. Takahashi, An asymptotic property of a gap sequence, *Proc. Japan Acad.*, 38 (1962), 101-104.

[21] S. Takahashi, The law of the iterated logarithm for a gap sequence with infinite gaps, *Tohoku Math. Journ.*, 15 (1963), 281-288.

[22] S. Takahashi, Probability limit theorem for lacunary trigonometric series, (in this volume).

[23] A. Zygmund, *Trigonometric series*, Vol. I, Cambridge University Press, 1959.

COLLOQUIA MATHEMATICA SOCIETATIS JÁNOS BOLYAI
11. LIMIT THEOREMS OF PROBABILITY THEORY, KESZTHELY (HUNGARY), 1974.

SOME NOTES ON THE LAW OF THE ITERATED LOGARITHM FOR EMPIRICAL DISTRIBUTION FUNCTION

E. CSÁKI

1. INTRODUCTION

Consider a sequence $X_1, X_2, \ldots, X_n, \ldots$ of independent random variables, each uniformly distributed on $(0, 1)$ and let $F_n(x)$ denote the empirical distribution function of the variables $X_1, X_2, \ldots, X_n$.

In this paper we deal with problems concerning the law of the iterated logarithm (LIL) for the generalized Kolmogorov – Smirnov statistics

$$(1.1) \qquad K_n(\tau) = \sup_{0 \leqslant x \leqslant 1} (\tau(x) | x - F_n(x)|),$$

where $\tau(x) \geqslant 0 \ (0 \leqslant x \leqslant 1)$ is a weight function.

For $\tau(x) \equiv 1$, i.e. for $D_n = K_n(1)$ the LIL has been proved by Smirnov [14] and Chung [3], and extensions have been given by Cassels [2], Kiefer [10], and Richter [13]. Functional (Strassen's type) LIL for empirical distribution function has been proved by Finkelstein [9], Richter [12] and Wichura [16].

We note that for fixed x, $|x - F_n(x)|\tau(x)$ is a (transformed) Bernoulli variable, hence from classical results,

$$\overline{\lim_{n\to\infty}} \left(\sqrt{\frac{n}{\log\log n}}\, |x - F_n(x)|\,\tau(x)\right) = \tau(x)\sqrt{2x(1-x)} \qquad \text{a.s.} \tag{1.2}$$

which implies that

$$\overline{\lim_{n\to\infty}} \left(\sqrt{\frac{n}{\log\log n}}\, K_n(\tau)\right) \geqslant A \qquad \text{a.s.} \tag{1.3}$$

where

$$A = \sup_{0\leqslant x\leqslant 1} \left(\tau(x)\sqrt{2x(1-x)}\right). \tag{1.4}$$

In Section 2 we consider the case of bounded $\tau(x)$ and show that (1.3) holds with $=$ (instead of $\geqslant$). The *LIL* however does not hold in general, when $\tau(x)$ is unbounded. It will be apparent in Section 3 that the *LIL* is not true for the weight function

$$\tau(x) = \frac{1}{\sqrt{x(1-x)}} \qquad 0 < x < 1\,. \tag{1.5}$$

We mention the related results of Eicker [8] and Kiefer [11]:

$$\overline{\lim_{n\to\infty}} \frac{n|\epsilon_n - F_n(\epsilon_n)|}{\sqrt{\epsilon_n(1-\epsilon_n)n\log\log n}} \leqslant \sqrt{2} \qquad \text{a.s.} \tag{1.6}$$

when $\epsilon_n \to 0$ and $\dfrac{n\epsilon_n}{\log\log n} \to \infty$ as $n \to \infty$.

Kiefer [11] considers also other sequences $\{\epsilon_n\}$ for which the *LIL* does not hold.

On the other hand Csörgő and Révész [6] consider the weight function

$$\tau_n(x) = \begin{cases} \dfrac{1}{\sqrt{x(1-x)}}, & a_n \leqslant x \leqslant 1 - a_n \\ 0 & \text{otherwise} \end{cases} \tag{1.7}$$

and show that

$$(1.8)\qquad \overline{\lim_{n\to\infty}} \left(\sqrt{\frac{n}{\log\log n}}\, K_n(\tau_n)\right) = 2 \qquad \text{a.s.}$$

provided that $\frac{1}{\sqrt{n}} \geqslant a_n \geqslant \frac{\log^4 n}{n}$.

Note the interesting fact that the constant on the right hand side of (1.8) is 2 instead of the "usual" $\sqrt{2}$.

2. THE CASE OF BOUNDED $\tau(x)$

Now we consider weight functions $\tau(x)$ such that

$$(2.1)\qquad 0 \leqslant \tau(x) \leqslant c', \qquad 0 \leqslant x \leqslant 1$$

with some positive constant c'.

Theorem 2.1. *Assume* (2.1) *and let* A *be given by* (1.4). *Then*

$$(2.2)\qquad \overline{\lim_{n\to\infty}} \left(\sqrt{\frac{n}{\log\log n}}\, K_n(\tau)\right) = A \qquad \textit{a.s.}$$

Here we only sketch the proof of Theorem 2.1 based on two lemmas stated below. For details we refer to [5].

First consider the weight function

$$(2.3)\qquad \tau_1(x) = \frac{1}{c\sqrt{x(1-x)} + b}, \qquad 0 \leqslant x \leqslant 1,$$

where $c \geqslant 0$, $b > 0$. Obviously

$$(2.4)\qquad \frac{1}{\frac{c}{2} + b} \leqslant \tau_1(x) \leqslant \frac{1}{b}.$$

Let furthermore

$$(2.5)\qquad K_n^+(\tau_1) = \sup_{0 \leqslant x \leqslant 1} \tau_1(x)(x - F_n(x)).$$

Lemma 2.1. *Let* $\mathscr{F}_n$ *be the* σ*-algebra generated by* $X_1, X_2, \ldots$ $\ldots, X_n$. *Then the sequence* $\{nK_n^+(\tau_1)\}$ *is a semi-martingale relative to*

$\{\mathcal{F}_n\}$, *i.e.*

$$\text{(2.6)} \qquad \mathsf{E}((n+1)K_{n+1}^{+}(\tau_1) \mid \mathcal{F}_n) \geqslant nK_n^{+}(\tau_1)\,.$$

Proof. Let ρ denote the point where $(x - F_n(x))\tau_1(x)$ takes its maximum, i.e.

$$\text{(2.7)} \qquad K_n^{+}(\tau_1) = (\rho - F_n(\rho))\tau_1(\rho)\,.$$

Then

$$(n+1)K_{n+1}^{+}(\tau_1) \geqslant (n+1)(\rho - F_{n+1}(\rho))\tau_1(\rho) =$$
$$= nK_n^{+}(\tau_1) + \rho\tau_1(\rho) + (nF_n(\rho) - (n+1)F_{n+1}(\rho))\tau_1(\rho)\,.$$

But $nF_n(\rho) - (n+1)F_{n+1}(\rho) = -1$ or 0 according as $X_{n+1} < \rho$ (having probability ρ under $\mathcal{F}_n$), or $X_{n+1} > 1 - \rho$ (having probability $1 - \rho$ under $\mathcal{F}_n$). Hence

$$\mathsf{E}((n+1)K_{n+1}^{+}(\tau_1) \mid \mathcal{F}_n) \geqslant$$
$$\geqslant nK_n^{+}(\tau_1) + (\rho - 1)\rho\tau_1(\rho) + \rho(1-\rho)\tau_1(\rho) = nK_n^{+}(\tau_1)\,,$$

proving our lemma.

We note that Lemma 2.1 obviously holds also for more general weight functions.

Lemma 2.2.

$$\text{(2.8)} \qquad \begin{aligned} &\mathsf{E}(e^{tK_n^{+}(\tau_1)}) \leqslant \\ &\leqslant 1 + t\mathsf{E}(K_n^{+}(\tau_1)) + \frac{nt^2}{b^2}\Big(1 + \frac{t^2}{2(c+2b)^2} + \frac{t^3 e^{\frac{t}{b}}}{6b^3}\Big)^n\,. \end{aligned}$$

The proof of Lemma 2.2 for $c = 0$, $b = 1$ (i.e. for $\tau(x) \equiv 1$) is given in [4]. For arbitrary c and b the proof is similar (see [5]).

Lemma 2.1 and Lemma 2.2 yield the proof of Theorem 2.1 for $\tau_1(x)$ by using Theorem 1.1 in [4].

For general $\tau(x)$ the conclusion of Theorem 2.1 follows immediately from (1.3) and from the inequality

$$(2.9) \qquad |x - F_n(x)|\,\tau(x) \leqslant \frac{|x - F_n(x)|}{\sqrt{2x(1-x)} + \frac{\epsilon}{c'}}\,(A + \epsilon)\,.$$

We remark that the statement of Theorem 2.1 would also be a consequence of functional *LIL* (Finkelstein [9]), but the proof of Theorem 2.1 via Lemma 2.1 and Lemma 2.2 may be of some interest. E.g. boundary crossing probabilities can be determined for $K_n^+(\tau_1)$ (see Stanley [15]) which in turn can be applied to Darling – Robbins type sequential tests [7]. Lemma 2.2 provides also an estimation of the tail of the distribution of $K_n^+(\tau_1)$.

Some particular weight functions for which Theorem 2.1 can be applied, are the following ones:

(i) Kolmogorov – Smirnov-type statistics:

$$\tau(x) = \begin{cases} 1 & a_1 \leqslant x \leqslant a_2 \qquad (0 \leqslant a_1 < a_2 \leqslant 1) \\ 0 & \text{otherwise.} \end{cases}$$

In this case

$$A = \begin{cases} \sqrt{2a_2(1-a_2)} & \text{if} \quad a_2 < \frac{1}{2} \\ \frac{1}{\sqrt{2}} & \text{if} \quad a_1 \leqslant \frac{1}{2} \leqslant a_2 \\ \sqrt{2a_1(1-a_1)} & \text{if} \quad \frac{1}{2} < a_1\,. \end{cases}$$

(ii) Rényi-type statistics:

$$\tau(x) = \begin{cases} \frac{1}{x} & a_1 \leqslant x \leqslant a_2 \qquad (0 < a_1 < a_2 \leqslant 1) \\ 0 & \text{otherwise.} \end{cases}$$

Here

$$A = \sqrt{\frac{2(1-a_1)}{a_1}}\,.$$

$$\tau(x) = \begin{cases} \dfrac{1}{1-x} & a_1 \leqslant x \leqslant a_2 \quad (0 \leqslant a_1 \leqslant a_2 \leqslant 1) \\ 0 & \text{otherwise.} \end{cases}$$

Here

$$A = \sqrt{\frac{2a_2}{1-a_2}}\,.$$

(iii)

$$\tau(x) = \begin{cases} \dfrac{1}{\sqrt{x(1-x)}} & a_1 \leqslant x \leqslant a_2 \quad (0 < a_1 < a_2 < 1) \\ 0 & \text{otherwise.} \end{cases}$$

Obviously

$$A = \sqrt{2}\,.$$

(iv) The case of discrete distribution:

$$\tau(x) = \begin{cases} 1 & x = a_1, a_2, \ldots \\ 0 & \text{otherwise.} \end{cases}$$

In this case

$$A = \max_{(i)} (\sqrt{2a_i(1-a_i)})\,.$$

3. THE CASE OF UNBOUNDED WEIGHT FUNCTION

Here we are not able to give a general result for arbitrary $\tau(x)$. We consider only the weight function

$$\tau_2(x) = \begin{cases} \dfrac{1}{\sqrt{x(1-x)}} & 0 < x < 1 \\ 0 & \text{otherwise} \end{cases} \tag{3.1}$$

which may be typical concerning the behaviour of $K_n(\tau)$ for which the *LIL* does not hold.

From (1.4) we have $A = \sqrt{2}$ for $\tau_2(x)$, but

$$(3.2) \qquad \overline{\lim_{n\to\infty}} \left(\sqrt{\frac{n}{\log \log n}} \, K_n(\tau_2) \right) = \infty \qquad \text{a.s.}$$

follows easily from the following theorem of Baxter [1]:

$$(3.3) \qquad \overline{\lim_{n\to\infty}} \left(\frac{n \log \log \log n}{\log \log n} \, F_n\left(\frac{1}{n}\right) \right) = 1 \qquad \text{a.s.}$$

Now we prove

Theorem 3.1.

(i) *If* $\sum_{n=1}^{\infty} a_n = \infty$, *then*

$$(3.4) \qquad \overline{\lim_{n\to\infty}} \, (n\sqrt{a_n} \, K_n(\tau_2)) = \infty \qquad a.s.$$

(ii) *If* $\sum_{n=1}^{\infty} b_n < \infty$, *then*

$$(3.5) \qquad \lim_{n\to\infty} \, (n\sqrt{b_n} \, K_n(\tau_2)) = 0 \qquad a.s.$$

Proof. Part (i) follows immediately from the following result of Kiefer [11]:

If $\sum a_n = \infty$, then $\min (X_1, \ldots, X_n) < a_n$ infinitely often with probability one.

Now we prove part (ii). Consider first

$$(3.6) \qquad U_n = \sup_{0 < x \leqslant \frac{1}{2}} \left(\frac{F_n(x) - x}{\sqrt{x}} \right)$$

and prove that $\lim_{n\to\infty} (n\sqrt{b_n} \, U_n) = 0$ a.s.

Define the following event:

$$C_n = \left\{ U_i \leqslant \frac{\epsilon}{i\sqrt{b_i}}, \quad i = 1, 2, \ldots, n-1; \; U_n > \frac{\epsilon}{n\sqrt{b_n}} \right\}.$$

Then by virtue of Borel – Cantelli lemma it suffices to prove that

$\sum P(C_n) < \infty$ for every $\epsilon > 0$.

Let

$$B_{n,k} = \{\exists x \ (x_{k-1} \leqslant x < x_k):$$

$$nF_n(x) > nx + \frac{\epsilon}{\sqrt{b_n}}\sqrt{x}\,,\ (n-1)F_{n-1}(x) < nx + \frac{\epsilon}{\sqrt{b_n}}\sqrt{x}\}\,,$$

where x_k is the solution of the equation

$$nx + \frac{\epsilon}{\sqrt{b_n}}\sqrt{x} = k\,, \tag{3.7}$$

i.e.

$$x_k = \frac{4k^2}{4nk + \frac{\epsilon^2}{b_n}\left(1 + \sqrt{1 + \frac{4nkb_n}{\epsilon^2}}\right)}\,. \tag{3.8}$$

Then

$$C_n \subset \{\exists x \ \left(0 < x \leqslant \tfrac{1}{2}\right):$$

$$F_n(x) > x + \frac{\epsilon}{n\sqrt{b_n}}\sqrt{x}\,,\ F_{n-1}(x) < x + \frac{\epsilon}{(n-1)\sqrt{b_{n-1}}}\sqrt{x}\} \subset$$

$$\subset \{\exists x \ \left(0 < x \leqslant \tfrac{1}{2}\right):$$

$$nF_n(x) > nx + \frac{\epsilon}{\sqrt{b_n}}\sqrt{x}\,,\ (n-1)F_{n-1}(x) < nx + \frac{\epsilon}{\sqrt{b_n}}\sqrt{x}\} =$$

$$= \bigcup_{k=1}^{[\frac{n}{2}]} B_{n,k}\,.$$

Hence

$$\mathsf{P}(C_n) \leqslant \sum_{k=1}^{[\frac{n}{2}]} \mathsf{P}(B_{n,k}) = \sum_{k=1}^{L_n} \mathsf{P}(B_{n,k}) + \sum_{k=L_n+1}^{[\frac{n}{2}]} \mathsf{P}(B_{n,k})\,,$$

where

(3.9) $$L_n = \left[\frac{\epsilon^2}{64nb_n}\right].$$

Obviously

$$B_{n,k} = \{\exists x\ (x_{k-1} \leqslant x < x_k):$$
$$(n-1)F_{n-1}(x) = k-1;\ X_n \leqslant x\},$$

thus

$$\mathsf{P}(B_{n,k}) \leqslant x_k \binom{n-1}{k-1} x_k^{k-1} = \frac{k}{n}\binom{n}{k} x_k^k \leqslant \frac{k}{n}\frac{(nx_k)^k}{k!}.$$

It can be seen from (3.8) that $x_k < \dfrac{2k^2 b_n}{\epsilon^2}$, hence

$$\mathsf{P}(B_{n,k}) \leqslant \frac{k}{n}\left(\frac{2nk^2 b_n}{\epsilon^2}\right)^k \frac{1}{k!}$$

and for $k \leqslant L_n$, we have

$$\frac{k}{n}\left(\frac{2nk^2 b_n}{\epsilon^2}\right)^k \frac{1}{k!} \leqslant \frac{2b_n}{\epsilon^2}\left(\frac{1}{2}\right)^{k-1}.$$

Thus

(3.10) $$\sum_{k=1}^{L_n} \mathsf{P}(B_{n,k}) \leqslant \frac{2b_n}{\epsilon^2}\sum_{k=1}^{L_n}\left(\frac{1}{2}\right)^{k-1} < \frac{4b_n}{\epsilon^2}.$$

For $k > L_n$ we use the estimation

$$\mathsf{P}(B_{n,k}) \leqslant \binom{n}{k} x_k^k (1-x_k)^{n-k} < \text{const}\ e^{-\frac{1}{2}\frac{(k-nx_k)^2}{k}}$$

and it is easy to see that for n large enough

$$\frac{1}{2}\frac{(k-nx_k)^2}{k} > 3\log n,$$

that yields for $k > L_n$

$$(3.11)\qquad \mathsf{P}(B_{n,k}) < \frac{c''}{n^3}, \quad \sum_{k=L_n+1}^{[\frac{n}{2}]} \mathsf{P}(B_{n,k}) < \frac{c''}{n^2}.$$

This together with (3.10) gives

$$(3.12)\qquad \mathsf{P}(C_n) < \frac{4}{\epsilon^2} b_n + \frac{c''}{n^2},$$

i.e. $\sum_{n=1}^{\infty} \mathsf{P}(C_n) < \infty$ for every $\epsilon > 0$.

Now let

$$(3.13)\qquad V_n = \sup_{0<x\leq\frac{1}{2}} \left(\frac{x - F_n(x)}{\sqrt{x}}\right).$$

We can see similarly that

$$(3.14)\qquad \mathsf{P}\left(V_n > \frac{\epsilon}{n\sqrt{b_n}}\right) \leq \sum_{k=0}^{[\frac{n}{2}]} \binom{n}{k} t_k^k (1 - t_k)^{n-k} < \frac{c'''}{n^2},$$

where

$$(3.15)\qquad t_k = \frac{k}{n} + \frac{\epsilon^2}{2n^2 b_n} + \frac{\epsilon}{n\sqrt{b_n}} \sqrt{\frac{\epsilon^2}{n^2 b_n} + \frac{4k}{n}}.$$

From (3.12) and (3.14) and from the obvious inequality

$$(3.16)\qquad \sup_{0<x<\frac{1}{2}} \left(\frac{|x - F_n(x)|}{\sqrt{x(1-x)}}\right) \leq \sqrt{2} \sup_{0<x<\frac{1}{2}} \left(\frac{|x - F_n(x)|}{\sqrt{x}}\right)$$

it follows that

$$(3.17)\qquad \lim_{n\to\infty} \left(n\sqrt{b_n} \sup_{0<x\leq\frac{1}{2}} \left(\frac{|x - F_n(x)|}{\sqrt{x(1-x)}}\right)\right) = 0 \quad \text{a.s.}$$

The same reasoning yields

$$(3.18)\qquad \lim_{n\to\infty} \left(n\sqrt{b_n} \sup_{\frac{1}{2}<x<1} \left(\frac{|x - F_n(x)|}{\sqrt{x(1-x)}}\right)\right) = 0 \quad \text{a.s.}$$

proving part (ii) of Theorem 3.1.

For more details we refer to [5].

From Theorem 3.1 one gets the following corollaries:

Corollary 3.1. For $K_n(\tau_2)$ lim sup *sequence does not exist, i.e. there is no numerical sequence* $\{\alpha_n\}$ *for which*

(3.19) $$\overline{\lim_{n\to\infty}} (\alpha_n K_n(\tau_2)) = \text{finite positive number a.s.}$$

Corollary 3.2.

(3.20) $$\overline{\lim_{n\to\infty}} (\sqrt{n}\, K_n(\tau_2))^{\frac{1}{\log\log n}} = \sqrt{e} \qquad a.s.$$

(Apply Theorem 3.1 for $a_n = \frac{1}{n \log n}$ and $b_n = \frac{1}{n(\log n)^{1+\epsilon}}$).

REFERENCES

[1] G. Baxter, An analogue of the law of the iterated logarithm, *Proc. Amer. Math. Soc.*, 6 (1955), 177-181.

[2] J.W.S. Cassels, An extension of the law of the iterated logarithm, *Proc. Cambridge Philos. Soc.*, 47 (1951), 55-64.

[3] K.L. Chung, An estimate concerning the Kolmogorov limit distribution, *Trans. Amer. Math. Soc.*, 64 (1948), 205-233.

[4] E. Csáki, An iterated logarithm law for semimartingales and its application to empirical distribution function, *Studia Sci. Math. Hung.*, 3 (1968), 287-292.

[5] E. Csáki, On the empirical distribution function, (in Hungarian), *MTA III. Oszt. Közl.*, (to appear).

[6] M. Csörgő – P. Révész, Some notes on the empirical distribution function and the quantile process, to appear in Coll. Math. Soc. J. Bolyai, Limit theorems of probability theory.

[7] D.A. Darling – H. Robbins, Some nonparametric sequential tests with power one, *Proc. Nat. Acad. Sci.*, 61 (1968), 804-809.

[8] F. Eicker, A loglog-law for double sequences of random variables, *Z. Wahrscheinlichkeitstheorie verw. Geb.*, 16 (1970), 107-133.

[9] H. Finkelstein, The law of the iterated logarithm for empirical distributions, *Ann. Math. Statist.*, 42 (1971), 607-615.

[10] J. Kiefer, On large deviations of the empiric distribution function of vector chance variables and a law of the iterated logarithm, *Pacific J. Math.*, 11 (1961), 649-660.

[11] J. Kiefer, Iterated logarithm analogues for sample quantiles when $p_n \downarrow 0$, *Proc. 6th Berkeley Sympos. Math. Statist. Probab.*, (1970), I. 227-244.

[12] H. Richter, Zum Gesetz vom iterierten Logarithmus für empirische Verteilungsfunktionen und empirisches Chi-Quadrat, *Manuscripta Math.*, 9 (1973), 187-199.

[13] H. Richter, Das Gesetz vom iterierten Logarithmus für empirische Verteilungsfunktionen im R^k, *Manuscripta Math.*, 11 (1974), 291-303.

[14] N.V. Smirnov, Approximate laws of distribution of random variables from empirical data, (in Russian), *Uspehi Mat. Nauk.*, 10 (1944), 179-206.

[15] R.M. Stanley, Boundary crossing probabilities for the Kolmogorov – Smirnov statistics, *Ann. Math. Statist.*, 43 (1972), 664-668.

[16] M.J. Wichura, Some Strassen-type laws of the iterated logarithm for multiparameter stochastic processes with independent increments, *Ann. Prob.*, 1 (1973), 272-296.

COLLOQUIA MATHEMATICA SOCIETATIS JÁNOS BOLYAI
11. LIMIT THEOREMS OF PROBABILITY THEORY, KESZTHELY (HUNGARY), 1974.

SOME NOTES ON THE EMPIRICAL DISTRIBUTION FUNCTION AND THE QUANTILE PROCESS

M. CSÖRGŐ – P. RÉVÉSZ

1. INTRODUCTION

Let $X_1, X_2, \ldots$ be a sequence of independent uniform- (0, 1) random variables, and, for each $n \geq 1$, let $0 = U_0^{(n)} \leq U_1^{(n)} \leq \ldots \leq U_n^{(n)} \leq \leq U_{n+1}^{(n)} = 1$ denote the order statistics of the random sample $X_1, X_2, \ldots, X_n$. Define the empirical distribution function $F_n(x)$ and the quantile process $Q_n(x)$ as follows:

$$F_n(x) = \frac{k}{n} \qquad \text{if} \quad U_k^{(n)} < x \leq U_{k+1}^{(n)} \qquad (k = 0, 1, 2, \ldots, n),$$

$$Q_n(x) = U_k^{(n)} \qquad \text{if} \quad \frac{k}{n+1} < x \leq \frac{k+1}{n+1} \quad (k = 0, 1, 2, \ldots, n).$$

It is of some interest to approximate these processes by appropriate Brownian Bridges (B.B. ≠ Brigitte Bardot) and a number of papers deal with this question. We first mention a result of Brillinger [3] (for a similar approach to convergence problems of the empirical process also refer to Breiman [2]).

Theorem A ([3]). *One can define, for each* n, *a B.B.* $\{B_n(x); 0 \leqslant x \leqslant 1\}$ *and a random function* $\{\widetilde{F}_n(x); 0 \leqslant x \leqslant 1\}$ *on a suitable probability space such that*

$$\sup_x |\sqrt{n}(\widetilde{F}_n(x) - x) - B_n(x)| =$$
$$= O(n^{-1/4}(\log n)^{1/2}(\log\log n)^{1/4})$$

with probability one (w.p. 1) as $n \to \infty$ *and, for each* n, *one has*

$$\{\widetilde{F}_n(x); 0 \leqslant x \leqslant 1\} \stackrel{\mathcal{D}}{=} \{F_n(x); 0 \leqslant x \leqslant 1\}.$$

Here and thereinafter $\stackrel{\mathcal{D}}{=}$ stands for equality in distribution and the B.B. $B_n(x)$ is a Gaussian process with covariance function $\min(x, y) - xy$ for each n.

Quite recently a much stronger form of this theorem was found by Komlós, Major and Tusnády [9].

Theorem B ([9]). *On a rich enough probability space one can define, for each* n, *a B.B.* $\{B_n(x); 0 \leqslant x \leqslant 1\}$ *such that*

$$\sup_x |\sqrt{n}(F_n(x) - x) - B_n(x)| = O\left(\frac{\log n}{\sqrt{n}}\right) \quad w.p.\ 1;$$

more precisely: there exists an absolute constant K *such that*

$$\mathsf{P}\left\{\overline{\lim_{n\to\infty}} \frac{\sqrt{n}}{\log n} \sup_x |\sqrt{n}(F_n(x) - x) - B_n(x)| \leqslant K\right\} = 1.$$

In fact their main result states:

Theorem C ([9]). *For a fixed* n *one can define positive absolute constants* A, B, C, *and a B.B.* $\{B_n(x); 0 \leqslant x \leqslant 1\}$ *such that*

$$\mathsf{P}\{\sup_x \sqrt{n}\, |\sqrt{n}(F_n(x) - x) - B_n(x)| \geqslant A \log n + z\} \leqslant Be^{-Cz}$$

for all real z.

Clearly Theorem B is a simple consequence of Theorem C.

Our first aim is to find analogous statements to Theorems B and C for quantile processes. This will be done in Section 2 with the help of another result of Komlós, Major and Tusnády [9], which we only quote here in a very special form as follows:

Theorem D ([9]). *Let* $Y_1, Y_2, \ldots$ *be independent random variables with distribution function* $F(x) = 1 - e^{-x}$ *if* $x > 0$ *and zero otherwise. If the underlying probability space of the* Y_i $(i = 1, 2, \ldots)$ *is rich enough then there exists a standard Wiener process* $\{W(t);\ 0 \leq t < \infty\}$ *and positive constants* A, B, C *such that*

$$\mathsf{P}\{\sup_{1 \leq k \leq n} |Y_1 + Y_2 + \ldots + Y_k - k - W(k)| \geq A \log n + z\} \leq$$

$$\leq Be^{-Cz}$$

for all real z *and hence*

$$\sup_{1 \leq k \leq n} \frac{|Y_1 + Y_2 + \ldots + Y_k - k - W(k)|}{\log n} = O(1) \quad w.p.\ 1,$$

as $n \to \infty$.

A deeper than a Brillinger type connection was found by Kiefer [8] between the empirical and Gaussian processes. In fact he introduced a Gaussian process $\{K(x, y);\ 0 \leq x \leq 1, 0 \leq y < \infty\}$ (will be called the Kiefer process) and proved that $K(x, n)$ is near to $\sqrt{n}(F_n(x) - x)$ uniformly in x if n is large enough.

Definition. Let $\{W(x, y);\ 0 \leq x < \infty, 0 \leq y < \infty\}$ be a Wiener process of two variables with zero expectation and covariance function $\min(x_1, x_2) \min(y_1, y_2)$. Then the Kiefer process $K(x, y)$ can be defined as

$$K(x, y) = W(x, y) - xW(1, y) \quad (0 \leq x \leq 1, 0 \leq y < \infty).$$

Now Kiefer's result can be formulated as follows:

Theorem E ([8]). *If the random variables* $X_1, X_2, \ldots$ *are defined on a rich enough probability space then one can define a Kiefer process* $K(x, y)$ *on the same space such that*

$$\sup_x |n(F_n(x) - x) - K(x, n)| = O(n^{1/3}(\log n)^{2/3}) \quad w.p.\ 1$$

as $n \to \infty$.

Again Komlós, Major and Tusnády, obtained a much stronger result in this direction too [9].

Theorem F ([9]). *If the random variables* $X_1, X_2, \ldots$ *are defined on a rich enough probability space then one can define a Kiefer process* $K(x, y)$ *on the same space and positive absolute constants* A, B, C *such that*

$$\mathsf{P}\{\sup_{1 \leqslant k \leqslant n} \sup_x |k(F_k(x) - x) - K(x, k)| > (A \log n + z) \log n\} \leqslant$$
$$\leqslant Be^{-Cz} \qquad \text{for all } z \text{ and } n,$$

and hence

$$\sup_x |n(F_n(x) - x) - K(x, n)| = O(\log^2 n) \quad w.p.\ 1,$$

as $n \to \infty$.

We formulate an immediate, but much weaker, analogous result for quantile processes in Section 3.

Our third problem is concerned with the law of iterated logarithm for empirical processes. The simplest form of this theorem says:

$$(1) \qquad \overline{\lim_{n \to \infty}} \frac{\sqrt{n}(F_n(x) - x)}{\sqrt{2 \log \log n}} = \sqrt{x(1 - x)} \leqslant 1/2 \quad \text{w.p. } 1$$

for all $x \in (0, 1)$.

Chung [4] and Smirnov [10] have also proved

Theorem G ([4] and [10]).

$$(2) \qquad \overline{\lim_{n \to \infty}} \sup_{0 < x < 1} \frac{\sqrt{n}(F_n(x) - x)}{\sqrt{2 \log \log n}} = \frac{1}{2} \quad w.p.\ 1.$$

Combining (1) and (2) it is natural to ask what we can say about

$$\overline{\lim_{n\to\infty}} \sup_{0<x<1} \frac{\sqrt{n}(F_n(x)-x)}{\sqrt{2x(1-x)\log\log n}}.$$

An answer (but not a complete solution) of this question is given in Section 4.

2. APPROXIMATION OF A QUANTILE PROCESS BY A B.B.

In this paragraph we prove our

Theorem 1. *If the random variables* $X_1, X_2, \ldots$ *are defined on a rich enough probability space then one can define, for each* n, *a B.B.* $\{B_n(x);\ 0 \leq x \leq 1\}$ *on the same probability space and a positive absolute constant* A *such that*

$$\mathsf{P}\{\sup_x \sqrt{n}\,|\sqrt{n}(Q_n(x)-x) - B_n(x)| > A\log n\} \leq \frac{1}{n^2}.$$

This result immediately implies our

Theorem 2. *If the random variables* $X_1, X_2, \ldots$ *are defined on a rich enough probability space then one can define a sequence* $\{B_n(x);\ 0 \leq x \leq 1\}_{n=1}^{\infty}$ *of B.B.'s and a positive constant* K *such that*

$$\mathsf{P}\left\{\overline{\lim_{n\to\infty}} \frac{\sqrt{n}}{\log n} \sup_x |\sqrt{n}(Q_n(x)-x) - B_n(x)| \leq K\right\} = 1.$$

Put

$$Y_k = \log\frac{1}{X_k} \qquad (k = 1, 2, \ldots),$$

$$S_0 = 0,\ S_k = \sum_{j=1}^{k} Y_j \qquad (k = 1, 2, \ldots),$$

$$\widetilde{Q}_n(x) = \frac{S_k}{S_{n+1}} \quad \text{if} \quad \frac{k}{n+1} < x \leq \frac{k+1}{n+1}$$

$$(k = 0, 1, 2, \ldots, n).$$

The following two formulae are well known and trivial

$$\mathsf{P}\{Y_k < a\} = \begin{cases} 0 & \text{if } a \leqslant 0 \\ 1 - e^{-a} & \text{if } a > 0, \end{cases}$$

$$\{\widetilde{Q}_n(x);\ 0 \leqslant x \leqslant 1\} \overset{\mathcal{D}}{=} \{Q_n(x);\ 0 \leqslant x \leqslant 1\} \quad \text{for each } n. \tag{3}$$

Instead of directly proving Theorem 1, the following will be proved.

Theorem 1*. *If the random variables* $X_1, X_2, \ldots$ *are defined on a rich enough probability space then one can define a standard Wiener process* $\{W(t);\ 0 \leqslant t < \infty\}$ *on the same probability space and a positive absolute constant* A *such that*

$$\mathsf{P}\{\sup_x | n(\widetilde{Q}_n(x) - x) - (W(nx) - xW(n)) | > A \log n\} \leqslant \frac{1}{n^2}. \tag{4}$$

Theorem 1* clearly implies Theorem 1, for $\dfrac{W(nx) - xW(n)}{\sqrt{n}}$ is a B.B. for every fixed n and because of (3).

Proof of Theorem 1*. A simple calculation yields

$$\begin{aligned} &(n+1)\left(\frac{S_k}{S_{n+1}} - \frac{k}{n+1}\right) = \\ &= \frac{n+1}{S_{n+1}}\left[(S_k - k) - \frac{k}{n+1}(S_{n+1} - (n+1))\right]. \end{aligned} \tag{5}$$

Instead of $n(\widetilde{Q}_n(x) - x) - (W(nx) - xW(n))$ of (4) we may consider $(n+1)(\widetilde{Q}_n(x) - x) - (W((n+1)x) - xW(n+1))$. First taking $x = \dfrac{k}{n+1}$ in the latter it follows from (5) that this random variable is equal to

$$\begin{aligned} &\frac{n+1}{S_{n+1}}\left[(S_k - k) - \frac{k}{n+1}(S_{n+1} - (n+1))\right] - \\ &- \left(W(k) - \frac{k}{n+1}W(n+1)\right). \end{aligned} \tag{6}$$

Adding and subtracting $\dfrac{n+1}{S_{n+1}}\left[W(k) - \dfrac{k}{n+1}W(n+1)\right]$ in (6) we get

$$
\begin{aligned}
(7)\qquad &\frac{n+1}{S_{n+1}}\Big[(S_k-k)-W(k)-\frac{k}{n+1}\,((S_{n+1}-(n+1))-W(n+1))\Big]+\\
&+\left(\frac{n+1}{S_{n+1}}-1\right)\Big[W(k)-\frac{k}{n+1}\,W(n+1)\Big].
\end{aligned}
$$

Now let $\{W(t),\ 0\leqslant t<\infty\}$ be the Wiener process of Theorem D. Then, as in Theorem D

$$
(8)\qquad \mathsf{P}\{\sup_{0\leqslant k\leqslant n}|(S_k-k)-W(k)|\geqslant A\log n+z\}\leqslant Be^{-Cz},
$$

and, by the well known large deviation theorem

$$
(9)\qquad \mathsf{P}\left\{\left|\frac{S_{n+1}}{n+1}-1\right|\geqslant 1\right\}\leqslant De^{-En}\qquad (n=1,2,\dots)
$$

for some E and D.

Since

$$
\mathsf{P}\left\{\left|\frac{n+1}{S_{n+1}}-1\right|\geqslant A_1\sqrt{\frac{\log n}{n}}\right\}\leqslant\frac{1}{2n^2}
$$

and

$$
\mathsf{P}\left\{\sup_{1\leqslant k\leqslant n}\left|W(k)-\frac{k}{n+1}\,W(n+1)\right|\geqslant A_2\sqrt{n\log n}\right\}\leqslant\frac{1}{2n^2}
$$

(if A_1 and A_2 are suitable positive constants), we have

$$
(10)\qquad \mathsf{P}\left\{\left|\frac{n+1}{S_{n+1}}-1\right|\sup_{1\leqslant k\leqslant n}\left|W(k)-\frac{k}{n+1}\,W(n+1)\right|\geqslant A_3\log n\right\}\leqslant\frac{1}{n^2}
$$

if A_3 is a big enough positive constant. Making use of (7) our inequalities (8), (9) and (10) imply:

$$
\begin{aligned}
\mathsf{P}\Big\{\sup_{1\leqslant k\leqslant n}\Big|(n+1)\Big(\tilde{Q}_n\Big(\frac{k}{n+1}\Big)-\frac{k}{n+1}\Big)-\\
-\Big(W(k)-\frac{k}{n+1}\,W(n+1)\Big)\Big|\geqslant A\log n\Big\}\leqslant\frac{1}{n^2}
\end{aligned}
$$

with an appropriate positive constant A.

Theorem 1* now follows from this latter inequality and from the simple fact that

$$\mathsf{P}\{\max_{1\leq k\leq n}\ \sup_{0\leq x\leq 1} |W(k+x)-W(k)| \geq \log n + z\} \leq e^{-z}\ .$$

3. APPROXIMATION OF QUANTILE PROCESS BY A KIEFER PROCESS

Bahadur [1] was the first to investigate the distance between the empirical and the quantile processes. The best results, concerning this problem, are due to Kiefer ([6] and [7]). Here we apply the following result of Kiefer:

Theorem H ([7]). *We have*

$$\overline{\lim_{n\to\infty}} \frac{n^{3/4}}{(\log n)^{1/2}(\log\log n)^{1/4}} \times$$

$$\times \sup_x |(F_n(x)-x)-(x-Q_n(x))| = 2^{-1/4} \qquad w.p.\ 1.$$

Combining this theorem and Theorem F, one immediately gets:

Theorem 3. *If the random variables $X_1, X_2, \ldots$ are defined on a rich enough probability space then one can define a Kiefer process $K(x,y)$ on the same probability space and a positive absolute constant K such that*

$$\overline{\lim_{n\to\infty}} \sup_x |n(Q_n(x)-x)-K(x,n)| \times$$

$$\times \frac{1}{(n\log\log n)^{1/4}(\log n)^{1/2}} \leq K \qquad w.p.\ 1.$$

This result seems to be far from the best possible one.

4. A LAW OF ITERATED LOGARITHM FOR THE EMPIRICAL PROCESS

It is easy to see that*

$$\lim_{n\to\infty} \sup_{0<x<1} \frac{\sqrt{n}(F_n(x) - x)}{\sqrt{2x(1-x)\log\log n}} = +\infty$$

with probability 1.

Towards this end one observes:

$$\text{(11)} \qquad \mathsf{P}\left\{ \overline{\lim_{n\to\infty}} \frac{\sqrt{n}\left(F_n\left(\frac{1}{n}\right) - \frac{1}{n}\right)}{\sqrt{2\frac{1}{n}\log\log n\sqrt[4]{\log\log n}}} \geq \frac{1}{2} \right\} = 1 .$$

Clearly we have

$$\text{(12)} \qquad \mathsf{P}\left\{F_n\left(\frac{1}{n}\right) \geq \frac{(\log\log n)^{3/4}}{n}\right\} \geq \frac{1}{(\log\log n)^{3/4(\log\log n)^{3/4}}} .$$

Let $F^{(n)}(x)$ be the empirical distribution function based on the sample elements $X_{2^n+1}, X_{2^n+2}, \ldots, X_{2^{n+1}}$ and consider the events

$$A_n = \left\{F^{(n)}\left(\frac{1}{2^n}\right) \geq \frac{(\log\log 2^n)^{3/4}}{2^n}\right\} \qquad (n = 1, 2, \ldots) .$$

Since the events $\{A_n\}$ are independent, it follows from (12) and the Borel – Cantelli lemma that $\mathsf{P}\{A_n \text{ i.o.}\} = 1$, (i.o. ≡ infinitely often). Now our statement is a consequence of the inequality

$$2^{n+1} F_{2^{n+1}}(x) \geq 2^n F^{(n)}(x) .$$

*The order of magnitude of

$$\sqrt{\frac{n}{2\log\log n}} \sup_{0<x<1} \frac{|F_n(x) - x|}{\sqrt{x(1-x)}}$$

is nicely characterized in a recent paper by Csáki [14].

Actually an earlier result of Baxter [12] (see also [13]) does give a more precise information in this respect. He proves

$$\overline{\lim_{n\to\infty}} \frac{\sqrt{n}\left(F_n\left(\frac{c}{n}\right) - \frac{c}{n}\right)}{\sqrt{2 \log\log n}\sqrt{\frac{c}{n}}} \cdot \frac{\sqrt{2c} \log\log\log n}{\sqrt{\log\log n}} = 1$$

with probability 1.

On the other hand a theorem of Finkelstein [5] implies

Theorem I ([5]). *For every* $\epsilon > 0$ *we have*

$$\mathsf{P}\left\{\overline{\lim_{n\to\infty}} \sup_{\epsilon < x < 1-\epsilon} \frac{\sqrt{n}(F_n(x) - x)}{\sqrt{2x(1-x)\log\log n}} = 1\right\} = 1 .$$

In the light of (11) and Theorem I it is natural to ask what happens if we replace ϵ in Theorem I by a sequence $\{\epsilon_n\}$ tending to zero slowly enough. As an answer to this question we prove:

Theorem 4. *Let* $\epsilon_n = \frac{\log^4 n}{n}$. *Then we have*

$$\mathsf{P}\left\{\overline{\lim_{n\to\infty}} \sup_{\epsilon_n < x < 1-\epsilon_n} \frac{\sqrt{n}(F_n(x) - x)}{\sqrt{2x(1-x)\log\log n}} = \sqrt{2}\right\} = 1 .$$

The proof of Theorem 4 is based on Theorem F and on the following result of Tusnády:

Theorem J ([14]). *Let* $W(x, y)$ *be a Wiener process then*

$$\overline{\lim_{y\to\infty}} \sup_{1 \leqslant x \leqslant f(y)} \frac{W(x, y)}{\sqrt{2xy \log\log xy}} = \sqrt{2}$$

with probability 1, *provided that* $\lim_{y\to\infty} \frac{\log\log f(y)}{\log\log y} = 1.$

This result immediately implies:

Lemma 1.

$$Q = \overline{\lim_{y\to\infty}} \sup_{\frac{1}{f(y)} \leq x \leq 1} \frac{W(x, y)}{\sqrt{2xy \log\log \frac{y}{x}}} = \sqrt{2}$$

with probability 1, *provided that* $\lim_{y\to\infty} \frac{\log\log f(y)}{\log\log y} = 1.$

Proof. Let $x = \frac{1}{z}$ then

$$Q = \overline{\lim_{y\to\infty}} \sup_{1 \leq z \leq f(y)} \frac{zW\left(\frac{1}{z}, y\right)}{\sqrt{2zy \log\log yz}}.$$

Since $zW\left(\frac{1}{z}, y\right) = W^*(z, y)$ is a Wiener process, we have our Lemma.

From this lemma and from the definition of a Kiefer process $K(x, y)$ we immediately get

Lemma 2. *Let* $\epsilon_n = \frac{\log^4 n}{n}$. *Then we have*

$$\mathsf{P}\left\{ \overline{\lim_{n\to\infty}} \sup_{\epsilon_n \leq x \leq 1-\epsilon_n} \frac{K(x, n)}{\sqrt{2nx(1-x) \log\log \frac{n}{x(1-x)}}} = \sqrt{2} \right\} = 1.$$

Proof of Theorem 4. It follows from Theorem F that

$$\sup_{\epsilon_n \leq x \leq 1-\epsilon_n} \frac{|n(F_n(x) - x) - K(x, n)|}{\sqrt{2nx(1-x) \log\log n}} =$$

$$= O\left(\frac{\log^2 n}{\sqrt{2n \frac{\log^4 n}{n} \log\log n}} \right) = o(1) \quad \text{w.p. 1 as } n \to \infty .$$

Now our theorem follows from Lemma 2 and from the following trivial remark:

$$\overline{\lim_{n\to\infty}} \sup_{\epsilon_n < x < 1-\epsilon_n} \frac{K(x,n)}{\sqrt{2nx(1-x)\log\log\frac{n}{x(1-x)}}} =$$

$$= \overline{\lim_{n\to\infty}} \sup_{\epsilon_n < x < 1-\epsilon_n} \frac{K(x,n)}{\sqrt{2nx(1-x)\log\log n}} \, .$$

No uniform results (in x) are known below the above given $\epsilon_n = \frac{(\log n)^4}{n}$. However Kiefer [13] does prove the following interesting pointwise law of iterated logarithm concerning the interval $\left[\frac{c}{n}, \frac{\log^4 n}{n}\right]$:

$$\overline{\lim_{n\to\infty}} \sqrt{n} \frac{|F_n(\pi_n) - \pi_n|}{\sqrt{2\pi_n(1-\pi_n)\log\log n}} =$$

$$= \begin{cases} 1 & \text{if } \dfrac{n\pi_n}{\log\log n} \to \infty \qquad \left(\pi_n \leqslant \frac{1}{2}\right) \\ K(\alpha) & \text{if } \dfrac{n\pi_n}{\log\log n} = \alpha > 0 \end{cases}$$

with probability 1 where $K(\alpha)$ is a positive constant depending on α.

REFERENCES

[1] R.R. Bahadur, A note on quantiles in large samples, *Ann. Math. Statist.*, 37 (1966), 577-580.

[2] L. Breiman, *Probability*, Reading, Mass, Addison-Wesley, 1968.

[3] D.R. Brillinger, An asymptotic representation of the sample distribution function, *Bull. Amer. Math. Soc.*, 75 (1969), 545-547.

[4] K.L. Chung, An estimate concerning the Kolmogorov limit distribution, *Trans. Amer. Math. Soc.*, 67 (1949), 36-50.

[5] H. Finkelstein, The law of the iterated logarithm for empirical distributions, *Ann. Math. Statist.*, 42 (1971), 607-615.

[6] J. Kiefer, On Bahadur's representation of sample quantiles, *Ann. Math. Statist.*, 38 (1967), 1323-1342.

[7] J. Kiefer, Deviations between the sample quantile process and the sample DF, *Proc. First Internat. Conf. Nonpar. Inf.*, (1969), Cambridge Univ. Press, 299-319.

[8] J. Kiefer, Skorohod embedding of multivariate RV's, and the sample DF, *Z. Wahrscheinlichkeitstheorie verw. Geb.*, 24 (1972), 1-35.

[9] J. Komlós – P. Major – G. Tusnády, An approximation of partial sums of independent RV's, and the sample DF, I., *Z. Wahrscheinlichkeitstheorie verw. Geb.*, (to appear).

[10] N. Smirnov, Sur les écarts de la course de distribution empirique, *Mat. Sbornik,* 6 (1939), 3-26.

[11] M.J. Wichura, Some Strassen type laws of the iterated logarithm for multiparameter stochastic processes with independent increments, *Ann. Prob.*, 1 (1973), 272-296.

[12] G. Baxter, An analogue of the law of iterated logarithm, *Proc. Amer. Math. Soc.*, 6 (1955), 177-181.

[13] J. Kiefer, Iterated logarithm Analogues for Sample Quantiles when $p_n \downarrow 0$, *Sixth Berkeley Symposium on Probability and Statistics* 1972, Vol. I, 227-244.

[14] G. Tusnády, A law of the iterated logarithm for multivariate Wiener processes, *Studia Sci. Math. Hung.*, (to appear).

COLLOQUIA MATHEMATICA SOCIETATIS JÁNOS BOLYAI
11. LIMIT THEOREMS OF PROBABILITY THEORY, KESZTHELY (HUNGARY), 1974.

LAW OF LARGE NUMBERS FOR MARKOV CHAINS HOMOGENEOUS IN TIME AND IN THE SECOND COMPONENT

I.I. EŽOV – T. GERGELY

A $\{\xi_n, \eta_n\}_{n=1}^{\infty}$ two component homogeneous Markov chain taking values in $T \times R^{(k)}$ $(T = \{1, \ldots, m\}$, $R^{(k)}$ is k-dimensional Euclidean space) is homogeneous in the second component if its transition probabilities satisfy the condition

$$\mathsf{P}\{\xi_n = j,\ \eta_n \in A \mid \xi_{n-1} = i,\ \eta_{n-1} = x\} =$$
$$= \mathsf{P}\{\xi_n = j,\ \eta_n \in A_{-x} \mid \xi_{n-1} = i,\ \eta_{n-1} = 0\} = P_{ij}(A_{-x})$$

where

$$A_{-x} = \{y \in R^{(k)}:\ y + x \in A\}\ ;$$
$$n \geqslant 1;\ \ i, j \in T;\ \ 0, x \in R^{(k)};\ \ A \subseteq R^{(k)}\ .$$

The first component $\{\xi_n\}_{n=1}^{\infty}$ of this process is a homogeneous Markov chain and the second one is a process with independent increments given on the sample functions of the Markov chain $\{\xi_n\}_{n=1}^{\infty}$.

This class of stochastic processes was discussed in [1]-[3], while [4],

[5] contain some results on the asymptotic behaviour of such processes.

The present paper is devoted to the investigation of the law of large numbers for the two component Markov chain $\{\xi_n, \eta_n\}_{n=1}^{\infty}$.

We point out that the law of large numbers under certain conditions is valid for the sequence $\{\eta_n - \eta_{n-1}\}_{n=1}^{\infty}$, that is that the sequence $\left\{\frac{1}{n}\eta_n\right\}_{n=1}^{\infty}$ converges to a constant as $n \to \infty$.

Let us suppose that

$$\int_{R^{(k)}} e^{i(\lambda, x)} \mathsf{P}\{\xi_{n+1} = j,\ \eta_{n+1} \in dx \mid \xi_n = i,\ \eta_n = 0\} = p_{ij}\varphi_{ij}(\lambda)$$

where

$$(\lambda, x) = \sum_{i=1}^{k} \lambda_i x_i \qquad (\lambda, x \in R^{(k)}) .$$

Here we introduce the following notations

$$\boldsymbol{P}(\lambda) = \| p_{ij}\varphi_{ij}(\lambda);\ i, j \in T \|, \quad \boldsymbol{P} = \| p_{ij};\ i, j \in T \| .$$

Theorem. *If*

$$\varphi_{ij}(\epsilon\lambda) = 1 + i\epsilon(\lambda, d_{ij}) + o(\epsilon) \qquad (\epsilon \to 0;\ d_{ij} = (d_{ij}^{(1)}, \ldots, d_{ij}^{(k)}))$$

and

$$\det(z\boldsymbol{E} - \boldsymbol{P}) = (z-1) \prod_{l=1}^{m-1} (z - a_l)$$

where $\boldsymbol{E}$ *denotes unit matrix,* $|a_l| < 1$ $(1 \leqslant l \leqslant m-1)$, *then*

$$\text{(1)} \qquad \lim \boldsymbol{P}^n\left(\frac{1}{n}\lambda\right) = \begin{pmatrix} \rho_1 & \rho_2 & \cdots & \rho_m \\ \rho_1 & \rho_2 & \cdots & \rho_m \\ \vdots & \vdots & & \vdots \\ \rho_1 & \rho_2 & \cdots & \rho_m \end{pmatrix} \exp\left\{i \sum_{l=1}^{m} \rho_l(\lambda, \beta_l)\right\},$$

where $(\rho_1, \ldots, \rho_m)$ *is the stationary distribution vector of the Markov chain* $\{\xi_n\}$ *and*

$$\beta_l = \sum_{j=1}^{m} p_{lj} d_{lj} .$$

Notes.

(a) There can be equals among the complex numbers $a_1, \ldots, a_{m-1}$.

(b) There exists a stationary distribution of the Markov chain $\{\xi_n\}$ because it is ergodic, for 1 is a simple root of the characteristic equation $\det (zE - \boldsymbol{P}) = 0$ and the other roots are in the circle $|z| < 1$.

Proof. Let

$$\boldsymbol{P}^n (\lambda\epsilon) = \| p_{jk}^{(n)}(\lambda, \epsilon);\ j, k \in T \|;$$

$z_{\epsilon 1}, \ldots, z_{\epsilon k}$ are the characteristic roots of the matrix $\boldsymbol{P}(\lambda\epsilon)$ and $t_1, \ldots, t_k$ are their multiplicities for which

$$\sum_{i=1}^{k} t_i = m .$$

Using Perron's formula [6] we obtain

$$p_{ij}^{(n)}(\lambda, \epsilon) = \sum_{l=2}^{k} \frac{1}{(t_l - 1)!} \left[\frac{d^{t_l - 1}}{dz^{t_l - 1}} \left(\frac{z^n A_{ij}(z, \lambda, \epsilon)}{\psi_l(z, \lambda, \epsilon)} \right) \right]_{z = z_{\epsilon l}} \tag{2}$$

where $A_{ij}(z, \lambda, \epsilon)$ is the cofactor of $z\delta_{ij} - p_{ij}(\lambda, \epsilon)$ in $zE - \boldsymbol{P}(\epsilon\lambda)$ and

$$\psi_l(z, \lambda, \epsilon) = \frac{\det (zE - \boldsymbol{P}(\epsilon\lambda))}{(z - z_{\epsilon l})^{t_l}} \qquad (1 \leqslant l \leqslant k) .$$

At sufficiently small ϵ, one of the characteristic roots of the matrix $\boldsymbol{P}(\epsilon\lambda)$ is near to 1 (let this root be $z_{\epsilon 1}$, then it is evident that $t_1 = 1$) and the modulus of the others is strictly less than 1, then from (2) it follows

$$p_{ij}^{(n)}\left(\lambda, \frac{1}{n}\right) = \left. \frac{z^n A_{ij}\left(z, \lambda, \frac{1}{n}\right)\left(z - z_{\frac{1}{n}1}\right)}{\det\left(zE - \boldsymbol{P}\left(\frac{\lambda}{n}\right)\right)} \right|_{z = z_{\frac{1}{n}1}} + o(1) \tag{3}$$

when $n \to \infty$.

We investigate the limit of (3) by $\epsilon \to 0$. This is done in two stages.

Using (2) with $\lambda = 0$ we have*

(4) $$\lim_{\epsilon\to 0} \frac{A_{ij}(z, \lambda, \epsilon)(z - z_{\epsilon 1})}{\det (zE - P(\epsilon\lambda))}\bigg|_{z=z_{\epsilon 1}} = \frac{A_{ij}(z)(z-1)}{\det (zE - P)}\bigg|_{z=1} = \rho_i .$$

Now all we have to do is to determine the limit $\lim_{\epsilon\to 0} z^n_{\epsilon 1}$ $(\epsilon n = 1)$ only. Let

(5) $$\Delta_\epsilon(z) = \det (zE - P(\epsilon\lambda)) = \sum_{l=0}^{m} \Delta_{\epsilon l}(z-1)^l ,$$

then

(6) $$\lim_{\epsilon\to 0} \Delta_{\epsilon 1} = \lim_{\epsilon\to 0} \frac{d}{dz} \Delta_\epsilon(z) = \frac{d}{dz} \det (zE - P)|_{z=1} =$$

$$= \frac{\det (zE - P)}{z-1}\bigg|_{z=1} = \Delta_1 .$$

Note that $\Delta_1 \neq 0$ for 1 is a simple root of the characteristic equation $\det (zE - P) = 0$.

Using the following equation for matrices

$$\sum_{k=1}^{m} a_{kl}A_{kj} = \delta_{lj} \det (A) \qquad (l, j = 1, \ldots, m)$$

(where δ_{lj} is the Kronecker's symbol, A_{kj} is the cofactor of a_{kj} in the matrix $A = \| a_{kj};\ k, j = 1, \ldots, m \|$) $\Delta_{\epsilon 0}$ takes the form

$$\Delta_{\epsilon 0} = \det (E - P(\epsilon\lambda)) = \frac{1}{m} \sum_{l=1}^{m} \sum_{j=1}^{m} \sum_{k=1}^{m} (\delta_{lj} - p_{lj})A_{lk}(1, \lambda, \epsilon) -$$

$$- \frac{i\epsilon}{m} \sum_{l=1}^{m} \sum_{j=1}^{m} \sum_{k=1}^{m} p_{lj}A_{lk}(1, \lambda, \epsilon)(\lambda, d_{lj}) + o(\epsilon) .$$

*$A_{ij}(z)$ is the cofactor of $z\delta_{ij} - p_{ij}$ in $zE - P$.

From (5) we have

$$z_{\epsilon 1} = 1 - \frac{\Delta_{\epsilon 0}}{\Delta_{\epsilon 1}} + o(\epsilon) . \tag{7}$$

Going over the limits in $\Delta_{\epsilon 0}$ while $\epsilon \to 0$ we have

$$\lim_{\epsilon \to 0} \frac{1}{m} \sum_{l=1}^{m} \sum_{j=1}^{m} \sum_{k=1}^{m} (\delta_{lj} - p_{lj}) A_{lk}(1, \lambda, \epsilon) = 0$$

and using (4) and (6)

$$\lim_{\epsilon \to 0} \frac{\sum_{l=1}^{m} \sum_{j=1}^{m} \sum_{k=1}^{m} p_{lj} A_{lk}(1, \lambda, \epsilon)(\lambda, d_{lj})}{m \Delta_{\epsilon 1}} =$$

$$= \frac{\sum_{l=1}^{m} \sum_{j=1}^{m} (\lambda, d_{lj}) p_{lj} A_{lj}(z)(z-1)}{\det (zE - P)} = \sum_{l=1}^{m} \rho_l(\lambda, \beta_l) .$$

By these from (7)

$$\lim_{\epsilon \to +0} z_{\epsilon 1}^{\frac{1}{\epsilon}} = \exp \left\{ i \sum_{l=1}^{m} \rho_l(\lambda, \beta_l) \right\} \tag{8}$$

can easily be obtained.

(1) now follows from (4) and (8), herewith the theorem is proved.

Corollary 1. *By the conditions of the theorem the series* $\left\{ \frac{1}{n} \eta_n \right\}$ *converges in probability to* $\sum_{l=1}^{m} \rho_l \beta_l$ *as* $n \to \infty$.

Remark. If $\xi_n = l$, then β_l is equal to the mean increments of $\eta_{n+1} - \eta_n$ i.e. $\beta_l = \mathsf{E}\{\eta_{n+1} - \eta_n \mid \xi_n = l\}$. Here the mathematical expectation of a vector means a vector mathematical expectations of its components, i.e. $\mathsf{E}(\xi_1, \ldots, \xi_k) = (\mathsf{E}\xi_k, \ldots, \mathsf{E}\xi_k)$.

Corollary 2. *Let the random variable* β_{ξ_n} *equal to* β_l *if and only if* $\xi_n = l$ *and the initial distribution of Markov chain* $\{\xi_n\}$ *corresponds to its stationary distribution, i.e. to* $(\rho_1, \ldots, \rho_m)$. *Then*

$E\beta_{\xi_n}$ *does not depend on* n *and it corresponds to* $\lim_{n\to\infty} \frac{1}{n} \eta_n$, *i.e. to* $\sum_{i=1}^{m} \rho_l \beta_l$.

Corollary 3. *If the Markov chain* $\{\xi_n\}$ *in the Theorem is homogeneous and the stochastic vectors with characteristic functions* $\varphi_{ij}(\lambda)$ *take values in a bounded parallelepiped with probability* 1 *then the strong law of large numbers can be applied to the series* $\{\eta_{n+1} - \eta_n\}$, *i.e.*

$$P\{\lim_{n\to\infty} \frac{1}{n} [\eta_n - \sum_{l=1}^{n-1} \beta_{\xi_l}] = 0\} = 1 .$$

This fact can be easily proved using the theorem of the strong law of large numbers of the sum of random variables which form a finite homogeneous Markov chain.

REFERENCES

[1] I.I. Ežov – A.V. Skorohod, Markov processes homogeneous in the second components, *Teorija Verojatn. i Primenen.*, 14 (1969), 3-14.

[2] E. Činlar, Markov additive processes, I-II, *Z. Wahrscheinlichkeitstheorie verw. Geb.*, 24 (1972), 85-121.

[3] T. Gergely – I.I. Yezhow, Markov chains homogeneous in the second component, Preprint KFKI-74-40, Budapest, 1974.

[4] J. Keilson – D.M.G. Wishart, A central limit theorem for processes defined on a finite Markov chain, *Proc. Cambridge Philos. Soc.*, 60 (1964), 547-567.

[5] M. Fukushima – M. Hitsuda, On a class of Markov processes taking values on lines and the central limit theorem, *Nagoya Math. Journal*, 30 (1967), 47-56.

[6] O. Perron, Über die Matrizen, *Math. Ann.*, 64 (1907), 248-263.

COLLOQUIA MATHEMATICA SOCIETATIS JÁNOS BOLYAI
11. LIMIT THEOREMS OF PROBABILITY THEORY, KESZTHELY (HUNGARY), 1974.

LEARNING FROM AN ERGODIC TRAINING SEQUENCE

J. FRITZ

Consider a Robbins – Monro type approximation procedure $x_1 = y_0$, $x_{n+1} = x_n - \frac{1}{n+1}(A_n x_n - y_n)$ for solving the linear equation $Ax = y$ in a Banach space X, where y_n and A_n are such estimators that their arithmetic means converge to y and A, respectively. Under some additional conditions implying $\| I - A \| < 1$, it is shown that x_n goes to the unique solution of this equation. As an auxiliary result, a recursive approximation method has been obtained for the inverse of A. The results can be applied to linear regression problems under very general conditions.

1. INTRODUCTION

Regression problems of pattern recognition, prediction theory and system identification usually reduce to the following one: We are given a sequence $y_0, y_1, \ldots, y_n, \ldots$ of elements, and a sequence $A_1, A_2, \ldots$ $\ldots, A_n, \ldots$ of operators in a Banach space X such that

(i) $$\lim_n \frac{1}{n+1} \sum_{i=0}^{n} y_i = y ,$$

(ii) $$\lim_n \frac{1}{n} \sum_{i=1}^{n} A_i = A$$

in the strong sense; and we have to find the unique solution φ of the equation $Ax = y$. Because of computational constraints it may happen that we are not able to determine y and A from (i) and (ii) directly, but we still have a possibility to approximate φ by a Robbins – Monro type procedure

(1) $$x_1 = y_0, \; x_{n+1} = x_n - \frac{1}{n+1} (A_n x_n - y_n) .$$

Unfortunately, stochastic approximation theory (e.g. the theorem of Venter [1] when X is a separable Hilbert-space) applies to this algorithm only if the (y_n, A_n)'s are samples from an independent sequence. Recently, several efforts have been made to get rid of independence; it can be replaced by strong mixing conditions (see Csibi [3]). However, nothing is known on the ergodic case even in this simple situation. The aim of this paper is to give conditions under which (i) and (ii) imply $\lim x_n = \varphi$. These conditions are formulated in terms of arithmetic means, thus their validity with probability one may be deduced from ergodic theorems.

Throughout this paper we use the following notations: X is a real or complex Banach space, and operators in X are linear, bounded transformations mapping X into X. The conjugate (dual) space of X is X^* and C^* denotes the adjoint of an operator C; I is the identity transformation in X. The norm of elements and of operators in X and in X^*, as well, is denoted by $\| \cdot \|$. Convergence of elements means convergence in the norm, while $\lim C_n = C$ for operators in X means $Cu = \lim C_n u$ for each $u \in X$. For convenience, we introduce $R_n = I - A_n$ for our sequence.

To prove $\lim x_n = \varphi$, the following additional assumptions are needed:

(iii) $$\sup_n \frac{1}{n} \sum_{m=1}^{n} \| A_m \| = a < +\infty .$$

(iv) There exist a $0 < q < 1$, and an n_0 such that for each $u^* \in X^*$ we have

$$\frac{1}{n}\sum_{m=1}^{n}\|R_m^* u^*\| \subseteq q\|u^*\| \quad \text{if} \quad n \geq n_0 .$$

We shall see that our assumptions imply $\|I - A\| < 1$, that is the inverse

$$(2) \qquad A^{-1} = \sum_{n=0}^{\infty} (I - A)^n$$

is defined and bounded on X; thus we may speak about the unique solution $\varphi = A^{-1}y$ of $Ax = y$. Let us remark that in case of a Hilbert space, $\|I - A\| < 1$ implies that $A + A^*$ is positive, which is necessary for $\lim x_n = \varphi$. However, even $\|I - A\| < 1$ is far from being a necessary condition of $\lim x_n = \varphi$. Further, if X is a Hilbert space, then (iv) can be replaced by the stronger, but more familiar condition that

$$(\text{iv}') \qquad \limsup \frac{1}{n}\Big\|\sum_{m=1}^{n} R_m R_m^*\Big\| < 1 ,$$

since

$$\frac{1}{n}\sum_{m=1}^{n}\|R_m^* u\| \leq \Big[\frac{1}{n}\sum_{m=1}^{n}\|R_m^* u\|^2\Big]^{\frac{1}{2}} =$$

$$= \Big[\Big(\frac{1}{n}\sum_{m=1}^{n} R_m R_m^* u, u\Big)\Big]^{\frac{1}{2}} \leq \|u\| \Big[\frac{1}{n}\Big\|\sum_{m=1}^{n} R_m R_m^*\Big\|\Big]^{\frac{1}{2}}$$

where $(.,.)$ denotes the inner product. Moreover, if each A_n is a positive operator with $\|A_n\| \leq 1$, then

$$\|R_m^* u\|^2 = (R_m u, R_m u) \leq (R_m u, u) ,$$

therefore (iv′) reduces to $\|I - A\| < 1$, provided that (ii) holds in the operator-norm convergence.

The study of (1) will be based on the following expression for x_{n+1}. Let

$$(3) \qquad T_m^{(n)} = \Big(I + \frac{1}{n} R_n\Big)\Big(I + \frac{1}{n-1} R_{n-1}\Big) \ldots \Big(I + \frac{1}{m+1} R_{m+1}\Big)$$

if $0 \leq m < n$, and $T_n^{(n)} = I$. Then

$$x_{n+1} = \left(I - \frac{1}{n+1} A_n\right) x_n + \frac{1}{n+1} y_n =$$

$$= \frac{n}{n+1} \left(I + \frac{1}{n} R_n\right) x_n + \frac{1}{n+1} y_n ,$$

whence immediately follows by induction that

$$(4) \qquad x_{n+1} = \frac{1}{n+1} \sum_{m=0}^{n} T_m^{(n)} y_m .$$

Given $T_m^{(n)}$ (i.e. the sequence $A_1, A_2, \ldots, A_n, \ldots$), this is a Toeplitz summation method for $y_0, y_1, \ldots, y_n, \ldots$; we prove that it transforms sequences of type (1) into convergent ones.

2. THE RESULTS

Lemma. *Consider a triangular array* $C_m^{(n)}$ $(0 \leqslant m \leqslant n)$ *of operators in* X, *and an arbitrary sequence* $y_n \in X$ $(n \geqslant 0)$. *Set*

$$s_n = \frac{1}{n+1} \sum_{m=0}^{n} y_m ,$$

$$x_{n+1} = \sum_{m=0}^{n} C_m^{(n)} y_m$$

and suppose that

$$\text{(a)} \qquad \lim_n \sum_{m=0}^{n} C_m^{(n)} = C ,$$

$$\text{(b)} \qquad \lim_n \| C_m^{(n)} \| = 0 \quad (m = 0, 1, \ldots, n) ,$$

$$\text{(c)} \qquad \sup_n \sum_{m=0}^{n} \| C_m^{(n)} \| < + \infty ;$$

then $\lim y_n = y$ *implies* $\lim x_n = Cy$. *Moreover, if*

$$\text{(d)} \qquad \sup_n \left[(n+1) \| C_n^{(n)} \| + \sum_{m=0}^{n-1} (m+1) \| C_m^{(n)} - C_{m+1}^{(n)} \|\right] < + \infty ,$$

then $\lim s_n = y$ *implies* $\lim x_n = Cy$.

We shall apply this lemma to $C_m^{(n)} = \frac{1}{n+1} T_m^{(n)}$; the Proposition states that (a) holds in our case.

Proposition. *We use the notations of Sec.* 1, *and suppose the validity of* (ii), (iii) *and* (iv). *Then*

$$\lim_n \frac{1}{n+1} \sum_{m=0}^{n} T_m^{(n)} \doteq A^{-1} .$$

Observe that the Proposition says that the recursive procedure

$$B_0 = I,\ B_{n+1} = \frac{1}{n+1} I + \left(I - \frac{1}{n+1} A_n\right) B_n \tag{5}$$

approximates the inverse of A. The main advantage of iteration rules like (1) and (5) is that any approximate solution of our problem can be refined on the basis of the available new information only.

Theorem. *Under assumptions* (i)-(iv) *we have* $\lim x_n = \varphi$ *for process* (1).

In view of this result, we can recursively approximate the solution of $Ax = y$ using sequences of strongly depending (ergodic, not necessarily stationary) estimators of y and A; what we merely need is the strong law of large numbers.

3. PROOF OF THE LEMMA

This proof is essentially the same as that of Toeplitz theorem. Denote $\mathscr{B}$ the Banach space of convergent sequences $\omega = (u_0, u_1, \ldots, u_n, \ldots)$ from X with norm $\|\omega\| = \sup \|u_n\|$, and consider the operators

$$\mathscr{C}_n \omega = \sum_{m=0}^{n} C_m^{(n)} u_m ,$$

$$\mathscr{C} \omega = Cu \quad \text{if} \quad \lim u_n = u ,$$

mapping $\mathscr{B}$ into X. Observe that

$$\| \mathscr{C}_n \omega \| \leqslant \sum_{m=0}^{n} \| C_m^{(n)} \| \| u_m \| \leqslant \| \omega \| \sum_{m=0}^{n} \| C_m^{(n)} \| ,$$

that is $\sup \| \mathscr{C}_n \| < +\infty$ follows from (c). On the other hand, (a) and (b) imply

$$\text{(6)} \qquad \lim_n \mathscr{C}_n \omega = \mathscr{C}\omega ,$$

at least if $u_n = u \in X$ in ω for n large enough. Since the set of such sequences is dense in $\mathscr{B}$, the validity of (6) follows from the Banach – Steinhaus theorem for each $\omega \in \mathscr{B}$, which proves the first statement of the Lemma.

The second statement is an immediate consequence of the first one, since

$$x_{n+1} = \sum_{m=0}^{n} C_m^{(n)} u_m =$$

$$= \sum_{m=0}^{n-1} (m+1)(C_m^{(n)} - C_{m+1}^{(n)}) s_m + (n+1) C_n^{(n)} s_n ,$$

further

$$\lim_n \sum_{m=0}^{n} (m+1)(C_m^{(n)} - C_{m+1}^{(n)}) + (n+1) C_n^{(n)} =$$

$$= \lim_n \sum_{m=0}^{n} C_m^{(n)} = C$$

from (a), while

$$\lim_n (m+1) \| C_m^{(n)} - C_{m+1}^{(n)} \| = 0$$

for each m follows from (b).

4. PROOF OF THE PROPOSITION

First we prove by induction that

$$\text{(7)} \qquad B_{n+1} = \frac{1}{n+1} \sum_{m=0}^{n} T_m^{(n)} = \sum_{i=0}^{n} S_n^{(i)} ,$$

where

$$S_n^{(0)} = I,\ \ S_n^{(1)} = \frac{1}{n+1} \sum_{m=1}^{n} R_m$$

for each n, and

$$(8) \qquad S_n^{(i+1)} = \frac{1}{n+1} \sum_{m=i}^{n-1} R_{m+1} S_m^{(i)}$$

for $0 \leqslant i < n$; $S_n^{(i)} = 0$ if $i > n$. $B_1 = I$, $B_2 = I + \frac{1}{2} R_1$, thus (7) is true for $n = 0$ and $n = 1$. Suppose that

$$B_n = \sum_{i=0}^{n-1} S_{n-1}^{(i)} ;$$

since $T_m^{(n)} = \left(I + \frac{1}{n} R_n\right) T_m^{(n-1)}$,

$$\begin{aligned}
B_{n+1} &= \frac{1}{n+1} I + \frac{n}{n+1} \left(I + \frac{1}{n} R_n\right) B_n = \\
&= \frac{1}{n+1} I + \frac{n}{n+1} \sum_{i=0}^{n-1} S_{n-1}^{(i)} + \frac{1}{n+1} \sum_{i=0}^{n-1} R_n S_{n-1}^{(i)} = \\
&= \frac{1}{n+1} I + \frac{n}{n+1} S_{n-1}^{(0)} + \frac{1}{n+1} R_n S_{n-1}^{(n-1)} + \\
&+ \sum_{i=1}^{n-1} \left(\frac{n}{n+1} S_{n-1}^{(i)} + \frac{1}{n+1} R_n S_{n-1}^{(i-1)} \right) = \\
&= I + \sum_{i=1}^{n} \left(\frac{n}{n+1} S_{n-1}^{(i)} + \frac{1}{n+1} R_n S_{n-1}^{(i-1)} \right)
\end{aligned}$$

as $S_{n-1}^{0} = I$ and $S_{n-1}^{(n)} = 0$. Therefore, (7) reduces to

$$(9) \qquad \frac{n}{n+1} S_{n-1}^{(i)} + \frac{1}{n+1} R_n S_{n-1}^{(i-1)} = S_n^{(i)} ,$$

where $1 \leqslant i \leqslant n$. We see from (8) that (9) is true if $n - i \leqslant 0$, suppose it for $n - i \leqslant k < n$. Let $j = n - k - 1$, then $n - 1 - j \leqslant k$, thus

$$\begin{aligned}
\frac{n}{n+1} S_{n-1}^{(j)} &= \frac{n}{n+1} \left(\frac{n-1}{n} S_{n-2}^{(j)} + \frac{1}{n} R_{n-1} S_{n-2}^{(j-1)} \right) = \\
&= \frac{n-1}{n+1} S_{n-2}^{(j)} + \frac{1}{n+1} R_{n-1} S_{n-2}^{(j-1)} .
\end{aligned}$$

Repeating this step $k+1$ times, we obtain

$$\frac{1}{n+1} S^{(j)}_{n-1} + \frac{1}{n+1} R_n S^{(j-1)}_{n-1} = \frac{n-k-1}{n+1} S^{(j)}_{j-1} +$$

$$+ \frac{1}{n+1} \sum_{m=j-1}^{n-1} R_{m+1} S^{(j-1)}_m = S^{(j)}_n$$

from (8), as $S^{(j-1)}_j = 0$; which proves (9). The proof of (7) is complete.

Observe now that

(10) $$\lim_n S^{(i)}_n = (I-A)^i \quad \text{for each } i ,$$

as follows immediately from (ii), (iii) and (8) by induction; we show that this convergence is a dominated one, whence by (7)

(11) $$\lim B_{n+1} = \lim_n \sum_{i=0}^{n} S^{(i)}_n = \sum_{i=0}^{\infty} (I-A)^i = A^{-1} .$$

Let n_0 and q be the same as in (iv); since convergent sequences are bounded, we have such a large constant c that

(12) $$\| S^{(i)}_n \| \leqslant cq^i \quad \text{for each } n ,$$

at least if $0 \leqslant i \leqslant n_0$. Fix this c, and suppose (12) for a $j \geqslant n_0$. Using $\| S \| = \| S^* \|$, we obtain from (8) that

$$\| S^{(j+1)}_n \| \leqslant \sup_{\|u^*\|=1} \frac{1}{n+1} \sum_{m=j}^{n-1} \| S^{(j)}_m \| \| R^*_{m+1} u^* \| \leqslant$$

$$\leqslant cq^j \sup_{\|u^*\|=1} \frac{1}{n+1} \sum_{m=0}^{n} \| R^*_m u^* \| \leqslant cq^{j+1} ;$$

that is (12) holds if $i \leqslant n$ and n is arbitrary. Since $0 < q < 1$ in (iv), this proves (11) and the proposition.

5. PROOF OF THE THEOREM

We want to apply the Lemma to $C^{(n)}_m = \frac{1}{n+1} T^{(n)}_m$; in view of the Proposition, it suffices to verify (b), (c) and (d). First we prove that

$$(13)\qquad \| T_m^{(n)} \| \leqslant \frac{\alpha}{\alpha - q} \left(\frac{n+1}{m}\right)^{\alpha} \quad \text{if} \quad n \geqslant m \geqslant n_0 ,$$

where n_0 and q are the same as in (iv), while $q < \alpha < 1$.

(13) is true for $n = m$ as $T_n^{(n)} = I$; fix $m \geqslant n_0$ and suppose that

$$\| T_m^{(i)} \| \leqslant b \left(\frac{i+1}{m}\right)^{\alpha} \quad \text{if} \quad m \leqslant i < n .$$

Since

$$T_m^{(n)} = \left(I + \frac{1}{n} R_n\right) T_m^{(n-1)} = T_m^{(n-1)} + \frac{1}{n} R_n T_m^{(n-1)} =$$

$$= I + \sum_{i=m}^{n-1} \frac{1}{i+1} R_{i+1} T_m^{(i)} ,$$

whence, with $u^* \in X$, $\| u^* \| = 1$ and

$$r_i = \frac{1}{i} \sum_{j=1}^{i} \| R_j^* u^* \|$$

we have from (iv) and $\| T \| = \| T^* \|$ that

$$\| T_m^{(n)*} u^* \| \leqslant 1 + \sum_{i=m}^{n-1} \frac{1}{i+1} \| T_m^{(i)} \| \| R_{i+1}^* u^* \| \leqslant$$

$$\leqslant 1 + b \sum_{i=m}^{n-1} \frac{1}{i+1} \left(\frac{i+1}{m}\right)^{\alpha} [(i+1) r_{i+1} - i r_i] =$$

$$= 1 - b \frac{m}{m+1} \left(\frac{m+1}{m}\right)^{\alpha} r_m + b \frac{n}{n+1} \left(\frac{n+1}{n}\right)^{\alpha} r_n +$$

$$+ b \sum_{i=m+1}^{n} \left[\frac{1}{i} \left(\frac{i}{m}\right)^{\alpha} - \frac{1}{i+1} \left(\frac{i+1}{m}\right)^{\alpha}\right] i r_i \leqslant$$

$$\leqslant 1 + bq \frac{n}{n+1} \left(\frac{n+1}{m}\right)^{\alpha} +$$

$$+ bq \sum_{i=m+1}^{n} \left[\left(\frac{i}{m}\right)^{\alpha} - \frac{i}{i+1} \left(\frac{i+1}{m}\right)^{\alpha}\right] .$$

However,

$$\| T_m^{(n)} \| = \| T_m^{(n)*} \| = \sup_{\|u^*\| = 1} \| T_m^{(n)*} u^* \| ,$$

thus

$$\| T_m^{(n)} \| \leqslant 1 + bq \frac{n}{n+1} \left(\frac{n+1}{m}\right)^\alpha +$$

$$+ bq \left(\frac{m+1}{m}\right)^\alpha - bq \left(\frac{n+1}{m}\right)^\alpha +$$

$$+ bq \sum_{i=m+2}^{n+1} \frac{1}{i} \left(\frac{i}{m}\right)^\alpha \leqslant 1 + bq \left(\frac{m+1}{m}\right)^\alpha +$$

$$+ bqm^{-\alpha} \int_{m+1}^{n+1} t^{\alpha-1} dt = 1 + bq \left(\frac{m+1}{m}\right)^\alpha +$$

$$+ \frac{bq}{\alpha} \left(\frac{n+1}{m}\right)^\alpha - \frac{bq}{\alpha} \left(\frac{m+1}{m}\right)^\alpha \leqslant$$

$$\leqslant 1 + \frac{bq}{\alpha} \left(\frac{n+1}{m}\right)^\alpha \leqslant b \left(\frac{n+1}{m}\right)^\alpha$$

if $b \geqslant \dfrac{\alpha}{\alpha - q}$, which proves (13).

On the other hand, if $m \leqslant n_0$, then

$$\| T_m^{(n)} \| \leqslant \| T_m^{(n_0)} \| \| T_{n_0}^{(n)} \| \leqslant \frac{\alpha}{\alpha - q} \left(\frac{n+1}{n_0}\right)^\alpha \prod_{j=1}^{n_0} \left(1 + \frac{1}{j} \| R_j \|\right),$$

that is

$$\| T_m^{(n)} \| \leqslant d\left(\frac{n+1}{m}\right)^\alpha \quad \text{if} \quad 0 < m \leqslant n, \tag{14}$$

where $0 < \alpha < 1$ and d is a positive constant, while $\| T_0^{(n)} \| \leqslant d(n+1)^\alpha$; whence (b) and (c) follow immediately as $\alpha < 1$ and

$$\sum_{m=2}^{n} m^{-\alpha} \leqslant \int_1^n t^{-\alpha} dt = \frac{1}{1-\alpha} [n^{1-\alpha} - 1]. \tag{15}$$

To check (d) observe that

$$T_m^{(n)} - T_{m+1}^{(n)} = T_{m+1}^{(n)} \left(I + \frac{1}{m+1} R_{m+1}\right) - T_{m+1}^{(n)} =$$

$$= \frac{1}{m+1} R_{m+1} T_{m+1}^{(n)}.$$

Therefore, using (14), (iii) and (15), we obtain

$$h_n = (n+1)\| C_n^{(n)} \| + \sum_{m=0}^{n-1} (m+1) \| C_m^{(n)} - C_{m+1}^{(n)} \| \leqslant$$

$$\leqslant 1 + \frac{1}{n+1} \sum_{m=1}^{n} \| T_m^{(n)} \| \| R_m \| \leqslant$$

$$\leqslant 1 + \frac{d}{n+1} \sum_{m=1}^{n} \left(\frac{n+1}{m}\right)^{\alpha} (mp_m - (m-1)p_{m-1})$$

where

$$p_m = \frac{1}{m} \sum_{i=1}^{m} \| R_m \| \leqslant 1 + a$$

in view of (iii). Hence

$$h_n \leqslant 1 + \frac{d}{n+1} \sum_{m=1}^{n} \left[\left(\frac{n+1}{m}\right)^{\alpha} - \left(\frac{n+1}{m+1}\right)^{\alpha}\right] mp_m +$$

$$+ dp_n \leqslant 1 + d(1+a) + \frac{d(1+a)}{n+1} [(n+1)^{\alpha} - (n+1)] +$$

$$+ \frac{d(1+a)}{n+1} \sum_{m=2}^{n+1} \left(\frac{n+1}{m}\right)^{\alpha} \leqslant 1 + d(1+a) +$$

$$+ \frac{d(1+a)}{(1-\alpha)(n+1)} [(n+1)^{\alpha}(n+1)^{1-\alpha} - (n+1)^{\alpha}] \leqslant$$

$$\leqslant 1 + d(1+a) \frac{2-\alpha}{1-\alpha}$$

which proves (d) and the theorem, as well.

6. AN EXAMPLE

Let X be a finite dimensional Euclidean space, and consider a jointly ergodic sequence $(\xi_1, \eta_1), (\xi_2, \eta_2), \ldots, (\xi_n, \eta_n), \ldots$ with finite second moments, where $\xi_n \in X$ and the η_n's are real variables. Define $y_n = \eta_n \xi_n$ and A_n by $A_n x = (x, \xi_n)\xi_n$; further, set $A = \mathsf{E}(A_1)$, $y = \mathsf{E}(y_1)$. Since A is just the covariance matrix of ξ_1, (1) is a recursive procedure for solving the linear regression problem

$$\mathsf{E}(\eta_1 - (x, \xi_1))^2 = \min!, \qquad x \in X .$$

Observe that $\| A_n \| = \| \xi_n \|^2$, thus our moment conditions and the ergodic theorem imply (i), (ii) and (iii); at least with probability one. Further, (iv) holds with probability one if and only if $\mathsf{E} \| R_1 u \| < 1$ for each $u \in X$, $\| u \| = 1$ where $R_n = I - A_n$. This statement follows immediately from the fact, that the functions

$$r_n(u) = \frac{1}{n} \sum_{m=1}^{n} \| R_m u \|$$

satisfy

$$| r_n(u) - r_n(v) | \leqslant (1 + a) \| u - v \|$$

if a is the constant in (iii); and the unit sphere in X is compact. Of course, a is a random variable here, but we need (iv) only for fixed realizations of the process.

In the case when A is not singular, and $\| \xi_1 \| \leqslant \beta < 2$ with probability one, this later condition is certainly satisfied, since, for

$$\mathsf{E} \| R_1 u \| = \mathsf{E}[1 - (u, \xi_1)^2 (2 - \| \xi_1 \|^2)]^{1/2} \leqslant$$

$$\leqslant [1 - (uA, u)(2 - \beta)]^{1/2} < 1 ,$$

as $\mathsf{E}(u, \xi_1)^2 = (uA, u)$. Let us remark that $\mathsf{E}(\eta_1^2) < + \infty$ is not needed if $\| \xi_1 \| \leqslant \beta < 2$.

REFERENCES

[1] J.H. Venter, On Dvoretzky stochastic approximation theorems, *Ann. Math. Stat.*, 37 (1966), 1534-1544.

[2] L.W. Kantorowitsh – G.P. Akilow, *Funktionalanalysis in normierten Räumen*, Akademie Verlag, Berlin, 1964.

[3] S. Csibi, *Stability and complexity of learning processes,* Lecture notes, International Center for Mechanical Sciences, Summer School, 1972, (1973).

[4] M. Loève, *Probability theory,* Van Nostrand, New York, 1963.

COLLOQUIA MATHEMATICA SOCIETATIS JÁNOS BOLYAI
11. LIMIT THEOREMS OF PROBABILITY THEORY, KESZTHELY (HUNGARY), 1974.

AROUND THE GLIVENKO – CANTELLI THEOREM

P. GAENSSLER

0. SUMMARY

The present paper is concerned with a new way of proving Rao's version of the Glivenko – Cantelli theorem for independent identically distributed R^k-valued random variables x_n $(n \in N)$, based on a uniform law of large numbers for sequences $h_t \circ x_n$ with certain functions $h_t: R^k \to \bar{R}$, where t is running through a compact parameter space T. Secondly some new results on the speed of (mean) Glivenko – Cantelli convergence recently obtained by W. Stute (Bochum) will be announced.

1. THE GLIVENKO – CANTELLI THEOREM FOR R^k-VALUED RANDOM VARIABLES

Let $(x_n)_{n \in N}$ be a sequence of independent identically distributed (i.i.d.) random variables on some probability space (p-space) $(\Omega, \mathscr{F}, \mathsf{P})$ with values in R^k $(k \geqslant 1)$ and distribution function (d.f.) F.

Denoting with F_n^ω the empirical d.f. pertaining to $x_1(\omega), \dots, x_n(\omega)$, $n \in N$, $\omega \in \Omega$, the classical Glivenko – Cantelli theorem $(k = 1)$ can be generalized to the following statement:

For arbitrary F it is true that

(1.1) $$\lim_{n\to\infty} \sup_{\lambda\in R^k} |F_n^\omega(\lambda) - F(\lambda)| = 0$$

for P-almost all (P-a.a.) $\omega \in \Omega$.

As to (1.1) see e.g. the recently published paper by H. Richter [16], where one can even find a result on the rate of convergence in (1.1), namely:

For arbitrary F and $(\varphi(n))_{n\in N}$

so that $\lim_{n\to\infty} \varphi(n) \sqrt{\frac{\log\log n}{n}} = 0$ one has

(1.2)

$$\lim_{n\to\infty} \varphi(n) \sup_{\lambda\in R^k} |F_n^\omega(\lambda) - F(\lambda)| = 0$$

for P-a.a. $\omega \in \Omega$.

Now, replacing in (1.1) the class $\{\{\xi \in R^k : \xi \leqslant \lambda\} : \lambda \in R^k\}$ by the class $\mathscr{C}_k$ of all measurable convex sets C in R^k and denoting with μ_n^ω and μ the empirical p-measure and distribution on the Borel σ-field $\mathscr{B}_k$ in R^k pertaining to F_n^ω and F, respectively, it was proved by R.R. Rao [15], Theorem 7.1, that

(1.3) $$\lim_{n\to\infty} \sup_{C\in\mathscr{C}_k} |\mu_n^\omega(C) - \mu(C)| = 0 \quad \text{for P-a.a. } \omega \in \Omega,$$

whenever μ fulfills the following condition

(+) $$\mu(\partial C) = 0 \quad \text{for all } C \in \mathscr{C}_k$$

(∂C denoting the boundary of C).

It can be easily shown by examples that in (1.3) the additional condition (+) on μ cannot be dispensed with in general.

There are several possibilities of proving (1.3), one of them will be sketched by the following considerations (a)-(c):

(a) According to a result of V.S. Varadarajan [21]

$$P(\{\omega: \mu_n^\omega \to \mu \text{ weakly}\}) = 1;$$

hence for P-a.a. $\omega \in \Omega$ one has $\lim_{n\to\infty} \mu_n^\omega(B) = \mu(B)$ for all $B \in \mathscr{B}_k$ with $\mu(\partial B) = 0$.

(b) In particular for any μ fulfilling (+) one obtains that for

$$\text{P-a.a. } \omega \in \Omega \quad \lim_{n\to\infty} \mu_n^\omega(C) = \mu(C) \text{ for all } C \in \mathscr{C}_k .$$

Using now the following result (c) of V. Fabian [6] one immediately obtains the assertion in (1.3).

(c) If $(\mu_n)_{n\in N}$ is a sequence of p-measures on $\mathscr{B}_k$ with $\lim_{n\to\infty} \mu_n(C) = \mu(C)$ for all $C \in \mathscr{C}_k$, where μ is a p-measure on $\mathscr{B}_k$ fulfilling (+), then $\lim_{n=\infty} \sup_{C\in\mathscr{C}_k} |\mu_n(C) - \mu(C)| = 0$.

Fabian's theorem (c) as well as the original proof of (1.3) given by Rao are based on the following lemma known as Blaschke's selection theorem (cf. H.G. Eggleston [5], pp. 64-67):

Lemma 1. *For any real* $a > 0$ *let* $\mathscr{C}_k^a$ *be the class of all closed convex and nonempty subsets of the ball* $B_a = \{\xi \in R^k : \|\xi\| \leqslant a\}$. *For* $C \in \mathscr{C}_k^a$ *and* $\delta > 0$ *let* $C^\delta = \{\xi \in B_a : \|\xi, C\| = \inf_{\eta\in C} \|\xi - \eta\| < \delta\}$. *Then introducing in* $\mathscr{C}_k^a$ *the so called Hausdorff metric* $d(C_1, C_2) = \inf\{\delta > 0: C_1 \subset C_2^\delta$ *and* $C_2 \subset C_1^\delta\}$, $C_1, C_2 \in \mathscr{C}_k^a$, $(\mathscr{C}_k^a, d)$ *becomes a compact metric space.*

Using again Lemma 1 we want to present here another short and rather direct way of obtaining (1.3) as an immediate consequence of the following Lemma 2 which is useful in the theory of estimation as well (cf. [9], Section 3). We remark that Lemma 2 may also be applied in deriving Glivenko – Cantelli results as obtained by J. Dehardt [3].

Lemma 2. *Let* $(X, \mathscr{A}, \mu)$ *be a* p*-space,* $(T, \mathscr{T})$ *a compact Hausdorff space and let* $h_t\colon X \to \bar{R}$, $t \in T$, *be a family of functions fulfilling the following set of conditions:*

(i) $\xi \to h_t(\xi)$ *is* $\mathscr{A}$*-measurable for every* $t \in T$;

(ii) *for any* $t_0 \in T$ *and for any open neighbourhood* $U(t_0)$ *of* t_0 *the functions*

$$\xi \to \inf_{t \in U(t_0)} h_t(\xi) \quad \textit{and} \quad \xi \to \sup_{t \in U(t_0)} h_t(\xi)$$

are $\mathscr{A}$*-measurable;*

(iii) *for any* $t_0 \in T$ *and* $\epsilon > 0$ *there exists an open neighbourhood* $U(t_0)$ *of* t_0 *such that*

(a) $\mathsf{E}_\mu(\inf_{t \in U(t_0)} h_t) > \mathsf{E}_\mu(h_{t_0}) - \epsilon$

(b) $\mathsf{E}_\mu(\sup_{t \in U(t_0)} h_t) < \mathsf{E}_\mu(h_{t_0}) + \epsilon$;

(iv) $-\infty < \mathsf{E}_\mu(\inf_{t \in T} h_t)$ *and* $\mathsf{E}_\mu(\sup_{t \in T} h_t) < +\infty$.

Then, if $(x_n)_{n \in N}$ *is a sequence of independent identically distributed random variables on some probability space* $(\Omega, \mathscr{F}, \mathsf{P})$ *with values in* $(X, \mathscr{A})$ *and distribution* μ, *it follows that*

$$(1.4) \qquad \lim_{n \to \infty} \sup_{t \in T} \left| \frac{1}{n} \sum_{i=1}^{n} h_t(x_i(\omega)) - \mathsf{E}_\mu(h_t) \right| = 0 \quad \textit{for } \mathsf{P}\textit{-a.a. } \omega \in \Omega .$$

Now, as to (1.3) we remark that $\lim_{n \to \infty} \sup_{C \in \mathscr{C}_k} |\mu_n^\omega(C) - \mu(C)| = 0$ for P-a.a. $\omega \in \Omega$ is (in view of (+)) implied by the following statement: For any real $a > 0$

$$(1.5) \qquad \lim_{n \to \infty} \sup_{C \in \mathscr{C}_k^a} |\mu_n^\omega(C) - \mu(C)| = 0 \quad \text{for } \mathsf{P}\text{-a.a. } \omega \in \Omega ,$$

where the latter holds true according to Lemma 1 and (1.4) with $T = \mathscr{C}_k^a$ provided the family $\{h_t = \chi_C : t = C \in \mathscr{C}_k^a\}$ fulfills (i)-(iv) of Lemma 2, where χ_C denotes the characteristic function of C. But this can be easily seen making essential use of condition (+) on μ. As to (iii) (a) for example, given any $C_0 \in \mathscr{C}_k^a$ and $\epsilon > 0$ there exists $\delta = \delta(\epsilon) > 0$ such that $\mathsf{E}_\mu(\inf_{C \in U(C_0)} \chi_C) = \mu((C_0)_\delta) > \mu(C_0) - \epsilon$, where $U(C_0) = \{C \in \mathscr{C}_k^a : d(C, C_0) < \delta\}$ and $C_\delta = C^\delta \setminus \partial_\delta C$, $\partial_\delta C$ being the δ-boundary of $C \in \mathscr{C}_k^a$ defined by

$$\partial_\delta C = \{\xi \in B_a : \| \xi, C \| < \delta, \ \| \xi, B_a \setminus C \| < \delta\} .$$

For the sake of completeness we will give a proof of Lemma 2 in the next section.

2. PROOF OF LEMMA 2.

We remark that the following proof of Lemma 2 is nearly the same as a proof given by J. Pfanzagl (in one of his lectures on estimation theory); for a similar result cf. Le Cam [12], Corollary 4.1, p. 300.

First, by (iii) and (iv) one obtains that $t \to \mathsf{E}_\mu(h_t)$ is a real valued continuous function on T. Thus it follows from (iii) (a) that for any $t_0 \in T$ and $\epsilon > 0$ there exists $U(t_0) \in \mathscr{T}$ with $t_0 \in U(t_0)$ such that $V(t_0) = \{\tau \in U(t_0): \mathsf{E}_\mu(\inf_{t \in U(t_0)} h_t) > \mathsf{E}_\mu(h_\tau) - \epsilon\} \in \mathscr{T}$ and $t_0 \in V(t_0) \subset$ $\subset U(t_0)$; since $\tau \in V(t_0)$ implies that

$$\mathsf{E}_\mu(h_\tau) \geqslant \mathsf{E}_\mu(\inf_{t \in V(t_0)} h_t) \geqslant \mathsf{E}_\mu(\inf_{t \in U(t_0)} h_t) > \mathsf{E}_\mu(h_\tau) - \epsilon ,$$

we obtain that for all $\tau \in V(t_0)$

$$\frac{1}{n} \sum_{i=1}^n [h_\tau \circ x_i - \mathsf{E}_\mu(h_\tau)] \geqslant$$

$$\geqslant \frac{1}{n} \sum_{i=1}^n [\inf_{t \in V(t_0)} h_t \circ x_i - \mathsf{E}_\mu(\inf_{t \in V(t_0)} h_t)] - \epsilon .$$

As by assumption $(T, \mathscr{T})$ is a compact space, there exist $V(t_1), \ldots$ $\ldots, V(t_m) \in \mathscr{T}$ such that $\bigcup_{i=1}^m V(t_i) = T$ and

$$\frac{1}{n} \sum_{i=1}^n h_\tau \circ x_i - \mathsf{E}_\mu(h_\tau) \geqslant$$

$$\geqslant \inf_{1 \leqslant j \leqslant m} \{\frac{1}{n} \sum_{i=1}^n [\inf_{t \in V(t_j)} h_t \circ x_i - \mathsf{E}_\mu(\inf_{t \in V(t_j)} h_t)]\} - \epsilon$$

for all $\tau \in T$.

Now, according to the strong law of large numbers it follows that there exists a P-null set $N_j(\epsilon)$ such that for all

$\omega \notin N_j(\epsilon)$:

$$\lim_{n\to\infty} \left\{\frac{1}{n}\sum_{i=1}^{n}\left[\inf_{t\in V(t_j)} h_t(x_i(\omega)) - \mathsf{E}_\mu\left(\inf_{t\in V(t_j)} h_t\right)\right]\right\} = 0\,.$$

It follows that for all $\omega \notin N(\epsilon) = \bigcup_{j=1}^{m} N_j(\epsilon)$:

$$\lim_{n\to\infty} \left(\inf_{1\leq j\leq m} \left\{\frac{1}{n}\sum_{i=1}^{n}\left[\inf_{t\in V(t_j)} h_t(x_i(\omega)) - \mathsf{E}_\mu\left(\inf_{t\in V(t_j)} h_t\right)\right]\right\}\right) = 0\,.$$

Hence for $\omega \notin N(\epsilon)$ we obtain

$$\varliminf_{n\to\infty}\ \inf_{\tau\in T} \left(\frac{1}{n}\sum_{i=1}^{n} h_\tau(x_i(\omega)) - \mathsf{E}_\mu(h_\tau)\right) \geq -\epsilon\,.$$

Let us put $N_0 = \bigcup_{k\in N} N\left(\frac{1}{k}\right)$; then $\mathsf{P}(N_0) = 0$ and $\omega \notin N_0$ implies

$$\varliminf_{n\to\infty}\ \inf_{t\in T} \left(\frac{1}{n}\sum_{i=1}^{n} h_t(x_i(\omega)) - \mathsf{E}_\mu(h_t)\right) \geq 0\,.$$

In the same way (replacing "inf" by "sup" and making use of (iii) (b) instead of (iii) (a)) one obtains that there exists a P-null set N_0' such that $\omega \notin N_0'$ implies

$$\varlimsup_{n\to\infty}\ \sup_{t\in T} \left[\frac{1}{n}\sum_{i=1}^{n} h_t(x_i(\omega)) - \mathsf{E}_\mu(h_t)\right] \leq 0\,.$$

Now, keep $\omega \notin N_0 \cup N_0'$ fixed and put $a_n(t) = \frac{1}{n}\sum_{i=1}^{n} [h_t(x_i(\omega)) - \mathsf{E}_\mu(h_t)]$; then from the considerations so far we obtain

$$\varlimsup_{n\to\infty}\ \sup_{t\in T} a_n(t) \leq 0 \quad \text{and} \quad \varliminf_{n\to\infty}\ \inf_{t\in T} a_n(t) \geq 0$$

i.e.

$$\varlimsup_{n\to\infty}\ \sup_{t\in T} (-a_n(t)) \leq 0$$

and therefore $\overline{\lim}_{n\to\infty} \max\{\sup_{t\in T} a_n(t), \sup_{t\in T} (-a_n(t))\} \leqslant 0$, i.e.

$$0 \leqslant \overline{\lim}_{n\to\infty} \sup_{t\in T} (\max\{a_n(t), -a_n(t)\} \leqslant 0$$

and therefore

$$\lim_{n\to\infty} \sup_{t\in T} |a_n(t)| = 0 .$$

3. SOME GENERALIZATIONS (W. STUTE)

The reason why a condition like (+) on μ is essential for (1.3) lies to a certain extent in the methods of proof as presented in Section 1; cf. F. Topsøe [20] for a more extensive and rather beautiful examination. When studying the question of how essential condition (+) on μ is for obtaining almost sure uniform convergence on $\mathscr{C}_k$ of the empirical p-measures, W. Stute and myself tried (partially stimulated by the author's work in [8]) to obtain Glivenko – Cantelli results by solving an associated problem of set-wise convergence. This led to a new framework as described in [10] and carried through by Stute in [18]. It follows from his results that under the assumptions preceeding (1.3) the following is true (cf. [18], Theorem 1.4):

$$(3.1) \qquad \lim_{n\to\infty} \sup_{C\in\mathscr{C}_k} |\mu_n^{\omega}(C) - \mu(C)| = 0 \text{ for P-a.a. } \omega \in \Omega ,$$

whenever μ fulfills the following condition

(++) there exist σ-finite measures μ_i on R ($i = 1, \ldots, k$) such that $\mu \ll \mu_1 \otimes \mu_2 \otimes \ldots \otimes \mu_k$.

We remark that (3.1) covers especially the case considered by W. Schlee in [17].

As to the speed of Glivenko – Cantelli-convergence let us consider the following question:

For which classes $\mathscr{C} \subset \mathscr{B}_k$ is it true that for $\mu = U_k[0, 1]$ (the uniform distribution in $[0, 1]^k$) one has

$$(3.2) \qquad \mathsf{P}\left(\left\{\omega \in \Omega:\ \lim_{n\to\infty} \frac{\sqrt{n}\,\sup_{C\in\mathscr{C}} |\mu_n^\omega(C) - \mu(C)|}{\sqrt{\log\log n}} = \frac{1}{\sqrt{2}}\right\}\right) = 1\,?$$

The following answers are known (cf. W. Philipp [14]):

(a) K.L. Chung [2]: (3.2) holds true for $k = 1$ and $\mathscr{C} = \{[0, t]:\ 0 \leqslant t \leqslant 1\}$;

(b) J.W.S. Cassels [1]: (3.2) holds true for $k = 1$ and $\mathscr{C} = \{]t_1, t_2]:\ 0 \leqslant t_1 < t_2 \leqslant 1\}$;

(c) J. Kiefer [11]: (3.2) holds true for $k \geqslant 1$ and with $\mathscr{C}$ being the class of all rectangles with one vertex at the origin;

(d) W. Philipp [13]: (3.2) holds true for $k \geqslant 1$ and with $\mathscr{C}$ being the class of general rectangles in R^k.

(e) W. Philipp [14]: (3.2) holds true for $k = 2$ and $\mathscr{C} = \mathscr{C}_2$.

At the 1973-Oberwolfach-Meeting W. Philipp posed the question whether (3.2) holds true for $\mathscr{C} = \mathscr{C}_k$ and $k \geqslant 3$.

Using some of the techniques as presented in a paper by S.K. Zaremba [22] Stute proved that the answer is negative for $\mathscr{C} = \mathscr{C}_k$, $k \geqslant 4$.

It is still an open problem whether the same negative answer is true for $\mathscr{C}_3$.

The only positive answer known to us for $\mathscr{C} = \mathscr{C}_k$ is contained in the following theorem proved by Stute:

Theorem 1. *Let $(x_n)_{n\in N}$ be a sequence of independent identically distributed random variables on some probability space $(\Omega, \mathscr{F}, \mathsf{P})$ with values in R^k $(k \geqslant 2)$ and distribution μ. Suppose that there exist non-atomic finite measures μ_i on R $(i = 1, \ldots, k)$ such that $\mu \ll \nu = \mu_1 \otimes \mu_2 \otimes \ldots \otimes \mu_k$, and $R = \left\| \frac{d\mu}{d\nu} \right\|_{\nu,\infty} < \infty$. Then for each $\delta > 0$*

$$\lim_{n\to\infty} n^{\frac{1}{k+\delta}} (\sup_{C\in\mathscr{C}_k} |\mu_n^\omega(C) - \mu(C)|) = 0 \quad \textit{for } \mathsf{P}\textit{-a.a. } \omega \in \Omega .$$

We remark that this result is in accordance with a conjecture of H. Niederreiter (oral communication to W. Philipp [14]), which states that in the case $\mu = U_k[0, 1]$

$$\sup_{C\in\mathscr{C}_k} |\mu_n^\omega(C) - \mu(C)| \geqslant n^{\frac{1}{k}}$$

infinitely often for any k-dimensional sequence ω.

As to the speed of the so called mean Glivenko – Cantelli convergence (cf. R.M. Dudley [4] and [7]) Stute obtained in [19] some general results based on the same techniques as applied in [18] which imply for example the following theorem ([19], Theorem 1.8):

Theorem 2. *Under the same assumptions as in Theorem* 1 *there exists a constant* $M > 0$ *depending only on* k *and* R *such that*

$$\mathsf{E}_\mathsf{P}(\sup_{C\in\mathscr{C}_k} |\mu_n(C) - \mu(C)|) \leqslant M \cdot n^{-\frac{1}{k+2}} .$$

REFERENCES

[1] J.W.S. Cassels, An extension of the law of the iterated logarithm, *Proc. Cambridge Philos. Soc.*, 47 (1951), 55-64.

[2] K.L. Chung, An estimate concerning the Kolmogoroff limit distribution, *Trans. A.M.S.*, 67 (1949), 36-50.

[3] J. Dehardt, Generalizations of the Glivenko – Cantelli theorem, *Ann. Math. Statist.*, 42 (1971), 2050-2055.

[4] R.M. Dudley, The speed of mean Glivenko – Cantelli convergence, *Ann. Math. Statist.*, 40 (1969), 40-50.

[5] H.G. Eggleston, *Convexity,* Cambridge University Press, Cambridge, 1958.

[6] V. Fabian, On uniform convergence of measures, *Z. Wahrsch. verw. Geb.*, 15 (1970), 139-143.

[7] P. Gaenssler, Note on a result of Dudley on the speed of mean Glivenko – Cantelli convergence, *Ann. Math. Statist.*, 41 (1970), 1339-1343.

[8] P. Gaenssler, Compactness and sequential compactness in spaces of measures, *Z. Wahrsch. verw. Geb.*, 17 (1971), 124-146.

[9] P. Gaenssler, Note on Minimum Contrast Estimates for Markov Processes, *Metrika*, 19 (1972), 115-130.

[10] P. Gaenssler, On convergence of sample distributions, *Bull. Int. Statist. Inst.*, Proceedings of the 39-th Session, 45 (1973), 427-432.

[11] J. Kiefer, On large deviations of the empiric d.f. of vector chance variables and a law of the iterated logarithm, *Pacific J. Math.*, 11 (1961), 649-660.

[12] L. Le Cam, On some asymptotic properties of maximum likelihood estimates and related Bayes estimates, *Univ. Calif. Publ. Statist.*, 1 (1953), 277-330.

[13] W. Philipp, Mixing sequences of random variables and probabilistic number theory, *Memoirs A.M.S.*, 114 (1971).

[14] W. Philipp, *Empirical distribution functions and uniform distribution mod* 1. *Diophantine approximation and its applications,* Academic Press, 1973.

[15] R.R. Rao, Relations between weak and uniform convergence of measures with applications, *Ann. Math. Statist.*, 33 (1962), 659-680.

[16] H. Richter, Das Gesetz vom iterierten Logarithmus für empirische Verteilungsfunktionen im R^k, *Manuscripta math.*, 11 (1974), 291-303.

[17] W. Schlee, Glivenko – Cantelli theoreme für endliche Dimension, *Z. Wahrsch. verw. Geb.*, 28 (1973), 1-4.

[18] W. Stute, On a generalization of the Glivenko – Cantelli theorem, RUB Preprint Series, No 3 (1973), Ruhr-Universität Bochum.

[19] W. Stute, On uniformity classes of functions with an application to the speed of mean Glivenko – Cantelli convergence, RUB Preprint Series, No. 5 (1974), Ruhr-Universität Bochum.

[20] F. Topsøe, On the Glivenko – Cantelli theorem, *Z. Wahrsch. verw. Geb.*, 14 (1970), 239-250.

[21] V.S. Varadarajan, On the convergence of probability distributions, *Sankhyā*, 19 (1958), 23-26.

[22] S.K. Zaremba, La discrépance isotrope et l'intégration numerique, *Ann. di Mat.*, 87 (1970), 125-135.

COLLOQUIA MATHEMATICA SOCIETATIS JÁNOS BOLYAI
11. LIMIT THEOREMS OF PROBABILITY THEORY, KESZTHELY (HUNGARY), 1974.

GAUSS DISTRIBUTIONS AND CENTRAL LIMIT THEOREM FOR LOCALLY COMPACT GROUPS

H. HEYER

1. INTRODUCTION

The most prominent and applicable distribution of classical probability theory is the Gauss distribution appearing in applied statistics as the basic object of all parametric procedures, in the framework of the central limit theorem as the most desired limiting distribution and in the theory of stochastic processes as the main tool in the description of the Brownian motion. On the real line R the Gauss distribution is defined as the measure $\nu_{a,\sigma^2} = n_{a,\sigma^2} \cdot \lambda$ (for $a \in R$, $\sigma^2 \in R_+^* = (0, \infty)$) with λ-density n_{a,σ^2} defined by

$$n_{a,\sigma^2}(x) = \frac{1}{\sqrt{2\pi}\,\sigma} \exp\left(-\frac{(x-a)^2}{2\sigma^2}\right)$$

for all $x \in R$, on the euclidean group R^p (for arbitrary $p \geqslant 1$) as the measure $\nu_{a,A} = n_{a,A} \lambda^p$ (for $a \in R^p$, $A \in M(p, R)$ symmetric positive definite) with λ^p-density $n_{a,A}$ given by

$$n_{a,A}(x) = \frac{1}{\sqrt{(2\pi)^p \det A}} \exp\left(-\frac{1}{2}\langle A^{-1}(x-a), x-a\rangle\right)$$

for all $x \in \boldsymbol{R}^p$. Clearly $\nu_{a,A}$ is an element of the vaguely topological (convolution) semi group $\mathscr{M}^1(\boldsymbol{R}^p)$ of all probability measures on $\boldsymbol{R}^p$ and infinitely divisible in the sense that to every $n \geqslant 1$ there exists a root $\nu_n \in \mathscr{M}^1(\boldsymbol{R}^p)$ such that $\nu_n^n = \nu_{a,A}$ holds. It is a deep and far-reaching result of classical probability theory that the class $\mathscr{I}(\boldsymbol{R}^p)$ of all infinitely divisible probability measures on $\boldsymbol{R}^p$ can be decomposed in two subclasses one of which is the class $\mathscr{G}(\boldsymbol{R}^p)$ of Gauss distributions.

An important problem of probability theory is the question of separating $\mathscr{G}(\boldsymbol{R}^p)$ within $\mathscr{I}(\boldsymbol{R}^p)$ from the class $\mathscr{P}(\boldsymbol{R}^p)$ of Poisson distributions on $\boldsymbol{R}^p$ of the form

$$\exp(\sigma) = e^{-\|\sigma\|} \sum_{k \geqslant 0} \frac{\sigma^k}{k!}$$

for σ from the set $\mathscr{M}^b(\boldsymbol{R}^p)$ of all bounded measures on $\boldsymbol{R}^p$ by algebraic-topological properties.

First results in this direction are due to Gnedenko, Kolmogorov [12], Khintchin, and P. Lévy [21]. We present a typical formulation: Let $\Delta = (\mu_{nj})_{j=1,\dots,k_n;\, n \geqslant 1}$ be a triangular system in $\mathscr{M}^1(\boldsymbol{R}^p)$ with the following properties:

(a) Δ is *infinitesimal,* i.e. for every U in the neighborhood filter $\mathfrak{B}(0)$ of $0 \in \boldsymbol{R}^p$ one has

$$\lim_{n\to\infty} \max_{1 \leqslant j \leqslant k_n} \mu_{nj}(\complement U) = 0 .$$

(b) Δ is *convergent with* (corresponding) *limit* $\mu \in \mathscr{M}^1(\boldsymbol{R}^p)$, i.e. for the sequence $(\mu_n)_{n \geqslant 1}$ of n-th partial convolution products $\mu_n = \mu_{n1} * \dots * \mu_{nk_n}$ one obtains

$$\lim_{n\to\infty} \mu_n = \mu \quad \text{(in the sense of the vague topology).}$$

It is known that infinitesimal triangular systems Δ in $\mathscr{M}^1(\boldsymbol{R}^p)$ can only be convergent with limits in $\mathscr{I}(\boldsymbol{R}^p)$. If the triangular system Δ satisfies the additional condition

(c) $\lim_{n\to\infty} \sum_{j=1}^{k_n} \mu_{nj}(\complement U) = 0$ for all $U \in \mathfrak{B}(0)$,

then the limit measure μ is in $\mathcal{G}(\boldsymbol{R}^p)$.

The main tool for establishing this result is the canonical representation of the measures in $\mathcal{I}(\boldsymbol{R}^p)$, the *Lévy – Khintchin formula:* To every $\mu \in \mathcal{I}(\boldsymbol{R}^p)$ there exist a constant $C \in \boldsymbol{R}_+^*$, a linear functional l on $\boldsymbol{R}^p$ of the form $l(x) = \sum_{i=1}^{p} a_i x_i$ for all $x = (x_1, \ldots, x_p) \in \boldsymbol{R}^p$, a symmetric positive semi definite form q on $\boldsymbol{R}^p$ of the form $q(x) = \sum_{i,j=1}^{p} a_{ij} x_i x_j$ for all $x = (x_1, \ldots, x_p) \in \boldsymbol{R}^p$ and a measure $\eta \in \mathcal{M}^b(\boldsymbol{R}^p)$ with $\eta(\{0\}) = 0$ such that the Fourier transform $\hat{\mu}$ of μ admits the representation $\hat{\mu} = \exp(-\psi)$ with

$$\psi = c + l + q + \int_{\boldsymbol{R}^p} \left[1 - e^{-i\langle \cdot, y\rangle} - \frac{i\langle \cdot, y\rangle}{1 + |y|^2}\right] \frac{1 + |y|^2}{|y|^2}\, \eta(dy)\,.$$

Here the items l, q and η are uniquely determined by the representation.

The Lévy – Khintchin formula is generally proved in two steps.

(i) *Embedding:* Every $\mu \in \mathcal{I}(\boldsymbol{R}^p)$ is continuously embeddable, i.e. to $\mu \in \mathcal{I}(\boldsymbol{R}^p)$ there exists a (one parameter) semi group $(\mu_t)_{t \in \boldsymbol{R}_+^*}$ in $\mathcal{M}^1(\boldsymbol{R}^p)$ with defining properties $\mu_t * \mu_s = \mu_{t+s}$ for all $t, s \in \boldsymbol{R}_+^*$ and $\lim_{t \downarrow 0} \mu_t = \epsilon_0$ such that $\mu_1 = \mu$ holds.

(ii) *Representation of* (one parameter) *semi groups:* To every semi group $(\mu_t)_{t \in \boldsymbol{R}_+^*}$ in $\mathcal{M}^1(\boldsymbol{R}^p)$ there exists a (negative definite) function ψ on $\boldsymbol{R}^p$ of the above form such that $\hat{\mu}_t = \exp(-t\psi)$ holds for all $t \in \boldsymbol{R}_+^*$.

The attempt to extend the notion of Gauss distributions to important types of groups other than $\boldsymbol{R}^p$ lead Lévy to a discussion of the circular normal distribution which is the Gauss distribution on the torus $\boldsymbol{T}$. It is defined as the image of ν_{a,σ^2} introduced at the beginning of the section under the homomorphism $\tau\colon t \to e^{it}$ from $\boldsymbol{R}$ into $\boldsymbol{T}$. Its density with respect to the invariant measure on T can be calculated. For a first discussion see [20]. A Lévy – Khintchin type formula for the class $\mathscr{I}(T)$ of all infinitely divisible probability distributions on T has been given for the first time by Bochner [2].

The aim of the paper is a sufficiently complete account of possible generalizations of the Gauss distribution on R^p and T to more general locally compact groups.

We shall discuss recent results pertaining to the embedding and representation theorem within the theory of probability measures on locally compact groups and give definition and properties of Gauss distributions in the most general sense. Furthermore we present contributions to the theory of absolutely continuous and diffuse Gauss distributions. The special case of central Gauss distributions serves as an example. Finally the rôle of the Gauss distribution in a general set up of a central limit problem for measures on locally compact groups in illustrated.

2. EMBEDDING INFINITELY DIVISIBLE MEASURES

In order to describe the theorems under (i) and (ii) of Sec. 1 for more general classes of locally compact groups containing the special cases R^p and T we need some preparations the details of which can be taken from [13], [24] or [16].

Let G be a locally compact group (multiplicatively written with neutral element e), $\mathscr{M}(G)$ the set of all Radon measures on G considered as linear functionals on the space $\mathscr{K}(G)$ of all continuous real valued functions on G with compact support. Subsets of interest of $\mathscr{M}(G)$ are the sets $\mathscr{M}^b(G)$ of bounded measures on G and $\mathscr{M}^1(G) = \{\mu \in \mathscr{M}^b_+(G) : \|\mu\| = 1\}$ of probability measures (distributions) on G. In $\mathscr{M}^b(G)$ one introduces the convolution defined for $\mu, \nu \in \mathscr{M}^b(G)$ by $\mu * \nu(f) = \int f(xy)\,\mu(dx)\,\nu(dy)$ for all $f \in \mathscr{K}(G)$. Furthermore $\mathscr{M}^b(G)$ is furnished with the vague topology, i.e. the topology of pointwise convergence on $\mathscr{K}(G)$. $\mathscr{M}^b(G)$ is an algebra and $\mathscr{M}^1(G)$ a semi group with unit ϵ_e, the Dirac measure in e. One shows that $\mathscr{M}^1(G)$ is a (vaguely) topological semi group in $\mathscr{M}^b(G)$. The class of all infinitely divisible measures in $\mathcal{M}^1(G)$ is defined analoguous to the classical situation and denoted by $\mathcal{I}(G)$. A semi group $(\mu_t)_{t \in R_+^*}$ in $\mathcal{M}^1(G)$ is defined to be *continuous,* if the homomorphism $t \to \mu_t$ from R_+^* into $\mathcal{M}^1(G)$ is continuous. For any continuous semi group $(\mu_t)_{t \in R_+^*}$ in $\mathcal{M}^1(G)$ one has $\lim_{t \downarrow 0} \mu_t = \mu_0$ with $\mu_0^2 = \mu_0$. Since the idempotents of $\mathcal{M}^1(G)$ are exactly the normed Haar measures ω_H of compact subgroups H of G, one concludes $\lim_{t \downarrow 0} \mu_t = \omega_H$ for some compact subgroup H of G. A semi group $(\mu_t)_{t \in R_+^*}$ in $\mathcal{M}^1(G)$ is called *e-continuous,* if $\lim_{t \downarrow 0} \mu_t = \epsilon_e$ holds.

For every $\mu \in \mathcal{M}^1(G)$ and $n \geqslant 1$ one defines the sets

$$R(n, \mu) = \{\nu \in \mathcal{M}^1(G) \colon \nu^n = \mu\}$$

and

$$R(\mu) = \bigcup_{n \geqslant 1} \{\nu^m : \nu \in \mathcal{M}^1(G) \text{ with } \nu^n = \mu \text{ for all } m = 1, \dots, n\}.$$

μ is called *root compact,* if $R(\mu)$ is relatively compact in $\mathcal{M}^1(G)$. The following general embedding theorem is in its final form proved in [31].

2.1 Theorem. *Let G be a locally compact group and $\mu \in \mathcal{I}(G)$ root compact. Let furthermore $S = (\mu_r)_{r \in Q_+^*}$ be a rational (one parameter) semi group in $\mathcal{M}^1(G)$ with $\mu_1 = \mu$. Then there exist*

(i) *a compact connected abelian group $E(S)$ in S, the continuity measuring group of S,*

(ii) *a compact subgroup H of G such that ω_H is the neutral element of $E(S)$, every μ_r admits ω_H as an idempotent factor and $\mu_r * \nu = \nu * \mu_r$ for all $\nu \in E(S)$ $(r \in Q_+^*)$.*

(iii) *a compact subgroup $H(S)$ of the normalizer $N(H)$ of H with $H(S)_0 H = H(S)$ such that $H(S)/H \cong E(S)$ and*

(iv) *to every* $r \in Q_+^*$ *an* x_r *in the connected component* $H(S)_0$ *of (the neutral element of)* $H(S)$ *such that* $(\epsilon_{x_r} * \mu_r)_{r \in Q_+^*}$ *is a rational semi group in* $\mathcal{M}^1(G)$ *with* $\lim_{r \downarrow 0} (\epsilon_{x_r} * \mu_r) = \omega_H$.

From this theorem one deduces that for compactly generated abelian Lie groups, arbitrary compact Lie groups, totally disconnected compact groups and connected nilpotent Lie groups G every $\mu \in \mathcal{I}(G)$ is *continuously embeddable* (with embedding semi group $(\mu_t)_{t \in R_+^*}$ in $\mathcal{M}^1(G)$), i.e., there exists a continuous semi group $(\mu_t)_{t \in R_+^*}$ in $\mathcal{M}^1(G)$ with $\mu_1 = \mu$.

For the proof of this conclusion one observes that the four types of groups listed are *strongly root compact* in the sense of the following definition: A locally compact group G is called *root compact,* if for every $n \geqslant 1$ and every compact subset K of G there exists a compact subset C_n of G which contains all sequences $\{x_1, \ldots, x_n\}$ in G with $x_n = e$ such that $Kx_iKx_j \cap Kx_{i+j} \neq \phi$ for all $i + j \leqslant n$, and *strongly root compact,* if the compact subset C_n *can be chosen independent of* n. If G is root compact, then for all $n \geqslant 1$ and every relatively compact subset $\mathcal{N}$ of $\mathcal{M}^1(G)$ the set $R(n, \mathcal{N}) = \bigcup_{\mu \in \mathcal{N}} R(n, \mu)$ is again relatively compact. In the case that G is strongly root compact, for every relatively compact subset $\mathcal{N}$ of $\mathcal{M}^1(G)$ the set $R(\mathcal{N}) = \bigcup_{\mu \in \mathcal{N}} R(\mu)$ is relatively compact.

Consequently the strong root compactnes of G implies the applicability of Theorem 2.1 to any measure $\mu \in \mathcal{I}(G)$.

By $\mathcal{E}(G)$ we denote the set of all continuously embeddable measures in $\mathcal{M}^1(G)$. Plainly $\mathcal{E}(G) \subset \mathcal{I}(G)$ and for the classes of locally compact groups G mentioned above one also has $\mathcal{I}(G) \subset \mathcal{E}(G)$.

It should be noted that $\mathcal{E}(G)$ contains the set $\mathcal{E}_e(G)$ of all *e-continuously embeddable* measures in $\mathcal{M}^1(G)$ which by definition are those measures $\mu \in \mathcal{M}^1(G)$ to which there exists an *e*-continuous semi group $(\mu_t)_{t \in R_+^*}$ in $\mathcal{M}^1(G)$ with $\mu_1 = \mu$.

3. CANONICAL REPRESENTATIONS

Canonical representations in the sense of Lévy – Khintchin formulae for e-continuous semi groups in $\mathscr{M}^1(G)$ have been established for general Lie groups for the first time by G. A. Hunt [19]. The case of a compact Lie group and associated homogeneous spaces has been analyzed in [16], where also an extensive bibliography of the problem is given.

Let G be an arbitrary Lie group of dimension $d > 0$ with Lie algebra $\mathscr{L}(G)$ and a basis $\{X_1, \ldots, X_d\}$ of $\mathscr{L}(G)$. By $\mathscr{D}(G)$ we denote the vector space of all infinitely differentiable functions on G with compact support. Furthermore we define the sets

$$\mathscr{D}_+^0(G) = \{f \in \mathscr{D}_+(G) \colon f(e) = 0\}$$

and

$\mathscr{F}(G) = \{f \in \mathscr{D}_+^0(G)$: there is no $g \in \mathscr{D}_+^0(G)$ nor U in the neighborhood filter $\mathfrak{B}(e)$ of e such that $f(x) \leqslant g(x)^2$ for all $x \in U$ holds$\}$.

A linear functional ψ on $\mathscr{D}(G)$ is called a *primitive form,* if for all $f, g \in \mathscr{D}(G)$ one has

$$\psi(fg^*) = \psi(f)g(e) - f(e)\psi(g)$$

and a *quadratic form,* if $\psi(f) \geqslant 0$ for all $f \in \mathscr{D}_+^0(G)$ and if for all $f, g \in \mathscr{D}(G)$ one has

$$\psi(fg) + \psi(fg^*) = 2[\psi(f)g(e) - f(e)\psi(g)] \, .$$

Here for $g \in \mathscr{D}(G)$ the function g^* is defined by $g(x) = g(x^{-1})$ for all $x \in G$.

It can be easily shown that to every primitive form ψ on $\mathscr{D}(G)$ there exist $a_1, \ldots, a_d \in R$ such that

$$\psi(f) = \sum_{i=1}^{d} a_i(X_i f)(e)$$

holds for all $f \in \mathscr{D}(G)$ and that to every quadratic form ψ on $\mathscr{D}(G)$ there exists a sysmmetric positive semi definite matrix $(a_{ij})_{i,j=1,\ldots,d} \in$ $\in M(d, \boldsymbol{R})$ such that

$$\psi(f) = \sum_{i,j=1}^{d} a_{ij}(X_i X_j f)(e)$$

holds for all $f \in \mathscr{D}(G)$.

To every basis $\{X_1, \ldots, X_d\}$ of $\mathscr{L}(G)$ and every canonical coordinate system $\{x_1, \ldots, x_d\}$ of G w.r.t. $\{X_1, \ldots, X_d\}$ we define a linear operator Γ on $\mathscr{D}(G)$ by

$$(*) \qquad \Gamma(f) = \sum_{i=1}^{d} (X_i f)(e) x_i$$

for all $f \in \mathscr{D}(G)$. Γ is a *Lévy mapping* for G in the sense of the following three defining properties:

(LM1) For every primitive form ψ on $\mathscr{D}(G)$ and every $f \in \mathscr{D}(G)$ one has $\psi(f - \Gamma(f)) = 0$.

(LM2) For every $f \in \mathscr{D}(G)$ one has $\Gamma(f)^* = -\Gamma(f)$.

(LM3) For every $x \in G$ the linear functional $f \to \Gamma(f)(x)$ is a primitive form on $\mathscr{D}(G)$.

It can be shown that all Lévy mappings for G are of the form $(*)$ for some basis $\{X_1, \ldots, X_d\}$ of $\mathscr{L}(G)$ and a canonical coordinate system $\{x_1, \ldots, x_d\}$ w.r.t. $\{X_1, \ldots, X_d\}$.

Any measure $\eta \in \mathscr{M}_+(G \setminus \{e\})$ such that $\int_{G \setminus \{e\}} f \, d\eta < \infty$ for all $f \in \mathscr{D}_+^0(G)$ and $\eta(\complement U) < \infty$ holds for all $U \in \mathfrak{B}(e)$ is called a *Lévy measure* for G.

If $\{X_1, \ldots, X_d\}$ and $\{x_1, \ldots, x_d\}$ are given as above and if $U, V \in \mathfrak{B}(e)$ are relatively compact with $\bar{U} \subset \mathring{V}$ and $\sum_{i=1}^{d} x_i(x)^2 > 0$ for all $x \in \bar{U} \setminus \{e\}$, then there exists an infinitely differentiable function

$\varphi \geqslant 0$ on G with the properties $\varphi(x) = \sum\limits_{i=1}^{d} x_i(x)^2$ for all $x \in \bar{U}$, $\varphi(x) = 1$ for all $x \in \complement V$ and $\varphi(G \setminus \{e\}) > 0$. Functions φ described this way are called *Hunt functions* for G. Given a Hunt function φ for G *a measure* $\eta \in \mathscr{M}_+(G \setminus \{e\})$ is a Lévy measure iff $\int\limits_{G \setminus \{e\}} \varphi d\eta < \infty$.

Following the approach of Siebert in [30] Hunt's famous theorem can be reformulated.

3.1 Theorem. *Let G be Lie group and Γ a Lévy mapping for G.*

(i) *For every e-continuous semi group $(\mu_t)_{t \in R_+^*}$ in $\mathscr{M}^1(G)$ the generating functional ψ defined by*

$$\text{(GF)} \qquad \psi(f) = \lim_{t \downarrow 0} \frac{1}{t} \int [f - f(e)]\, d\mu_t$$

exists for all $f \in \mathscr{D}(G)$, and there are uniquely a primitive form ψ_1, a quadratic form ψ_2 on $\mathscr{D}(G)$ and a Lévy measure η for G such that

$$\text{(LK)} \qquad \psi(f) = \psi_1(f) + \psi_2(f) + \int\limits_{G \setminus \{e\}} [f - f(e) - \Gamma(f)]\, d\eta$$

holds. For all $f \in \mathscr{K}(G \setminus \{e\})$ one obtains

$$\int\limits_{G \setminus \{e\}} f\, d\eta = \lim_{t \downarrow 0} \frac{1}{t} \int\limits_G f\, d\mu_t \,.$$

(ii) *Let ψ_1, ψ_2 and η be given as in* (i). *Then to ψ defined by* (LK) *there exists exactly one e-continuous semi group $(\mu_t)_{t \in R_+^*}$ in $\mathscr{M}^1(G)$ such that* (GF) *of* (i) *holds.*

If for the generating functional ψ of an e-continuous semi group $(\mu_t)_{t \in R_+^*}$ in $\mathscr{M}^1(G)$ the formula (LK) holds, then we call (ψ_1, ψ_2, η) or more specifically $(a_i, (a_{ij}), \eta)$ the *representation of* $(\mu_t)_{t \in R_+^*}$.

Let now G be an arbitrary locally compact group, Rep (G) the set of all finite dimensional unitary continuous representations of G furnished with the compact open topology and let $\mathscr{R}(G)$ be the algebra of coefficients of representations in Rep (G).

It should be noted that Theorem 3.1 for Lie groups G can now be formulated also with $\mathscr{D}(G) \oplus \mathscr{R}(G)$ in place of G. This modification enables us to establish a general Lévy – Khintchin representation for a large class of locally compact groups which admits an extensive representation theory.

For every $\mu \in \mathscr{M}^b(G)$ the Fourier transform $\hat{\mu}$ of μ is defined by $\hat{\mu}(f) = \int f\,d\mu$ for all $f \in \mathscr{R}(G)$. If G is *almost periodic* in the sense that Rep (G) separates the points of G, then the mapping $\mu \to \hat{\mu}$ is injective. It is also sequentially bicontinuous, if G is a *Moore group,* i.e. a locally compact group whose irreducible (continuous, unitary) representations are finite dimensional.

In analogy to the discussion above we define

$$\mathscr{R}(G)_+^0 = \{f \in \mathscr{R}_+(G) \colon f(e) = 0\}$$

and call a linear functional ψ on $\mathscr{R}(G)$ a *negative definite form,* if $\psi(1) \geqslant 0$ and $\psi(f) \leqslant 0$ holds for all $f \in \mathscr{R}(G)_+^0$. One notes, that in the case of an almost periodic group G there exists a one to one correspondence between e-continuous semi groups $(\mu_t)_{t \in \boldsymbol{R}_+^*}$ in $\mathscr{M}^1(G)$ and continuous negative definite forms ψ on $\mathscr{R}(G)$ with $\psi(1) = 0$ defined by $\hat{\mu}_t = \exp(-t\psi)$ for all $t \in \boldsymbol{R}_+^*$, where the exponential Exp of a linear functional on $\mathscr{R}(G)$ is introduced in a natural way. In order to classify all continuous negative definite forms on $\mathscr{R}(G)$ we need the appropriate notions of primitive, quadratic form on $\mathscr{R}(G)$ as well as Lévy function and Lévy measure for G.

A linear functional ψ on $\mathscr{R}(G)$ is called a *primitive form,* if for all $f, g \in \mathscr{R}(G)$ the relation

$$\psi(fg^*) = \psi(f)g(e) - f(e)\,\psi(g)$$

holds, and a *quadratic form,* if $\psi(D)$ is positive semi definite for every $D \in$ Rep (G) and if for all $f, g \in \mathscr{R}(G)$ one has

$$\psi(fg) + \psi(fg^*) = 2[\psi(f)g(e) + f(e)\,\psi(g)]\,.$$

A mapping $\Gamma\colon G \times \text{Rep}\,(G) \to \boldsymbol{C}$ is called a *Lévy function* for G, if it satisfies the following conditions:

(LF1) For every $n \geqslant 1$ the mapping $\Gamma\colon G \times \mathrm{Rep}_n(G) \to \boldsymbol{M}(n, \boldsymbol{C})$ is continuous.

(LF2) For every compact subset C of $\mathrm{Rep}\,(G)$ one has

$$\sup\{\|\Gamma(x, D)\|\colon x \in G, D \in C\} < \infty$$

and

$$\lim_{x \to e} \sup_{D \in C} \|\Gamma(x, D)\| = 0 .$$

(LF3) To every $x \in G$ there exists a one parameter subgroup $(x_t)_{t \in R}$ of G such that

$$D(x_t) = \exp t\Gamma(x, D)$$

for all $D \in \mathrm{Rep}\,(G)$ and $t \in \boldsymbol{R}$.

(LF4) To every compact subset C of $\mathrm{Rep}\,(G)$ there exists a neighborhood $U \in \mathfrak{B}(e)$ such that

$$D(x) = \exp \Gamma(x, D)$$

holds for all $D \in C$ and $x \in U$.

Defining for every $D \in \mathrm{Rep}\,(G)$ the function f_D on G by $f_D(x) = \mathrm{Re}\,[\mathrm{tr}\,(E_{n(D)} - D(x))]$ for all $x \in G$ we observe $f_D \in \mathscr{R}(G)$ and $\ker D = f_D^{-1}(\{0\})$.

A measure $\eta \in \mathscr{M}_+(G \setminus \{e\})$ is called a *Lévy-measure* for G, if $\int_{G \setminus \{e\}} f_D\, d\eta < \infty$ and $\eta(\complement U) < \infty$ for all $U \in \mathfrak{B}(e)$.

The following Theorem is a generalization due to Siebert [30] of Hunt's theorem (see Theorem 3.1).

3.2 Theorem. *Let G be a Lie projective almost periodic group and Γ a Lévy function for G.*

(A) *To any e-continuous semi group $(\mu_t)_{t \in R_+^*}$ in $\mathscr{M}^1(G)$ with* *corresponding negative definite form* ψ *on* $\mathscr{R}(G)$ *there exist*

(i) *a continuous primitive form* ψ_1 *on* $\mathscr{R}(G)$,

(iii) *a continuous quadratic form* ψ_2 *on* $\mathscr{R}(G)$ *and*

(iii) *a Lévy measure* η *for* G

such that for all $f \in \mathscr{R}(G)$ *one has the representation* (ψ_1, ψ_2, η) *of* ψ *defined by*

$$\text{(LK)} \qquad \psi(f) = \psi_1(f) + \psi_2(f) - \int_{G \setminus \{e\}} [f - f(e) - \Gamma(f)]\, d\eta .$$

Furthermore ψ_2 *and* η *are uniquely determined by* $(\mu_t)_{t \in R_+^*}$, *and*

$$\int_{G \setminus \{e\}} f\, d\eta = \lim_{t \downarrow 0} \frac{1}{t} \int_G f\, d\mu_t$$

holds for all $f \in \mathscr{K}(G \setminus \{e\})$.

(B) *Let, conversely,* ψ_1, ψ_2 *and* η *be given as above and let* G *be a Moore group. Then the representation* (LK) *defines a continuous negative definite form* ψ *on* $\mathscr{R}(G)$, *and there exists an* e-*continuous semi group in* $\mathscr{M}^1(G)$ *whose corresponding negative definite form is just* ψ.

The proof of the theorem reduces to the case of a Lie group, since by assumption G is a projective limit of Lie groups.

Remark. As well known, every connected locally compact group is Lie projective.

4. GAUSS DISTRIBUTIONS ON A LOCALLY COMPACT GROUP

Gauss distributions on a locally compact group G are defined within the class $\mathscr{E}_e(G)$ of e-continuously embeddable measures in $\mathscr{M}^1(G)$. The following definition is due to Courrège [10] for the euclidean group R^p and has been discussed in the more general set up by Siebert [30].

Definition. A non degenerate measure $\nu \in \mathscr{M}^1(G)$ is called a *Gauss distribution,* if the following conditions hold:

(G1) There is an e-continuous semi group $(\nu_t)_{t \in R_+^*}$ in $\mathscr{M}^1(G)$ with $\nu_1 = \nu$.

(G2) For any $U \in \mathfrak{V}(e)$ one has

$$\lim_{t \downarrow 0} \frac{1}{t} \nu_t(\complement U) = 0 .$$

More precisely we shall call ν a *Gauss distribution with embedding semi group* $(\nu_t)_{t \in R_+^*}$.

The set of all Gauss distributions on G will be denoted by $\mathscr{G}(G)$. It can be shown easily that every $\nu \in \mathscr{G}(G)$ is supported by the connected component G_0 of (e in) G.

4.1 Theorem. *Let G be a Lie projective almost periodic group and ν a non degenerate measure in $\mathscr{E}_e(G)$ with embedding semi group $S = (\nu_t)_{t \in R_+^*}$. Let ψ be the negative definite form on $\mathscr{R}(G)$ corresponding to S with representation (ψ_1, ψ_2, η). The following statements are equivalent:*

(i) $\nu \in \mathscr{G}(G)$.

(ii) $\eta = 0$.

(iii) *For all* $f \in \mathscr{K}(G \setminus \{e\})$ *one has* $\lim_{t \downarrow 0} \frac{1}{t} \int f \, d\nu_t = 0$.

(iv) *If* $\psi = \psi' + \psi''$ *is the representation of* ψ *as the sum of its skew symmetric and symmetric part, then* ψ' *is a primitive and* ψ'' *is a quadratic form on* $\mathscr{R}(G)$.

(v) $\psi(f_D^2) = 0$ *for all irreducible* $D \in \mathrm{Rep}\,(G)$.

(vi) *For all irreducible* $D \in \mathrm{Rep}\,(G)$ *the Gauss condition holds*

(G) $$0 < |\det(\hat{\nu}(D \otimes D))| \, |\det(\hat{\nu}(D \otimes \bar{D}))| = |\det(\hat{\nu}(D))|^{4n(D)} .$$

4.2 Corollary. *The definition of a Gauss distribution is independent of the choice of its embedding semi group.*

The class $\mathscr{G}(G)$ admits the following *properties:*

1. Let G be a Lie projective almost periodic group and $\mu, \nu \in \mathscr{G}(G)$ such that $\mu * \nu \in \mathscr{E}_e(G)$. Then $\mu * \nu \in \mathscr{G}(G)$.

2. For the embedding semi group $(\nu_t)_{t \in R_+^*}$ of a measure $\nu \in \mathscr{G}(G)$ one has $\nu_t \in \mathscr{G}(G)$ for all $t \in R_+^*$.

3. Let G, G' be locally compact groups and p a homomorphism from G into G'. If $\nu \in \mathscr{G}(G)$, then $p(\nu) \in \mathscr{G}(G'))$.

4. Let $G = \prod_{\alpha \in A} G_\alpha$ be a locally compact group and $\nu_\alpha \in \mathscr{G}(G_\alpha)$ for every $\alpha \in A$. Then $\bigtimes_{\alpha \in A} \nu_\alpha \in \mathscr{G}(G)$.

5. Let G be a locally compact group of the from $\varprojlim_{K \in \mathscr{N}} G/K$, where $\mathscr{N}$ denotes a descending family of compact normal subgroups K of G with $\bigcap_{k \in \mathscr{N}} K = \{e\}$. Let furthermore $(\nu^K)_{K \in \mathscr{N}}$ be a projective system of measures $\nu^K \in \mathscr{G}(G/K)$ $(K \in \mathscr{N})$. Then the measure $\nu = \varprojlim_{K \in \mathscr{N}} \nu^K$ is in $\mathscr{G}(G)$.

6. Let G, G' be Lie projective groups, G connected and p a continuous epimorphism from G onto G' such that $\ker p$ is a Lie group. To every $\nu' \in \mathscr{G}(G')$ exists a $\nu \in \mathscr{G}(G)$ with $p(\nu) = \nu'$.

7. The classical Cramér theorem on normal classes [11] is in general false. More precisely for $G = T$ there exists $\nu \in \mathscr{G}(G)$ with $\nu = \sigma * \tau$ such that σ and τ are not in $\mathscr{G}(G)$.

8. The class $\mathscr{G}(G)$ is closed in $\mathscr{E}_e(G)$.

Concerning the proofs of the properties one should note that properties 1 to 4 and 8 for Lie projective almost periodic groups G can be directly derived from Theorem 4.1.

In the more general case the proof of 8 requires different tools. The proofs of 5 and 6 happen to be more sophisticated. Examples supporting 7 are to be found in [4] and [13].

In order to establish the existence of Gauss distributions on an arbitrary locally compact group G we proceed as follows.

(1) *If G is a connected locally compact abelian group, then $\mathcal{G}(G) \neq \phi$.*

In fact $G = \boldsymbol{R}^n \times K$, where $n \geqslant 0$ and K is a connected compact abelian group. Clearly $\mathcal{G}(\boldsymbol{R}^n) \neq \phi$ for all $n \geqslant 1$. For $n = 0$ we have $K^\wedge = G^\wedge$, where the character group $K^\wedge$ of K is a torsion free discrete abelian group such that for $\chi_0 \in G^\wedge$ with $\chi_0 \neq 1$ the group $\langle \chi_0 \rangle$ generated by χ_0 is isomorphic to $\boldsymbol{Z}$. Defining a symmetric bilinear form φ on $G^\wedge$ by

$$\varphi(\xi, \eta) = \begin{cases} nm, & \text{if } \xi = \chi_0^n \text{ and } \eta = \chi_0^m \qquad (n, m \in \boldsymbol{Z}) \\ 0 & \text{otherwise} \end{cases}$$

and a quadratic form ψ on $G^\wedge$ by

$$\psi(\chi) = \varphi(\chi, \chi) \qquad \text{for all} \qquad \chi \in G^\wedge \cong \boldsymbol{Z}$$

we obtain that $\exp(-\psi)$ is the Fourier transform of a Gauss distribution on G.

(2) *For any connected Lie group G one has $\mathcal{G}(G) \neq \phi$.*

In fact: If $\nu \in \mathcal{E}_e(G)$ with embedding semi group $(\nu_t)_{t \in \boldsymbol{R}_+^*}$ whose generating functional admits the representation $(a_i, (a_{ij}), \eta)$, then, in view of Theorem 3.1, the following statements are equivalent:

(i) $\nu \in \mathcal{G}(G)$ with embedding semi group $(\nu_t)_{t \in \boldsymbol{R}_+^*}$.

(ii) $\eta = 0$ and $(a_{ij}) \neq 0$.

(3) *If G is a connected compact group, then $\mathcal{G}(G) \neq \phi$.*

By a structure theorem $G = (L \times A)/H$, where $L = \prod_{\alpha \in A} L_\alpha$ is a product of connected compact Lie groups L_α $(\alpha \in A)$, A is a connected compact abelian group an H is a normal subgroup of $L \times A$.

Using (1) and (2) together with properties 3 and 4 one obtains the result.

4.3 Theorem. *Let* G *be a connected locally compact group. Then* $\mathscr{G}(G) \neq \phi$.

Proof.

1. Let G admit a connected compact subgroup $H \neq \{e\}$ of G. Then it suffices to establish the existence of Gauss distributions in $\mathscr{M}^1(H)$. This, however, follows from step (3) above.

2. Let G does not have a connected compact subgroup $H \neq \{e\}$. Then G is finite dimensional.

In fact there exists a compact normal subgroup K of G such that G/K is a Lie group. By assumption $K_0 = \{e\}$, thus K is totally disconnected.

Therefore by a known theorem there are aconnected Lie group L and a continuous monomorphism f from L into G with $\overline{f(L)} = G$. In $\mathscr{M}^1(L)$ there exist Gauss distributions ν by the preceding step (2), thus we obtain $f(\nu) \in \mathscr{G}(G)$ by property 3.

The various definitions of Gauss distributions to be found in the literature [3], [35] and [22] have been compared by Siebert in [30].

In order to give some details we draw consequences from Theorem 4.1.

4.4 Theorem. *Let* G *be a Lie projective almost periodic group. Then for any non degenerate measure* $\nu \in \mathscr{E}_e(G)$ *the following statements are equivalent:*

(i) $\nu \in \mathscr{G}(G)$,

(ii) *for every irreducible* $D \in \mathrm{Rep}\,(G)$ *the measure* $D(\nu)$ *is either in* $\mathscr{G}(\overline{D(G)})$ *or degenerate in* $\mathscr{M}^1(\overline{D(G)})$.

In the special cases of a compact group G the Gauss distributions in the sense of Carnal [3] are in $\mathscr{G}(G)$, if they are in $\mathscr{E}_e(G)$.

If G is abelian locally compact, $\mathscr{G}(G)$ contains also the Gauss distributions in the sense of Urbanik [35].

The abelian locally compact case is of particular interest for an important though not extremely convenient definition of Gauss distribution given by Parthasarathy, Rao and Varadhan, in [22] (see also [24]).

A measure $\mu \in \mathcal{M}^1(G)$ is called *Poisson distribution,* if there exists a measure $\sigma \in \mathcal{M}^b(G)$ with $\mu = \exp(\sigma) = e^{-\|\sigma\|} \sum_{k \geq 0} \frac{\sigma^k}{k!}$.

4.5 Theorem. *Let* G *be an abelian locally compact group and* ν *a non degenerate measure in* $\mathcal{E}_e(G)$. *The following statements are equivalent:*

(i) $\nu \in \mathcal{G}(G)$.

(ii) *If* $\nu = \rho * \tau$ *with a Poisson distribution* $\rho \in \mathcal{M}^1(G)$ *and a measure* $\tau \in \mathcal{E}_e(G)$, *then* $\rho = \epsilon_e$.

(iii) *There are* $x \in G$, *a one parameter subgroup* $(x_t)_{t \in R}$ *of* G *with* $x = x_1$ *and a quadratic form* ψ_2 *on* $\mathcal{R}(G)$, *continuous on* $G^\wedge$, *such that for all* $\chi \in G^\wedge$ *the relation*

$$\hat{\nu}(\chi) = \chi(x) \exp(-\psi_2(\chi))$$

holds.

A measure $\mu \in \mathcal{M}^1(G)$ is called *weakly infinitely divisible,* if to every $n \geq 1$ there are a $\mu_n \in \mathcal{M}^1(G)$ and an $x_n \in G$ such that $\mu = \mu_n^n * \epsilon_{x_n}$. The class $\mathcal{I}_0(G)$ of all weakly infinitely divisible measures in $\mathcal{M}^1(G)$ is a closed subsemigroup of $\mathcal{M}^1(G)$.

Gauss distributions in the sense of Parthasarathy are defined as elements ν of $\mathcal{I}_0(G)$ with the property that whenever $\nu = \rho * \tau$ with a Poisson distribution ρ and a measure $\tau \in \mathcal{I}_0(G)$, then $\rho = \epsilon_e$.

The class of Gauss distributions in the sense of Parthasarathy will be abbreviated by $\mathcal{G}_p(G)$.

It can be deduced from Theorem 4.5 that a non degenerate measure $\nu \in \mathcal{E}_e(G)$ is in $\mathcal{G}_p(G)$ iff it is in $\mathcal{G}(P)$.

Finally we shall mention a generalization due to Corwin [6], [7], [8] and [9] of a classical version of the Gauss distribution based on the well known theorem of Bernstein [1] (see also [26]).

The new definition appears as condition (i) of the following result.

4.6 Theorem. *Let* G *be an abelian locally compact group with the property that the mapping* $x \to x^2$ *from* G *into itself is an automorphism and that* $G^\wedge$ *is connected.*

Then the following statements for $\nu \in \mathcal{M}^1(G)$ *are equivalent:*

(i) *With* n: $G \times G \to G \times G$ *being defined by* $n(x, y) = (xy, xy^{-1})$ *for all* $x, y \in G$ *one has*

$$n(\nu \otimes \nu) = (\nu * \nu) \otimes (\nu * \nu^\sim) .$$

(ii) $\nu \in \mathcal{G}(G)$.

In the special case of an abelian locally compact group with a countable base of its topology statement (i) of the Theorem is equivalent to the following condition (Bernstein's theorem):

There exists a probability space $(\Omega, \mathfrak{A}, \mathrm{P})$ and independent G-valued random variables X, Y on $(\Omega, \mathfrak{A}, \mathrm{P})$ with $X(\mathrm{P}) = Y(\mathrm{P}) = \nu$ such that XY and XY^{-1} are independent.

More generally one can describe the class $\mathcal{G}_B(G)$ of all Gauss distributions in the sense of Bernstein on an abelian locally compact group G with the property that $x \to x^2$ is an automorphism as the class $\mathcal{G}_P(G) * \mathcal{I}_B(G)$, where $\mathcal{I}_B(G)$ denotes the set of all idempotent elements in $\mathcal{G}_B(G)$. For details see [17].

Extensions of Bernstein's classical result to arbitrary locally compact groups have been given in the framework of positive definite functions by K. Schmidt [27], [28] on the basis of a theorem of C.R. Rao [25].

5. ABSOLUTE CONTINUITY AND DIFFUSION OF GAUSS DISTRIBUTION

For the p-dimensional Gauss distribution $\nu_{a,A} = n_{a,A}\lambda^p$ defined (in Section 1) for $a \in \boldsymbol{R}^p$ and a symmetric, positive definite matrix $A \in \in M(p, \boldsymbol{R})$ the Fourier transform $\hat{\nu}_{a,A}$ is given by

$$\hat{\nu}_{a,A}(t) = e^{i\langle t,a\rangle - \frac{1}{2}\langle At,t\rangle}$$

for all $t \in \boldsymbol{R}^p$. An analogous representation with A replaced by a symmetric merely positive *semi* definite matrix in $M(p, \boldsymbol{R})$ could be used to define a slightly more general Gauss distribution via injectivity of the Fourier mapping. In this case it remains to check whether the extended definition will again provide a λ^p-absolutely continuous measure or possibly even a λ^p-singular (Gauss) distribution on $\boldsymbol{R}^p$.

The classical results available are as follows:

(1) If ν is a p-dimensional Gauss distribution (with positive definite A) then $\nu = f\lambda^p$ with an analytic λ^p-density $f > 0$.

(2) If $\nu \in \mathscr{G}(\boldsymbol{R}^p)$, then $\nu \ll \lambda^p$ iff $\operatorname{supp}(\nu) = \boldsymbol{R}^p$.

(3) If $\nu \in \mathscr{G}(\boldsymbol{R}^p)$, then either $\nu \ll \lambda^p$ or $\nu \perp \lambda^p$. More precisely one obtains

(4) To any $\nu \in \mathscr{G}(\boldsymbol{R}^p)$ there exists a linear subspace V of dimension k of $\boldsymbol{R}^p$ with $\operatorname{supp}(\nu) = V$.

(5) Considered as a measure on V the measure ν is a k-dimensional Gauss distribution on V and hence admits an analytic ω_V-density $f > 0$.

(6) If $k < p$, then $\nu \perp \lambda^p$.

The problem described immediately carries over to the framework of an arbitrary Lie group G with Lie algebra $\mathscr{L}(G)$ and basis $\{X_1, \ldots, X_d\}$ of $\mathscr{L}(G)$.

Given a vector $(a_1, \ldots, a_d) \in \boldsymbol{R}^p$ and a symmetric positive definite matrix $(a_{ij})_{i,j=1,\dots,d} \in M(d, \boldsymbol{R})$ the linear functional ψ on $\mathscr{D}(G)$ defined by

$$\psi(f) = \sum_{i=1}^{d} a_i(X_i f)(e) + \sum_{i,j=1}^{d} a_{ij}(X_i X_j f)(e)$$

for all $f \in \mathscr{D}(G)$ is the generating functional of an e-continuous semi group $(\nu_t)_{t\in \boldsymbol{R}_+^*}$ in $\mathscr{G}(G)$ by Theorem 3.1. Thus $(\nu_t)_{t\in \boldsymbol{R}_+^*}$ is represented by the triple $(a_i, (a_{ij}), 0)$.

5.1 Theorem. *Let G be a connected Lie group of dimension $d > 0$ and ν a symmetric element of $\mathscr{G}(G)$ with embedding semi group represented by $(a_i, (a_{ij}), 0)$.*

If $(a_{ij})_{i,j=1,\dots,d}$ is positive definite, then there exists a (strictly) positive analytic ω_G-density f of ν such that $\nu = f\omega_G$ holds.

The proof of this theorem is based on results of the theory of parabolic differential operators [32].

Let now G be a Lie projective group such that there exists a descending family $(K_\alpha)_{\alpha\in A}$ of compact normal subgroups K_α of G with $\bigcap_{\alpha\in A} K = \{e\}$ such that $G_\alpha = G/K_\alpha$ is a Lie group for all $\alpha \in A$.

Denoting for every $\alpha \in A$ (or $\alpha, \beta \in A$ with $K_\beta \subset K_\alpha$) by p_α (or $p_{\alpha\beta}$) the canonical epimorphisms from G onto G_α (or from G_β onto G_α) we define

$$\mathscr{D}(G) = \bigcup_{\alpha\in A} \{f_\alpha \circ p_\alpha : f_\alpha \in \mathscr{D}(G_\alpha)\}$$

and

$$\mathscr{F}(G) = \bigcup_{\alpha\in A} \{f_\alpha \circ p_\alpha : f_\alpha \in \mathscr{F}(G_\alpha)\}.$$

A quadratic form ψ on $\mathscr{D}(G)$ is called *strict,* if $\psi(f) > 0$ for all $f \in \mathscr{F}(G)$.

We note that if G is a Lie group and ψ a quadratic form on $\mathscr{D}(G)$ of the form

$$\psi(f) = \sum_{i,j=1}^{d} a_{ij}(X_i X_j f)(e)$$

for all $f \in \mathscr{D}(G)$, then ψ is strict iff $(a_{ij})_{i,j=1,\ldots,d}$ is positive definite.

For every $\alpha \in A$ let ψ_α be a quadratic form on $\mathscr{D}(G_\alpha)$ such that for all $\beta, \gamma \in A$ with $K_\gamma \subset K_\beta$ we have $p_{\beta\gamma}(\psi_\gamma) = \psi_\beta$. Then

(a) there exists exactly one quadratic form $\psi = \varprojlim_{\alpha \in A} \psi_\alpha$ on $\mathscr{D}(G)$ with $p_\alpha(\psi) = \psi_\alpha$ for all $\alpha \in A$,

(b) ψ is strict iff ψ_α is strict for all $\alpha \in A$,

In [32] it is proved that for any connected locally compact group G there exists a strict quadratic form on $\mathscr{D}(G)$ and thus

5.2 Theorem. *If G is a connected locally compact group, then there exists a measure $\nu \in \mathscr{G}(G)$ with* $\operatorname{supp}(\nu) = G$.

This result strengthens the statement of Theorem 4.3.

Let $\nu \in \mathscr{G}(G)$ be a symmetric Gauss distribution with corresponding quadratic form ψ on $\mathscr{D}(G)$.

In the case of a Lie group G the strictness of ψ implies $\nu \ll \omega_G$.

For non Lie groups G this statement is in general false: An example showing this is given by $G = \prod_{n \geq 1} G_n$ with $G_n = T$ for all $n \geq 1$, $\nu_n \in \mathscr{G}(G_n)$ defined by $\hat{\nu}_n(m) = \exp(-m^2)$ for all $m \in Z \cong T$ $(n \geq 1)$ and $\nu = \bigtimes_{n \geq 1} \nu_n \in \mathscr{G}(G)$.

Clearly $\nu \perp \omega_G$, but the quadratic form ψ corresponding to ν is strict.

On the other hand it should be observed that $\operatorname{supp}(\nu) = G$ does not in general imply the strictness of ψ.

We give an example of an abelian locally compact group G and a non ω_G-absolutely continuous measure $\nu \in \mathscr{G}(G)$ with $\operatorname{supp}(\nu) = G$: Let $G = T^2$, $f\colon R \to G$ be defined by $f(t) = (e^{it}, e^{it\alpha})$ for all $t \in R$, where $\alpha \in \boldsymbol{R}$ is irrational.

Denoting $f(\boldsymbol{R})$ by H we obtain $\bar{H} = G$, but $H \neq G$, thus $\omega_G(H) = 0$. Let now μ be a symmetric Gauss distribution in $\mathcal{G}(\boldsymbol{R})$. Then $\nu = f(\mu) \in \mathcal{G}(G)$ with $\text{supp}(\nu) = \overline{f(\text{supp}(\mu))} = \overline{f(\boldsymbol{R})} = \bar{H} = G$. But $\nu(H) = 1$ and $\omega_G(H) = 0$ imply $\nu \perp \omega_G$.

The following theorem is a special case of a more general result of Hazod [14].

5.3 Theorem. *Let G be a Lie projective locally compact group and $\mu \in \mathcal{E}_e(G)$ with embedding semi group $(\mu_t)_{t \in \boldsymbol{R}_+^*}$ in $\mathcal{M}^1(G)$ whose generating functional on $\mathcal{D}(G)$ is denoted by ψ. Let $\mu_t^{\sim} * \mu_t = \mu_t^{\sim} * \mu_t$ for all $t \in \boldsymbol{R}_+^*$. Then the following statements are equivalent:*

(i) *μ is diffuse (atomless),*

(ii) *the symmetric part ψ^s of ψ is not bounded.*

5.4 Corollary. *Any measure $\nu \in \mathcal{G}(G)$ with embedding semi group $(\nu_t)_{t \in \boldsymbol{R}_+^*}$ such that $\nu_t^{\sim} * \nu_t = \nu_t * \nu_t^{\sim}$ holds for all $t \in \boldsymbol{R}_+^*$ is diffuse. In particular every $\nu \in \mathcal{G}(G)$ with symmetric generating functional is diffuse.*

6. CENTRAL GAUSS DISTRIBUTIONS

Let G be a connected locally compact group and ν a symmetric measure in $\mathcal{G}(G)$. For any topological automorphism α of G the measure $\alpha(\nu)$ is again a symmetric Gauss measure in $\mathcal{G}(G)$. A symmetric measure $\nu \in \mathcal{G}(G)$ is called *central,* if $\alpha(\nu) = \nu$ for all inner automorphisms α of G. Obviously $\nu \in \mathcal{G}(G)$ is central iff $\epsilon_x * \nu * \epsilon_{x^{-1}} = \nu$ for all $x \in G$. In this case ν belongs to the centre of $\mathcal{M}^1(G)$.

Central Gauss measures on locally compact groups have been studied in special cases first by E. M. Stein [34], under the general hypothesis recently by Siebert [32] (see also [33]).

Let now ν be a symmetric measure in $\mathcal{G}(G)$ with embedding semi group $(\nu_t)_{t \in \boldsymbol{R}_+^*}$ in $\mathcal{M}^1(G)$ and generating functional ψ on $\mathcal{D}(G)$.

For every $f \in \mathscr{D}(G)$ and $x \in G$ the function f^* on G defined by $f^x(y) = f(xyx^{-1})$ for all $y \in G$ is in $\mathscr{D}(G)$. Given $x \in G$ we define a linear functional ψ^x on $\mathscr{D}(G)$ by $\psi^x(f) = \psi(f^x)$ for all $f \in \mathscr{D}(G)$. ψ^x is a quadratic form generating the semi group $(\epsilon_x * \nu_t * \epsilon_{x^{-1}})_{t \in R_+^*}$ (which is a symmetric *Gauss semi group* in the obvious sense) and strict iff ψ is strict.

A quadratic form ψ on $\mathscr{D}(G)$ is called *G-invariant*, if $\psi^x = \psi$ for all $x \in G$.

Let ν be a symmetric measure in $\mathscr{G}(G)$ with embedding semi group $(\nu_t)_{t \in R_+^*}$ and generating functional ψ.

Then ν is central iff ψ is G-invariant.

6.1 Theorem. *Let G be a connected locally compact group. There exists a strict G-invariant quadratic form on $\mathscr{D}(G)$ iff G is a Z-group, i.e. a locally compact group G such that the quotient group $G/Z(G)$ by the centre $Z(G)$ of G is compact.*

6.2 Corollary. *On any connected Z-group G there exists a central Gauss distribution ν with* $\text{supp}(\nu) = G$.

By a more detailed study of the Fourier transform of a Gauss distribution one establishes

6.3 Theorem. *Let G be a connected, locally connected compact group with a countable base of its topology. Then there exists a central Gauss distribution $\nu \in \mathscr{G}(G)$ with the following properties:*

(i) $\text{supp}(\nu) = G$,

(ii) $\nu = f\omega_G$ *with* $f \in \mathscr{L}^2(\omega_G)$ *(i.e. ω_G-square integrable).*

In the case of a finite dimensional group the proof can be reduced to known facts, since the local connectednes implies that G is a Lie group and hence the result follows from Theorem 5.1 together with Theorem 6.1.

6.4 Theorem. *Let G be a connected almost periodic group with a countable base of its topology. The following statements are equivalent:*

(i) *There exists a* $\nu \in \mathcal{G}(G)$ *with* $\nu \ll \omega_G$.

(ii) G *is locally connected.*

The proof of the implication (ii) ⇒ (i) reduces to the discussion of a connected compact group K (by the Freudenthal – Weil theorem). But since K is locally connected, Theorem 6.3 implies the existence of the Gauss distribution desired. The proof of (i) ⇒ (ii) depends on the existence of a dense (Borel) measurable subgroup M of G with $M \neq G$ such that $\nu(M) = 1$ holds.

7. CONVERGENCE OF TRIANGULAR SYSTEMS TO GAUSS DISTRIBUTIONS

We proceed in the case of an almost periodic group G in complete analogy to the classical situation which was described in Section 1.

A triangular system $\Delta = (\mu_{nj})_{j=1,\ldots,k_n, n \geq 1}$ (of measures) in $\mathcal{M}^1(G)$ is called *infinitesimal,* if for each $U \in \mathfrak{B}(e)$ one has

$$\lim_{n\to\infty} \sup_{1 \leq j \leq k_n} \mu_{nj}(\complement U) = 0 .$$

In the case of a Moore group G the infinitesimality condition can be reformulated in the language of Fourier transforms of measures as follows: For every $D \in \operatorname{Rep}(G)$ and any vector ξ (or just the vector $(1, \ldots, 1)$) in the representing Hilbert space $\mathcal{H}(D)$ of D one has

$$\lim_{n\to\infty} \sup_{1 \leq j \leq k_n} \| (\hat{\mu}_{nj}(D) - I_{n(D)})\xi \| = 0 ,$$

where $I_{n(D)}$ denotes the identity operator on $\mathcal{H}(D)$. The triangular system Δ in $\mathcal{M}^1(G)$ is called *commutative,* if for all $n \geq 1$, $1 \leq j, \ k \leq k_n$ one obtains

$$\mu_{nj} * \mu_{nk} = \mu_{nk} * \mu_{nj} ,$$

and *convergent with limit* μ, if for the sequence $(\mu_n)_{n \geq 1}$ of n-th partial products

$$\mu_n = \mu_{n1} * \ldots * \mu_{nk_n} \qquad (n \geq 1)$$

there exists $\mu \in \mathcal{M}^1(G)$ such that $\lim_{n\to\infty} \mu_n = \mu$ holds.

7.1 Theorem. *Let G be a root compact Moore group and $\nu \in \mathcal{M}^1(G)$ non degenerate. The following statements are equivalent:*

(i) $\nu \in \mathcal{G}(G)$.

(ii) *There exists an infinitesimal and commutative triangular system $\Delta = (\mu_{nj})_{j=1,\dots,k_n,\, n\geq 1}$ in $\mathcal{M}^1(G)$ convergent with limit ν and satisfying the following conditions*

(a) $\lim_{n\to\infty} \sum_{j=1}^{k_n} \mu_{nj}(\complement U) = 0$ *for all* $U \in \mathfrak{B}(e)$.

(b) *To every irreducible $D \in \mathrm{Rep}\,(G)$ there is a $V \in \mathfrak{B}(e)$ with the property*

$$\overline{\lim_{n\geq 1}} \sum_{j=1}^{k_n} \left\| \int_V [D(x) - E_{n(D)}]\mu_{nj}(dx) \right\| < \infty ,$$

where $E_{n(D)}$ denotes the $n(D) \times n(D)$ unit matrix.

The proof of this (central limit) theorem is based as in the case of an abelian group [22], [24] on an accompanying laws result which has been established for general Moore groups in [29]. Special cases of the theorem have been proved previously for the rotation group by Parthasarathy in [23], for connected compact Lie groups by the author in [15]. Similar results in the framework of a general Lie group are due to Wehn [36] (see also [13]). A sufficiently complete treatment of the central limit problem for locally compact groups will be presented in a forthcoming monograph [18].

The connection between condition (b) of (ii) of the theorem and analogous conditions in [15] and [36] can be indicated as follows:

(1) Let $k_n = n$ and $\mu_{n1} = \ldots = \mu_{nn} = \lambda_n$ for all $n \geq 1$.

If the triangular system $\Delta = (\mu_{nj})_{j=1,\dots,k_n;\, n\geq 1}$ satisfies for all $D \in \mathrm{Rep}\,(G)$ and $\xi \in \mathcal{H}(D)$ the condition

$$\overline{\lim_{n \geq 1}} \sum_{j=1}^{k_n} \| (\hat{\mu}_{nj}(D)) - I_{n(D)})\xi \| < \infty ,$$

then Δ is infinitesimal. Furthermore for every $D \in \mathrm{Rep}\,(G)$ and $n \geq 1$ one obtains

$$1 - |\det (\hat{\lambda}_n(D))| \leq \hat{\lambda}_n(f_D) ,$$

thus the above condition implies

$$\overline{\lim_{n \geq 1}}\; n(1 - |\det (\hat{\lambda}_n(D))|) < \infty .$$

If now Δ is convergent with limit λ, it can be shown that λ admits no idempotent factor (in the sense of convolution).

(2) Let G be a Moore group which also is a Lie group of dimension $d > 0$ with Lie algebra $\mathscr{L}(G)$, basis $\{X_1, \ldots, X_d\}$ of $\mathscr{L}(G)$ and canonical coordinate system $\{x_1, \ldots, x_d\}$ w.r.t. $\{X_1, \ldots, X_d\}$. Let φ be a Hunt function for G.

For any infinitesimal and commutative triangular system $\Delta = (\mu_{nj})_{j=1,\ldots,k_n,\, n \geq 1}$ in $\mathscr{M}^1(G)$ the following two conditions imply the first condition of (1):

(α) $$\overline{\lim_{n \geq 1}} \sum_{j=1}^{k_n} \int \varphi d\mu_{nj} < \infty ,$$

(β) there exists $U \in \mathfrak{B}(e)$ with

$$\overline{\lim_{n \geq 1}} \sum_{j=1}^{k_n} \left| \int_U x_i d\mu_{nj} \right| < \infty \qquad \text{for all} \qquad i = 1, \ldots, d .$$

Finally we quote a result essentially due to Carnal [5]. For an abelian locally compact group G this result also follows from the discussion in [24].

7.2 Theorem. *Let* G *be a root compact Moore group and* $\Delta = (\mu_{nj})_{j=1,\ldots,k_n;\, n \geq 1}$ *an infinitesimal triangular system in* $\mathscr{M}^1(G)$ *convergent with limit* $\nu \in \mathscr{M}^1(G)$. *If* $\nu \in \mathscr{G}(G)$, *then for all* $U \in \mathfrak{B}(e)$ *the condition*

$$\lim_{n \to \infty} \sum_{j=1}^{k_n} \mu_{nj}(\complement U) = 0$$

is satisfied.

REFERENCES

[1] S.N. Bernstein, On a property characterizing the Gaussian law, in *Collected Works,* IV: Theory of probability, Nauka, Moscow (1964), 394-395 (in Russian).

[2] S. Bochner, *Harmonic analysis and the theory of probability,* University of California Press, 1955.

[3] H. Carnal, Unendlich oft teilbare Wahrscheinlichkeitsverteilungen auf kompakten Gruppen, *Math. Annalen,* 153 (1964), 351-383.

[4] H. Carnal, Non-validité du théorème de Lévy – Cramér sur le cercle, *Publ. de l'ISUP,* 13 (1964), 55-56.

[5] H. Carnal, Systèmes infinitésimaux sur les groupes topologiques compacts. Les Probabilités sur les Structures Algébriques, *Colloques Internationaux du CNRS,* 186 (1970), 43-49.

[6] L. Corwin, A "functional equation" for measures and a generalization of Gaussian measures, *Bull. Amer. Math. Soc.,* 75 (1969), 829-832.

[7] L. Corwin, Generalized Gaussian measures and a "functional equation" I, *Journ. of Functional Analysis,* 5 (1970), 412-427.

[8] L. Corwin, Generalized Gaussian measures and a "functional equation" II, *Journ. of Functional Analysis,* 6 (1970), 481-505.

[9] L. Corwin, Generalized Gaussian measures and a "functional equation" III. Measures on R^n, *Advances in Mathematics,* 6 (1971), 239-251.

[10] Ph. Courrège, Générateur infinitésimal d'un semi-groupe de convolution sur R^n et formule de Lévy – Khinchine, *Bull. Soc. Math.*, Ser. 2, 88 (1964), 3-30.

[11] H. Cramér, Über eine Eigenschaft der normalen Verteilungsfunktion, *Math. Z.*, 41 (1936), 405-414.

[12] B.V. Gnedenko – A.N. Kolmogorov, *Grenzverteilungen von Summen unabhängiger Zufallsgrössen,* Akademie-Verlag, Berlin, 1960.

[13] U. Grenander, *Probabilities on Algebraic Structures,* John Wiley, New York, 1963.

[14] W. Hazod, Symmetrische Gaussverteilungen sind diffus, *Manuscripta Math.*, 14 (1974), 283-295.

[15] H. Heyer, A central limit theorem for compact Lie groups, Papers from the "Open House for Probabilists", Matematisk Institut, Aarhus Universitet, Various Publ. Series, No 21, (1972), 101-117.

[16] H. Heyer, *Infinitely divisible probability measures on compact groups,* Lectures Notes in Mathematics, 247, Springer, 1972, 55-249.

[17] H. Heyer – Chr. Rall, Gaussche Wahrscheinlichkeitsmasse auf Corwinschen Gruppen, *Math. Z.*, 128 (1972), 343-361.

[18] H. Heyer, *Probability measures on locally compact groups,* in preparation for Ergebnisse der Mathematik und ihrer Grenzgebiete, Springer, Berlin – Heidelberg – New York.

[19] G.A. Hunt, Semi-groups of measures on Lie groups, *Trans. Amer. Math. Soc.*, 81 (1956), 264-293.

[20] P. Lévy, L'addition des variables aléatoires définies sur une circonférence, *Bull. Soc. Math. France,* 67 (1939), 1-41.

[21] P. Lévy, *Théorie de l'addition des variables aléatoires,* 2nd éd., Gauthier-Villars, 1954.

[22] K.R. Parthasarathy – R. Ranga Rao – S.R. Varadhan, Probability distributions on locally compact abelian groups, *Illinois J. Math.*, 7 (1963), 337-369.

[23] K.R. Parthasarathy, The central limit theorem for the rotation group, *Theory Prob. Applications,* 9 (1964), 248-257.

[24] K.R. Parthasarathy, *Probability measure on metric spaces,* Academic Press, 1967.

[25] C.R. Rao, Characterization of the distribution of a random variable in linear structural relations, *Sankhyā*, Ser. A, 28 (1966), 251-260.

[26] A.L. Ruhin, Some statistical and probabilistic problems on groups, *Proc. Steklov Inst. Math.*, 111 (1970), 59-129.

[27] K. Schmidt, On a characterization of certain infinitely divisible positive definite functions and measures, *Journal London Math. Soc.*, Ser. 2, 4 (1972), 401-407.

[28] K. Schmidt, A class of infinitely divisible positive definite functions on topological groups, Preprint, 1973.

[29] E. Siebert, Wahrscheinlichkeitsmasse auf lokalkompakten maximal fastperiodischen Gruppen, Dissertation Tübingen, 1972.

[30] E. Siebert, Stetige Halbgruppen von Wahrscheinlichkeitsmassen auf lokalkompakten maximal fastperiodischen Gruppen, *Z. Wahrscheinlichkeitstheorie verw. Geb.*, 25 (1973), 269-300.

[31] E. Siebert, Einbettung unendlich teilbarer Wahrscheinlichkeitsmasse auf topologischen Gruppen, *Z. Wahrscheinlichkeitstheorie verw. Geb.*, 28 (1974), 227-247.

[32] E. Siebert, Absolut-Stetigkeit und Träger von Gaussverteilungen auf lokalkompakten Gruppen, *Math. Annalen,* 210 (1974), 129-147.

[33] E. Siebert, Einige Bemerkungen zu den Gaussverteilungen auf lokalkompakten abelschen Gruppen, *Manuscripta Math.*, 14 (1974), 41-55.

[34] E.M. Stein, *Topics in harmonic analysis,* Annals of Math. Studies No 63, Princeton University Press, 1970.

[35] K. Urbanik, Gaussian measures on locally compact abelian topological groups, *Studia Math.*, 19 (1960), 77-88.

[36] D.F. Wehn, Probabilities on Lie groups, *Proc. Nat. Acad. Science,* 48 (1962), 791-795.

COLLOQUIA MATHEMATICA SOCIETATIS JÁNOS BOLYAI
11. LIMIT THEOREMS OF PROBABILITY THEORY, KESZTHELY (HUNGARY), 1974.

LIMIT PROBLEMS ON TOPOLOGICAL STOCHASTIC GROUPS AND BOHR COMPACTIFICATION

J. KLASA

0. INTRODUCTION

Let $(X_i)_{i\in N}$ be a sequence of independent, identical distributed (i.i.d.) random variables with a (non-degenerate) distribution function F and let

$$S_n = X_1 + X_2 + \ldots + X_n \qquad (n \in N).$$

It can be shown that for any fixed numbers a and b the probability of the event $A_n = \{a \leqslant S_n \leqslant b\}$ converges to zero when n tends to infinity. If (X_i) is viewed as a sequence of i.i.d. random elements of the compact Bohr line, then in many cases S_n will tend to be "uniformly" distributed on the compact subgroup generated by the support of F. We shall study the general problem of the limit distribution of partial products $X_1 \cdot X_2 \cdot \ldots \cdot X_n$ of i.i.d. random elements in a locally compact group G. For compact groups the problem was completely solved in 1940 by Y. Kawada and K. Itô. Therefore for a general locally compact group G, it appeared possible to answer the "weak" question of convergence:

When does the distribution of the partial product $X_1 \cdot X_2 \cdot \ldots \cdot X_n$ converge in the compact Bohr group of G? Kawada and Itô condition is shown to be necessary for the convergence in G.

1. PRELIMINARIES AND NOTATIONS

By a measure m on a locally compact space X we shall mean a complex linear continuous form on the topological vector space $K(X)$ of continuous complex-valued functions with compact supports. Instead of writing $m(f)$ we may write also the integral $\int_X f(x)\, dm(x)$.

The set of all measures on X will be denoted $M(X)$. $M(X)$ is equipped with the weak topology defined by: the sequence (m_n) converges weakly to a measure m if the sequence $(m_n(f))$ converges to $m(f)$ for any function f lying in $K(X)$.

The subset of continuous linear forms on $C^\infty(X)$, space of bounded continuous functions on X, is denoted $M_b(X)$ and called the set of *bounded measures on* X. It may be shown that any such bounded measure m on X is a bounded form on $C^\infty(X)$ with the norm

$$\|m\| = \sup_{\|f\|_\infty \leqslant 1} |m(f)| .$$

Let us denote by $P(X)$ the subset of positive real bounded measures of norm 1, i.e. *probabilities* on X. $P(X)$ will be equipped with the weak topology induced by $M(X)$. We may say: the sequence (p_n) of probabilities converges weakly to p if the sequence of numbers $p_n(f)$ converges to $p(f)$ for any bounded positive continuous function f on X.

Let us remark that the subspace $\delta(X)$ of $P(X)$ of Dirac measures is homeomorphic to X.

Definition. The support $S(m)$ of a measure m on X is given by

$$X \setminus (\cup \{O \text{ is open, } m \text{ is zero on } O\}) .$$

m is zero on the open set O if $m(f) = O$ for any continuous function, with a compact support inside O. The support $S(m)$ is always closed.

Image of a measure

Let $F\colon X \to Y$ be a continuous mapping between two locally compact spaces X and Y. With any bounded measure m on X we associate the bounded measure $\widetilde{F}(m)$ on Y defined by:

$$\widetilde{F}(m)(g) = m(F \circ g)\,.$$

Properties of the image measure:

(1) $\|\widetilde{F}(m)\| = \|m\|$.

(2) $S(\widetilde{F}(m)) = \overline{F(S(m))}$.

(3) The image of a probability is again a probability.

Convolution of bounded measures on a locally compact group G.

Let $(G, \cdot)$ be a locally compact topological group. On $M_b(G)$ we may define the convolution $*$ as follows:

$$(m * m')(f) = \int_G \Big(\int_G f(gg')\, dm(g) \Big)\, dm'(g') =$$

$$= \int_G \Big(\int_G f(gg')\, dm'(g') \Big)\, dm(g)\,.$$

Notation: $\underbrace{m}_{1} * \ldots * \underbrace{m}_{n} = m^{*n}$.

Some properties of the convolution:

(1) $(M_b(G), *)$ is a topological convex semigroup.

(2) $S(m * m') = S(m) \cdot S(m')$.

(3) $\delta_g * \delta_{g'} = \delta_{g \cdot g'}$

(4) $(P(G), *)$ is a closed convex subsemigroup of $M_b(G)$.

(5) The convolution is distributive with respect to any convex linear combination.

(6) The semigroup $(P(G), *)$ is commutative if and only if $(G, \cdot)$ is commutative.

(7) The convolution may be defined between a bounded measure and any other measure.

Haar measures on locally compact groups

Definition. A *left* (resp. *right*) *Haar measure* on the locally compact group G is a measure m such that we have:

$$\delta_g * m = m \quad \text{for any element } g \text{ in } G$$

(resp. $m * \delta_g = m$).

On a locally compact group there exist left (resp. right) Haar measure. They are all proportional one with each other. Furthermore, we know that Haar measures are bounded only for compact groups.

2. LIMIT THEOREMS ON COMPACT STOCHASTIC GROUPS

Let p be a probability on a compact group G. Can we find a limit for the iterated sequence p^{*n}?

Let us remark first of all that the space $P(G)$ is a compact semigroup with the kernel reduced to an element π, the identical left and right Haar probability on G. In particular, π is idempotent and stationary. As we are dealing with iterated sequences in compact semigroups we shall give the following result.

Theorem 2.1 (Koch – Numakura [16], [18]). *For* x *in a compact semigroup* S, *let* $\Gamma_n(x) = \{x^p : p \geqslant n\}^-$ *(–: closure),* $\Gamma(x) = \Gamma_1(x)$ *and* $K(x) = \bigcap_{n \geqslant 1} \Gamma_n(x)$. $K(x)$ *is an ideal of* $\Gamma(x)$ *and moreover a subgroup, containing an idempotent of* S *as identity.*

Remarks.

(a) In the finite case, we will find $K(x) = \Gamma(x)$ is a finite group with the idempotent e equal to a power of x.

(b) If $\lim_n x^n$ exists, this limit is an idempotent e such that $ex = xe = e$. It looks like a "zero" element.

Because of Koch – Numakura's theorem, we would like to determine all idempotents of the compact semigroup $P(G)$. Idempotent probabilities on a compact group G are known to be exactly Haar probabilities on compact subgroups of G. Let us remark that idempotent probabilities on compact semigroups are also well characterized (cf. (11), (19)).

Kawada and Itô, by using Fourier analysis on compact groups, gave a necessary and sufficient condition for the sequence p^{*n} to converge.

Theorem 2.3 (Kawada – Itô [14]). *For a given probability p on a compact group G, the limit of (p^{*n}) exists if and only if the support $S(p)$ is not contained in a proper two-sided coset of a compact subgroup of G. The limit of (p^{*n}) is then the Haar probability on the closed subgroup generated by $S(p)$.*

Corollary 2.4. *Let p be a probability on a compact group G, such that $S(p)$ contains the neutral element of G. Then the sequence (p^{*n}) converges to the Haar probability on some closed subgroup of G.*

Remark. If $S(p)$ is symmetric in G, then the subsequence (p^{*2n}) converges.

Illustration. Let us take $G = S^1$ (the unit circle). The possible limit distributions on S^1 will be the Haar probability $\frac{d\theta}{2\pi}$, and any uniform distribution $\frac{1}{n}$ on finite subgroups of rotations $\left\{\frac{k}{n} 2\pi,\ k = 0, 1, 2, \ldots \ldots, n-1\right\}$.

3. BOHR COMPACTIFICATION AND ITS FUNCTORIALITY

Alfsen, Fenstad and Holm (cf. (1), (2)) proved the following theorem.

Theorem 3.1. *Let G be a topological (not necessarily Hausdorff) group. Then, up to isomorphism, there exists an unique quasi-compact* *group $B(G)$ and a continuous homomorphism η_G onto a dense subgroup of $B(G)$ such that each continuous homomorphism σ of G into a quasi-compact group K may be uniquely extended to a continuous homomorphism σ_B of $B(G)$ into K in the sense that $\sigma = \sigma_B \circ \eta_G$. This group $B(G)$ is called the Bohr compactification of G.*

Remarks. If G is compact, then $B(G)$ is isomorphic to G. In the case of a locally compact abelian group G, the compact group $B(G)$ is the classical Bohr group of G. Then $B(G)$ is isomorphic to $\hat{\hat{G}}^d$, the whole group of characters on the discrete group $\hat{G}^d$. The map η_G is injective and is the inclusion of the topological group $G = \hat{\hat{G}}$ of continuous characters on $\hat{G}$ (with the compact-open topology) into the compact group of all (not necessarily continuous) characters on $\hat{G}$, with the pointwise convergence topology. The Banach space of all continuous complex-valued functions on $B(G)$ is isomorphic to the closed subspace of $C^\infty(G)$ of almost periodic functions on G.

For any topological group G, Alfsen and Holm showed that almost periodicity is also a necessary and sufficient condition for a continuous complex-valued function on G to be extendable by continuity to $B(G)$. Only if η_G is injective, $C(B(G))$ is isomorphic to the space of almost periodic functions on G. In [12] Heyer describes the class of *maximal almost periodic* (denoted MAP) groups, those groups for which η is injective. By the universality property of Bohr compactification we see easily that any topological group embeddable in a MAP group is MAP; then any subgroup of a MAP group is MAP. On the other hand, if H is a MAP subgroup of G with $[G:H] < \infty$, then G is also MAP. A quotient group G/H of a MAP group G is MAP if H is either compact or equal to the center of G. MAP groups may be characterized by the fact that only for them, the class of their finite unitary representations is separating (i.e. for any element g in G, there exists a finite unitary representation r such that $r(g) \neq r(e)$). By using this property Heyer lists following subclasses of MAP groups:

(a) compact groups,

(b) locally compact abelian groups,

(c) any free (non-abelian) group with more than one generator.

H. Leptin and L. Robertson [17] proved that any MAP locally compact group is unimodular. Moreover S. Grosser and M. Moskowitz [10] showed that a connected locally compact group is MAP if and only if it is central; a locally compact group is called *central* if the quotient $G/Z(G)$ ($Z(G)$: center of G) is compact.

Now we shall mention some functorial properties of the operation B.

At first, whenever we are given a continuous homomorphism

$$h : G \to H$$

then by universality, we may construct a continuous homomorphism

$$B(h) : B(G) \to B(H)$$

defined by

$$B(h) = h_B \circ \eta_G \, .$$

Now if we are given the sequence of continuous homomorphisms

$$G \xrightarrow{h} H \xrightarrow{k} K \, ,$$

commutativity of diagrams implies the equality

$$B(k \circ h) = B(k) \circ B(h) \, .$$

How good is B with respect to mono- and epimorphisms of topological groups? (See §4, [12].)

B is *right exact:* for any given exact sequence of topological groups

$$e \longrightarrow G_1 \xrightarrow{i} G \xrightarrow{s} G_2 \longrightarrow e$$

we may deduce the following exact sequence

$$B(G_1) \xrightarrow{B(i)} B(G) \xrightarrow{B(s)} B(G_2) \longrightarrow e$$

where $B(G_2)$ is isomorphic to the topological quotient group $B(G)/B(i)(B(G_1))$.

B happens to be *left exact* if G is a MAP group and G_1 is a compact normal subgroup of G. Then the compact group $B(G_2)$ is isomorphic to the quotient $B(G)/B(G_1)$ ($B(G_1)$ is isomorphic to its image in $B(G)$).

Theorem 3.2. *Let* G_1 *be a closed normal subgroup of a topological group* G, *then the compact group* $B(G/G_1)$ *is isomorphic to the quotient* $B(G)/\overline{\eta_G(G_1)}$.

For the proof see [12], p. 128-129. The right exactness of B and the equality $\overline{\eta_G(G_1)} = B(i)(B(G_1))$ are used in the proof.

Corollary 3.3. *If* G *is a* MAP *group and* G_1 *is a compact normal subgroup of* G, *then the compact group* $B(G/G_1)$ *is isomorphic to the quotient* $B(G)/B(G_1)$.

Consequence. *The topological group* $\eta_{G_2}(G/G_1)$ *is always dense in the quotient compact group* $B(G)/B(i)(B(G_1))$.

4. LIMIT THEOREMS ON LOCALLY COMPACT STOCHASTIC GROUPS

Let p be a probability on a locally compact group G. If $(X_i)_{i \in N}$ is a sequence of i.i.d. random elements in G, can we find the limit distribution of $X_1 \cdot X_2 \cdot \ldots \cdot X_n$? In the euclidean context, we used to look for some norming process (f_n): a sequence of continuous maps from G to G, such that the limit distribution of $f_n(X_1 \cdot X_2 \cdot \ldots \cdot X_n)$ does exist. Here we shall behave differently. Instead of norming, we shall embed our problem in the compact Bohr group $B(G)$. That will mean: given any sequence (m_n) of measures on G, try to find the limit measure on $B(G)$ of the image sequence $(\tilde{\eta}_G(m_n))$. For simplicity we shall denote the image $\tilde{\eta}_G(m_n)$ by $\tilde{m}_n$. Whenever the sequence (m_n) converges in $M(G)$, so will do $(\tilde{m}_n)$ in $M(B(G))$. But the converse is obviously false. We shall get very often limit measures of $(\tilde{m}_n)$ which do not come from one on G. For the locally compact (non-compact) abelian case, this will be the translation of the fact that the sequence of Fourier transforms $F(m_n)$, continuous functions on the dual group $\hat{G}$, will converge pointwise to a non-continuous function.

We may rewrite Kawada – Itô's theorem in the following way: Given any probability p on a locally compact group G, the sequence $(\widetilde{p}^{*n})$ converges if and only if the support $\overline{\eta_G(S(p))} = S(\widetilde{p})$ is not contained in any proper closed two-sided coset of a compact subgroup of $B(G)$.

To give more sense to this restatement, one should analyze for which probabilities is it true that their supports are included in a proper closed two-sided coset of a subgroup of the compact Bohr group.

Theorem 4.1. *Let p be a probability on the locally compact* MAP *group G. The sequence $(\widetilde{p}^{*n})$ converges if and only if the support $S(p)$ is not contained in a proper closed two-sided coset of a subgroup of G. The limit of $\widetilde{p}^{*n}$ is then the Haar probability on the compact subgroup generated by $S(\widetilde{p})$.*

Proof. Let p be a probability on a MAP locally compact group G. The closed subgroup generated by $S(p)$ is again a MAP locally compact group. Then for the sake of simplicity we shall suppose further that $S(p)$ generates the whole group G.

(a) Let p be a probability such that $S(p)$ is included in a closed proper coset A of G. Let us associate with A an element γ $(\gamma \neq e)$ of a quotient group $G_2 = G/G_1$ where G_1 is a normal closed subgroup of G, homeomorphic to A. The exact sequence

$$e \to G_1 \to G \to G_2 \to e$$

may be embedded into the commutative diagram

$$\begin{array}{ccccccccc} e & \longrightarrow & G_1 & \longrightarrow & G & \xrightarrow{\psi} & G_2 & \longrightarrow & e \\ & & \downarrow & & \downarrow \eta_G & & \downarrow \eta_{G_2} & & \\ e & \longrightarrow & \overline{\eta_G(G_1)} & \longrightarrow & B(G) & \xrightarrow{B(\psi)} & B(G_2) & \longrightarrow & e \end{array}$$

The support $\overline{\eta_G(S(p))}$ of the image probability $\widetilde{p}$ is included in $\overline{\eta_G(A)}$. It is clear that $\overline{\eta_G(A)}$ is equal to the closed coset $B(\psi)^{-1}(\eta_{G_2}(\gamma))$. Because of MAP property $\eta_{G_2}(\gamma) \neq e$ and $S(\widetilde{p})$ is included in a proper closed coset of $B(G)$ and by Kawada – Itô's theorem $\lim_n \widetilde{p}^{*n}$ does not exist.

(b) Let us suppose now that we are given a probability p on G such that $S(\widetilde{p})$ is contained in a proper closed coset C of $B(G)$. Then we may associate with C an element γ of a quotient group $B(G)/K$ where K is homeomorphic to C.

We can embed the exact sequence

$$e \longrightarrow K \xrightarrow{\varphi} B(G)/K \longrightarrow e$$

into the following commutative diagram

$$\begin{array}{ccccccccc} & & & & & & e & & \\ & & & & & & \downarrow & & \\ e \rightarrow & \psi^{-1}(e) & \rightarrow & G & \xrightarrow{\psi} & & G_2 & \rightarrow & e \\ & \downarrow & & \downarrow \eta_G & & & \downarrow \epsilon & & \\ e \rightarrow & K & \rightarrow & B(G) & \xrightarrow{\varphi} & & B(G)/K & \rightarrow & e \end{array}$$

where G_2 is equal to $\varphi \cdot \eta_G(G)$ and where ϵ is the inclusion of this image in $B(G)/K$. As $\eta_G(G)$ is dense in $B(G)$, so is $\epsilon(G_2)$ in $B(G)/K$. Is it possible for γ not to be in G_2? Any element g in $S(p)$ satisfies

$$\psi(g) = \varphi(\eta_G(g)) = \varphi(c) = \gamma$$

because c is an element of $\eta_G(S(p)) \subset C$. Then γ is necessarily an element in G_2. Furthermore we have:

$$\psi^{-1}(\gamma) = \eta_G^{-1}(\varphi^{-1}(\gamma)) = \eta_G^{-1}(C)$$

and

$$S(p) \subset \eta_G^{-1}(S(\widetilde{p})) \subset \eta_G^{-1}(C)\,.$$

Then $S(p)$ is contained in the proper closed coset $\psi^{-1}(\gamma) = \eta_G^{-1}(C)$.

We just showed that if p is a probability such that $S(\widetilde{p})$ is contained in a proper closed coset of $B(G)$, then $S(p)$ is contained in a proper closed coset of G.

(c) From parts (a) and (b) we deduce that the support $S(p)$ is not contained in a proper closed coset of G if and only if the support $S(\widetilde{p})$ is not contained in a proper closed coset of $B(G)$.

Corollary 4.2. *Let* p *be a probability on a locally compact group* G *such that the support* $S(p)$ *contains the neutral element* e *of* G. *Then the image sequence* $(\widetilde{p}^{*n})$ *converges to the Haar probability of the compact group generated by* $\overline{\eta_G(S(p))}$.

This is an obvious consequence of Theorem 4.1 as if $S(p)$ contains the neutral element of G so does $S(\widetilde{p})$.

Remarks. We know many distributions on the real line satisfying the condition given in Corollary 4.2. If we choose the probability p to be the normal distribution $n_{\mu,\sigma} \cdot \lambda$ then the image sequence $(n_{\mu,\sigma} \cdot \lambda)^{*n}$ converges to the Haar probability on $B(R) = \hat{R}_d$ = compact group of not necessarily continuous characters on the real line.

Let us think now either of the binomial distribution $b(k, p)$ or of the Poisson distribution $p(\lambda)$. Both of them give a strictly positive mass at the number 0. Then we may deduce that $\widetilde{b}(kn, p)$ and $\widetilde{p}(n\lambda)$ converge to the same distribution, the Haar probability on $B(Z)$, compact subgroup of $B(R)$. Any element of $B(Z)$ may be viewed as the (pointwise) limit of a sequence (γ_n) of characters on R, where $\gamma_n(x) = e^{ik_n x}$ and (k_n) is a sequence of integers.

As we did for locally compact groups, we might give the same kind of study for semigroups. Almost periodic compactifications of topological semigroups were constructed by J. S. Pym, A. and G. Baker and others. Unfortunately, for compact semigroups we do not know necessary and sufficient conditions of convergence of iterated sequence of probabilities.

Hewitt – Zuckerman gave in 1955 [9], [15] necessary and sufficient conditions of convergence for a finite semigroup. Rosenblatt [9], [15] and [19] showed that if the compact semigroup S generated by the support of the probability p admits a kernel K for which

$$kS = k \qquad (\text{resp. } Sk = k)$$

for any element k in K, then the sequence (p^{*n}) converges to an idempotent probability supported by K. The family of 0-compact semigroups satisfies the Rosenblatt's condition. In this case, the limit distribution is the Dirac measure at 0.

REFERENCES

[1] E.M. Alfsen – I.E. Fenstad, A note on completion and compactification, *Math. Scand.*, 10 (1960), 97-104.

[2] E.M. Alfsen – P. Holm, A note on compact representations and almost periodicity in topological groups, *Math. Scand.*, 10 (1962), 127-136.

[3] A.C. Baker – J.W. Baker, Algebras of measures on a locally compact semigroup, I-II, *J. London Math. Soc.*, 1 (1969), 249-259, 2 (1970), 651-659.

[4] J.W. Baker, Convolution measure algebra with involution, *Proc. Amer. Math. Soc.*, 27 (1971), 91-96.

[5] R. Bellman, Limit theorems for non-commutative operations, I, *Duke Math. J.*, 21 (1954), 491-500.

[6] N. Bourbaki, *Topologie générale,* Chapitre 3, Hermann.

[7] N. Bourbaki, *Intégration,* Chapitres 7, 8, Hermann.

[8] I. Glicksberg, Convolution semigroup of measures, *Pac. J. Math.*, 9 (1959), 51-67.

[9] U. Grenander, *Probabilities on algebraic structures,* University of Stockholm, John Wiley & Sons, Inc., 1963.

[10] S. Grosser – M. Moskowitz, (I) On central topological groups, *Trans. Amer. Math. Soc.*, 27 (1967), 317-340. (II) Representation theory of central topological groups, *Trans. Amer. Math. Soc.*, 129 (1967), 361-390.

[11] M. Heble – M. Rosenblatt, Idempotent measures on a compact topological semigroup, mimeographed report.

[12] H. Heyer, (I) *Dualität localkompakter Gruppen,* Springer-Verlag, Lecture Notes in Mathematics, No. 150, 1970. (II) *Lectures on operator algebras, Infinitely divisible probability measures on compact groups,* Springer-Verlag Lectures Notes in Mathematics, No. 247, (1972), 55-249.

[13] K. Hofman – P. Mostert, *Elements of compact semigroups,* Merrill, Columbus, Ohio, 1966.

[14] Y. Kawada – K. Itô, On the probability distribution on a compact group, *Proc. Phys. Mat. Soc. Japan,* 22 (1940), 977-998.

[15] J. Klasa, Random walks on compact semigroups, Queens University preprint 1973-20.

[16] R. Koch – D. Wallace, Maximal ideals in compact semigroups, *Duke Math. J.*, 21 (1954), 681-685.

[17] H. Leptin – L. Robertson, Every locally compact MAP group is unimodular, *Proc. Amer. Math. Soc.*, 19 (1968), 1079-1082.

[18] K. Numakura, On bicompact semigroups, *Math. J. Okayama Univ.*, 1 (1954), 99-108.

[19] M. Rosenblatt, Limits of convolution sequences of measures on a compact topological semigroup, *J. Math. Mech.*, 9 (1960).

[20] W. Rudin, (I) Measure algebras on abelian groups, *Bull. Amer. Math. Soc.*, 65 (1959), 227-247. (II) *Idempotent measures on abelian groups, Pac. J. Math.*, 9 (1959), 195-209.

[21] A. Tortrat, Lois tendues sur un demigroupe topologique complitement simple, *Z. Wahrscheinlichkeitstheorie und verw. Geb.*, 6 (1964), 145-160.

[22] A. Weil, *L'intégration dans les groupes topologiques et ses applications,* Paris, 1940.

COLLOQUIA MATHEMATICA SOCIETATIS JÁNOS BOLYAI
11. LIMIT THEOREMS OF PROBABILITY THEORY, KESZTHELY (HUNGARY), 1974.

WEAK CONVERGENCE AND EMBEDDING

J. KOMLÓS – P. MAJOR – G. TUSNÁDY

1. INTRODUCTION

Let $X_1, X_2, \ldots$ be independent, identically distributed random variables (i.i.d.r.v.) with distribution function $F \in \mathscr{F}_r$, where

$$\mathscr{F}_r = \{F\colon F \text{ is a distribution function}, \quad \int_{-\infty}^{\infty} x\, dF = 0, \quad \int_{-\infty}^{\infty} x^2\, dF = 1, \quad \int_{-\infty}^{\infty} |x|^r\, dF < \infty\}. \tag{1.1}$$

Let the function s_n be defined on $[0, 1]$ by

$$s_n(t) = \frac{1}{\sqrt{n}} \left[X_1 + \ldots + X_{k-1} + n\left(t - \frac{k-1}{n}\right) X_k\right] \quad \text{for} \quad \frac{k-1}{n} \leqslant t \leqslant \frac{k}{n}; \qquad k = 1, 2, \ldots, n; \tag{1.2}$$

and let the probability measure S_n^F be generated by $s_n(t)$ on the space $C(0, 1)$ of continuous functions on $[0, 1]$. It is well known that the sequence S_n^F converges to the Wiener measure W on $C(0, 1)$ for any

$F \in \mathcal{F}_2$. Similarly, if $Y_1, Y_2, \ldots$ are i.i.d.r.v.-s uniformly distributed on $[0, 1]$, the function z_n is defined by

$$z_n(t) = \sqrt{n}\Big(\frac{1}{n} \sum_{i:\, Y_i < t} 1 - t\Big) \quad \text{for} \quad 0 \leqslant t \leqslant 1\,, \tag{1.3}$$

and Z_n is the distribution of z_n on the space $D(0, 1)$ of real functions on $[0, 1]$ without discontinuities of second kind, then Z_n tends weakly to the distribution B of the Brownian bridge.

The weak convergence can be metrized by the Prohorov distance, which is defined in a metric space M by

$$\begin{aligned} \rho(\mathsf{P}_0, \mathsf{P}_1) = \inf\{\epsilon > 0\colon\ & \mathsf{P}_0(E) \leqslant \epsilon + \mathsf{P}_1\{y\colon \exists x \in E, d(x, y) < \epsilon\} \\ & \text{for all closed } E\}\,, \end{aligned} \tag{1.4}$$

where d is the metric of the space, especially on $C(0, 1)$ it is

$$d(x, y) = \sup_{0 \leqslant t \leqslant 1} |x(t) - y(t)|\,, \tag{1.5}$$

and the metric on $D(0, 1)$ is

$$\begin{aligned} d_0(x, y) = \inf\{\epsilon > 0\colon\ & \exists \text{ a homeomorphism } \varphi \\ & \text{of } [0, 1]\colon |\varphi(t) - t| \leqslant \epsilon, \text{ and } \sup_{0 \leqslant t \leqslant 1} |x(\varphi(t)) - y(t)| \leqslant \epsilon\}\,. \end{aligned} \tag{1.6}$$

Hence $\rho(\mathsf{S}_n^F, \mathsf{W})$ tends to 0 for any $F \in \mathcal{F}_2$, and also $\lim\limits_{n \to \infty} \rho(\mathsf{Z}_n, \mathsf{B}) = 0$.

The investigation of the rate of convergence of $\rho(\mathsf{S}_n^F, \mathsf{W})$ or $\rho(\mathsf{Z}_n, \mathsf{B})$ is usually based on the following remark. Let M be any metric space with a metric d, and let $\mathsf{P}_0, \mathsf{P}_1$ be probability measures on $(M, \mathcal{B})$, where $\mathcal{B}$ is the σ-algebra of Borel-measurable sets of M. Let $p_0(\omega)$, $p_1(\omega)$ be Borel-measurable mappings from a probability space $(\Omega, \mathcal{A}, \mathsf{P})$ to $(M, \mathcal{B})$ such that p_i generates the measure P_i on M $(i = 0, 1)$. Then

$$\rho(\mathsf{P}_0, \mathsf{P}_1) \leqslant \inf_{\epsilon > 0} (\epsilon + \mathsf{P}(d(p_0, p_1) \geqslant \epsilon))\,. \tag{1.7}$$

We shall call such a pair p_0, p_1 a *coupling* of the measures $\mathsf{P}_0, \mathsf{P}_1$. Especially, if $(\Omega, \mathscr{A}, \mathsf{P})$ equals $(M, \mathscr{B}, \mathsf{P}_0)$, and φ_0 is the identity, then φ_1 will be called an embedding of P_1 into P_0.

The first coupling of S_n^F and W was made by Skorohod, and it is the following. For any $F \in \mathscr{F}_2$ there is a Wiener process $w(x)$ and a sequence of i.i.d.r.v.-s τ_j such that the distribution of the function $s_n(t)$ is S_n^F, where

$$(1.8)\qquad \begin{aligned} s_n(t) &= \frac{\vartheta_k - t}{\vartheta_k - \vartheta_{k-1}}\, w(\vartheta_{k-1}) + \frac{t - \vartheta_{k-1}}{\vartheta_k - \vartheta_{k-1}}\, w(\vartheta_k) \\ &\text{for } \vartheta_{k-1} \leqslant t \leqslant \vartheta_k, \qquad k = 1, 2, \ldots, n; \end{aligned}$$

and $\vartheta_k = \tau_1 + \ldots + \tau_k$, $\tau_0 = 0$. Here $\mathsf{E}\tau_1 = 1$, and if $F \in \mathscr{F}_4$ then $\mathsf{E}\tau_1^2 < \infty$. Using this coupling of S_n^F and W, Dudley [8] proved that if $F \in \mathscr{F}_r$, then

$$(1.9)\qquad \rho(\mathsf{S}_n^F, \mathsf{W}) = \begin{cases} O\left((\log n)^{\frac{1}{2}} n^{-\frac{r-2}{2(r+1)}}\right) & \text{for} \quad 2 < r \leqslant 4, \\ O(n^{-\frac{1}{2}} \log n) & \text{for} \quad r \geqslant 5, \end{cases}$$

and

$$(1.10)\qquad \rho(\mathsf{Z}_n, \mathsf{B}) = O(n^{-\frac{1}{4}} \log n).$$

Sawyer [14] showed that the Skorohod embedding method cannot yield a speed of convergence faster than $O(n^{-\frac{1}{4}})$. Borovkov [3] proved that $\rho(\mathsf{S}_n^F, \mathsf{W}) = o\left(n^{\frac{r-2}{2(r+1)}}\right)$ for $2 \leqslant r \leqslant 3$.

The goodness of a coupling can be characterized in different ways. Let $\mathscr{C}(\mathsf{P}_0, \mathsf{P}_1)$ be the set of all possible couplings of $\mathsf{P}_0, \mathsf{P}_1$ (where also the space $(\Omega, \mathscr{A}, \mathsf{P})$ may vary). Strassen and Dudley [7] proved that if M is separable, then

$$(1.11)\qquad \rho(\mathsf{P}_0, \mathsf{P}_1) = \inf_{(p_0, p_1) \in \mathscr{C}(\mathsf{P}_0, \mathsf{P}_1)} \inf_{\epsilon > 0} (\epsilon + \mathsf{P}(d(p_0, p_1) \geqslant \epsilon)).$$

In the light of this theorem we can find couplings which yield good estimations for the Prohorov distance. An other possibility for measuring the goodness of coupling is to check whether $\mathsf{E}d(p_0, p_1)$ is near to the Wasserstein-distance of $\mathsf{P}_0, \mathsf{P}_1$ which is defined by

$$(1.12) \qquad \rho_0(\mathsf{P}_0, \mathsf{P}_1) = \inf_{(p_0, p_1) \in \mathscr{C}(\mathsf{P}_0, \mathsf{P}_1)} \mathsf{E}d(p_0, p_1) .$$

One may also try to find the coupling, which minimizes the probability $\mathsf{P}(d(p_0, p_1) > \epsilon)$ for a given ϵ.

A pair of random functions $\widetilde{s}(t), \widetilde{w}(t)$ defined for $0 \leqslant t < \infty$ will be called an infinite coupling of $\mathsf{S}_n^F, \mathsf{W}$ if the pair

$$(1.13) \qquad s_n(t) = \frac{\widetilde{s}(nt)}{\sqrt{n}}; \; w_n(t) = \frac{\widetilde{w}(nt)}{\sqrt{n}}, \qquad 0 \leqslant t \leqslant 1$$

is a coupling of $\mathsf{S}_n^F, \mathsf{W}$ for $n = 1, 2, \ldots$. Strassen extended the Skorohod embedding to an infinite coupling, and proved in [15] that if $F \in \mathscr{F}_4$, then for the corresponding infinite coupling

$$(1.14) \qquad \sup_{0 \leqslant t \leqslant n} |\widetilde{s}(t) - \widetilde{w}(t)| = O(n^{\frac{1}{4}} (\log n)^{\frac{1}{2}} (\log \log n)^{\frac{1}{4}})$$

holds true with probability 1. It was widely guessed that the Skorohod embedding, at least asymptotically, is best possible. This guess was disproved by Csörgő and Révész [4]. Following their and Bártfai's ideas we proved in [13] the following theorems.

Theorem A. *If* $F \in \mathscr{F}_2$, *and* $\int_{-\infty}^{\infty} e^{tx} F(dx) < \infty$ *for* $|t| < t_0$ $(t_0 > 0)$, *then there is an infinite coupling* $\widetilde{s}, \widetilde{w}$ *of* $\mathsf{S}_n^F, \mathsf{W}$ *such that for all* $x > 0$ *and every* n

$$(1.15) \qquad \mathsf{P}(\sup_{0 \leqslant t \leqslant n} |\widetilde{s}(t) - \widetilde{w}(t)| \geqslant x) \leqslant K n^C e^{-\lambda x} ,$$

where C, K, λ *are positive constants depending only on* F.

Theorem B. *If* $F \in \mathscr{F}_r$, $r > 3$, *then there is a constant* C *and a sequence* ϵ_n *tending to* 0 *with* $n \to \infty$ *such that for every* n *and* x, $n^{\frac{1}{r}} < x < C n^{\frac{1}{2}} (\log n)^{\frac{1}{2}}$, *there is a coupling* s_n, w, *of* $\mathsf{S}_n^F, \mathsf{W}$ *such that*

$$\text{(1.16)} \qquad \mathsf{P}\Big(\sup_{0 \leq t \leq 1} n^{\frac{1}{2}} \, | s_n(t) - w(t) | \geq x \Big) \leq n \epsilon_n x^{-r} \, .$$

Theorem C. *For every n there is a coupling z_n, b of Z_n and B such that for all $x > 0$*

$$\text{(1.17)} \qquad \mathsf{P}\Big(\sup_{0 \leq t \leq 1} n^{\frac{1}{2}} \, | z_n(t) - b(t) | \geq x \Big) \leq K n^C e^{-\lambda x} \, ,$$

where C, K, λ are positive absolute constants.

Our couplings are, in fact, embeddings of S_n^F (or Z_n) into W (or into B), and they are constructed by a new method called conditional quantile transformation on a diadic scheme. As we shall see, the investigation of couplings is closely related to the so-called stochastic geyser problem, so this is the topic of the next section.

2. THE STOCHASTIC GEYSER PROBLEM

Once upon a time there was a man who lived on a desolate island, and the only companion he had was a geyser. The geyser burst out periodically, and the man wanted to report the distribution of the random period of the consecutive bursts to his homeland. He had no watch and no possibility whatever to measure the hours. So he created a primitive calendar and put down carefully, day by day, the total number of bursts. Our man had a very long, let us say an infinitely long life, and only after he, and the geyser had died, found his fellow-countrymen the whole infinite sequence of his records. Can they figure out the distribution of the burst-time of the geyser?

The answer is yes, and it was given by B á r t f a i [1]. He investigated the following problem. Let $X = \{X_n;\ n = 1, 2, \ldots\}$ be i.i.d.r.v.-s with distribution function F, and $S_F = \{X_1 + \ldots + X_n;\ n = 1, 2, \ldots\}$ the sequence of partial sums. Let $e = \{e_n;\ n = 1, 2, \ldots\}$ be an arbitrary sequence of r.v.'s such that

$$\text{(2.1)} \qquad \mathsf{P}\Big(\limsup_{n \to \infty} \frac{e_n}{a_n} \leq 1 \Big) = 1 \, ,$$

where $a = \{a_n;\ n = 1, 2, \ldots\}$ is a given monotone increasing sequence. We call the sequence a estimation-permitting in a set $\mathcal{F}$ of distributions, if the infinite sample

$$(2.2)\qquad S_F(e) = \{X_1 + \ldots + X_n + e_n;\ n = 1, 2, \ldots\}$$

determines the distribution F with probability 1 for all $F \in \mathcal{F}$ and for all e having the property (2.1). This means that given a and $\mathcal{F}$ we can construct a system $\{A_F,\ F \in \mathcal{F}\}$ of disjoint Borel-measurable sets of infinite sequences of real numbers in such a way that for any $F \in \mathcal{F}$

$$(2.3)\qquad \mathsf{P}(S_F(e) \in A_F) = 1$$

for any choice of S_F and e such that e satisfies (2.1). Let $E(\mathcal{F})$ be the set of all monotone increasing sequences, estimation-permitting in $\mathcal{F}$. Combining Theorem A and the theorem of Bártfai we get

Theorem 1. *Let the set* $\mathcal{F}_\infty$ *be defined by*

$$(2.4)\qquad \mathcal{F}_\infty = \{F\colon \text{ there is a } t_0 > 0 \text{ such that } \int_{-\infty}^{\infty} e^{tx} F(dx) < \infty \text{ for } |t| < t_0\},$$

then $a \in E(\mathcal{F}_\infty)$ *if and only if*

$$(2.5)\qquad \liminf_{n\to\infty} \frac{a_n}{\log n} = 0\,.$$

This theorem will be proved later. First we define two other sets similar to $E(\mathcal{F})$. The first of them is the set $T(F_0, \mathcal{F})$ of monotone increasing test-permitting sequences in $\mathcal{F}$ with respect to F_0. A sequence a is test-permitting in $\mathcal{F}$ with respect to F_0 if the infinite sample $S_F(e)$ determines, with probability 1, whether $F = F_0$ or $F \in \mathcal{F}$ (of course $F_0 \notin \mathcal{F}$). This means that given $a, F_0, \mathcal{F}$ there is a measurable set A_0 such that for any choice of the error e satisfying (2.1) we have

$$(2.6)\qquad \mathsf{P}(S_{F_0}(e) \in A_0) = 1\,,$$

for any choice of S_{F_0} and

(2.7) $\mathsf{P}(S_F(e) \in A_0) = 0$

for any choice of $F \in \mathscr{F}$ and S_F.

Lemma 1. *For any* $F_0 \notin \mathscr{F}_1$, $\mathscr{F} = \{F_0\} \cup \mathscr{F}_1 \subset \tilde{\mathscr{F}}$, $\tilde{\mathscr{F}}_1 \subset \mathscr{F}_1$

(2.8) $E(\tilde{\mathscr{F}}) \subset E(\mathscr{F}) \subset T(F_0, \mathscr{F}_1) \subset T(F_0, \tilde{\mathscr{F}}_1)$

holds true.

Proof. The monotonity of the sets $E(\mathscr{F})$, $T(F_0, \mathscr{F}_1)$ is a trivial consequence of their definition. For proving the third statement choose $A_0 = A_{F_0}$.

A sequence a is couple-permitting with respect to F_0 and F_1 if there is an infinite coupling $\tilde{s}_0, \tilde{s}_1$ of $\mathsf{S}_n^{F_0}$ and $\mathsf{S}_n^{F_1}$ such that

(2.9) $\mathsf{P}\left(\limsup_{n\to\infty} \frac{|\tilde{s}_0(n) - \tilde{s}_1(n)|}{a_n} \leqslant 2\right) = 1\,.$

The set of all monotone increasing couple-permitting sequences with respect to F_0 and F_1 will be denoted by $C(F_0, F_1)$.

Lemma 2. *The sets* $C(F_0, F_1)$, $T(F_0, F_1)$ *are disjoint for any* F_0, F_1.

Proof. Assume that there is a sequence a such that $a \in C(F_0, F_1) \cap \cap T(F_0, F_1)$. Then there is a set such that (2.6) and (2.7) hold true with $\mathscr{F} = \{F_1\}$, and there is an infinite coupling $\tilde{s}_0, \tilde{s}_1$ such that (2.9) holds true. Put $S_{F_0} = \{\tilde{s}_0(n);\ n = 1, 2, \ldots\}$, $S_{F_1} = \{\tilde{s}_1(n);\ n = 1, 2, \ldots\}$,

$e = \left\{\frac{\tilde{s}_0(n) - \tilde{s}_0(n)}{2};\ n = 1, 2, \ldots\right\}$, then e satisfies (2.1), and

$$\mathsf{P}(S_{F_0}(e) \in A_0) = \mathsf{P}(S_{F_1}(-e) \in A_0) =$$
$$= \mathsf{P}\left(\left\{\frac{1}{2}(\tilde{s}_0(n) + \tilde{s}_1(n));\ n = 1, 2, \ldots\right\} \in A_0\right),$$

hence (2.6) and (2.7) can not hold true simultaneously.

Theorem 2. *For any* $F_0, F_1 \in \mathscr{F}_2 \cap \mathscr{F}_\infty$ *(cf. (1.1) and (2.4)) there are positive constants* $t(F_0, F_1) \leqslant c(F_0, F_1)$ *such that if a monotone increasing sequence* a *satisfies*

$$\text{(2.10)} \qquad \liminf_{n\to\infty} \frac{a_n}{\log n} < t(F_0, F_1),$$

then $a \in T(F_0, F_1)$, *and if*

$$\text{(2.11)} \qquad \liminf_{n\to\infty} \frac{a_n}{\log n} \geqslant c(F_0, F_1),$$

then $a \in C(F_0, F_1)$.

Proof. If $F_0, F_1 \in \mathscr{F}_2 \cap \mathscr{F}_\infty$, then Theorem A implies that there are infinite couplings $\tilde{s}_i, \tilde{w}$ of $\mathsf{S}_n^{F_i}$ and W such that

$$\text{(2.12)} \qquad \mathsf{P}\left(\limsup_{n\to\infty} \frac{|\tilde{s}_i(n) - \tilde{w}(n)|}{\log n} \leqslant C_i\right) = 1 \qquad (i = 1, 2)$$

where C_0, C_1 are positive constants. As we have remarked, our couplings are embeddings of $\mathsf{S}_n^{F_i}$ in W, hence in the couplings $(\tilde{s}_0, \tilde{w}), (\tilde{s}_1, \tilde{w})$ the process $\tilde{w}$ may be chosen the same. Hence $(\tilde{s}_0, \tilde{s}_1)$ is an infinite coupling of $\mathsf{S}_n^{F_0}$ and $\mathsf{S}_n^{F_1}$, and (2.9) holds true with $a_n = \frac{1}{2}(C_0 + C_1)\log n$. Thus the second statement of Theorem 2 holds true with $c(F_0, F_1) = \frac{1}{2}(C_0 + C_1)$. The proof of the first statement is based on the following theorem of Erdős and Rényi [10].

Theorem D. *Let* $X_1, X_2, \ldots$ *be i.i.d.r.v.-s with distribution function* $F \in \mathscr{F}_\infty$. *Let* $R(t)$ *be the moment-generating function of* F, $A^+ = \inf\{x\colon F(x) = 1\}$, $A^- = \sup\{x\colon F(x) = 0\}$ *and* $\pi(x) = \sup_t (tx - \log R(t))$. *Then for any* $\mathsf{E}X_1 < x < A^+$

$$\text{(2.13)} \qquad \mathsf{P}\Big(\lim_{n\to\infty} \sup_{1\leqslant j\leqslant n-m} \frac{1}{m}\sum_{k=j}^{j+m} X_k = x\Big) = 1\,,$$

and for any $A^- < x < \mathsf{E}X_1$

$$\text{(2.14)} \qquad \mathsf{P}\Big(\lim_{n\to\infty} \inf_{1\leqslant j\leqslant n-m} \frac{1}{m}\sum_{k=j}^{j+m} X_k = x\Big) = 1\,,$$

where $m = \left[\dfrac{\log n}{\pi(x)}\right]$.

Let us denote the corresponding quantities for F_i by A_i^+, A_i^- and $\pi_i(x)$ for $i = 0, 1$ and let $B_i^+ = \lim\limits_{x=A_i^+-0} \pi_i(x)$, $B_i^+ = \lim\limits_{x=A_i^-+0} \pi_i(x)$, $B^+ = \min(B_0^+, B_1^-)$, $B^- = \min(B_0^-, B_1^-)$. The functions $\pi_i(x)$ are monotone increasing for $x \geqslant 0$, let us denote their inverse here by $u_i(x)$, and let $v_i(x)$ be the inverse of $\pi_i(x)$ for $x \leqslant 0$. Then we prove the first statement of Theorem 2 with the following constant

$$t(F_0, F_1) = \frac{1}{4}\max\left(\sup_{0<x<B^+} \frac{|u_0(x) - u_1(x)|}{x},\; \sup_{0<x<B^-} \frac{|v_0(x) - v_1(x)|}{x}\right).$$

Indeed, if a monotone increasing sequence a statisfies (2.10) with this $t(F_0, F_1)$, then there are real numbers x_0, x_1 such that $x_0 x_1 > 0$, $\pi_0(x_0) = \pi_1(x_1) = A$, and there is a sequence n_k such that

$$\lim_{k\to\infty} \frac{a_{n_k}}{\log n_k} < \frac{|x_0 - x_1|}{4A}\,.$$

We may assume that $0 < x_0 < x_1$. Let A_0 be the set of all sequences $\{c_k\}$ of real numbers such that

$$\limsup_{k\to\infty} \sup_{1\leqslant j\leqslant n_k - m_k} \frac{1}{m_k}(c_{j+m_k} - c_j) < \frac{x_0 + x_1}{2}\,,$$

where $m_k = \left[\dfrac{\log n_k}{A}\right]$, then (2.6) and (2.7) hold true with this A_0, hence $a \in T(F_0, F_1)$.

Proof of Theorem 1. It is easy to see that for any $\epsilon > 0$ there are distributions F_i such that (2.12) holds with a $C_i < \epsilon$ (e.g. let F_i be the convolution power of some functions in $\mathscr{F}_\infty$). Hence Theorem 2,

Lemma 1 and Lemma 2 imply that (2.5) is necessary to $a \in E(\mathscr{F}_\infty)$. The sufficiency is a consequence of Theorem D and the fact that the function $\pi(x)$ determines the distribution function F.

It is easy to see that Theorem D remains valid if we substitute the set $\mathscr{F}_\infty$ by

$$\widetilde{\mathscr{F}}_\infty = \{F\colon \text{ there is a } t \neq 0 \text{ such that } \int_{-\infty}^{\infty} e^{tx} F(dx) < \infty\} .$$

Hence Theorem 1 and the first statement of Theorem 2 hold true also for this $\widetilde{\mathscr{F}}_\infty$.

It is a natural question, what is the situation if in the above theorems we substitute $\mathscr{F}_\infty$ by $\mathscr{F}_r$. One can expect that functions with few moments are far from each other, farther than functions in $\mathscr{F}_\infty$. Surprisingly enough, this is not so. Halász and Major [12] proved that there are distributions F_0, F_1 such that there is an infinite coupling $\widetilde{s}_0$, $\widetilde{s}_1$ of $\mathsf{S}_n^{F_0}, \mathsf{S}_n^{F_1}$ such that

$$\mathsf{P}(|\widetilde{s}_0(n) - \widetilde{s}_1(n)| \leq K, \ n = 1, 2, \ldots) = 1$$

with some positive constant K. Actually they proved that even this K may be arbitrarily small and still $F_0, F_1 \in \bigcap_{r=2}^{\infty} \mathscr{F}_r$. Hence $E\left(\bigcap_{r=2}^{\infty} \mathscr{F}_r\right)$ is empty. On the other hand, it is easy to see that for any F_0, F_1 there is an ϵ such that the sequence $\{a_n = \epsilon, \ n = 1, 2, \ldots\}$ is an element of $T(F_0, F_1)$. It is also trivial that

$$\mathsf{P}(\lim_{n \to \infty} e_n = 0) = 1$$

implies that $S_F(e)$ determines F with probability 1 within any family $\mathscr{F}$.

One can expect that the sets $E(\mathscr{F})$, $T(F_0, \mathscr{F})$, $C(F_0, F_1)$ determine mutually each other in the sense that

$$E(\mathscr{F}) = \bigcap_{F_0 \in \mathscr{F}} T(F_0, \mathscr{F} \setminus \{F_0\}) ,$$

$$T(F_0, \mathscr{F} \setminus \{F_0\}) = \bigcap_{F_1 \in \mathscr{F} \setminus \{F_0\}} T(F_0, F_1),$$

and $T(F_0, F_1) \cup C(F_0, F_1)$ is the set of all monotone increasing sequences. Let $C_0(F_0, F_1)$ be the set of all monotone increasing sequences a such that there is an infinite coupling $\tilde{s}_0, \tilde{s}_1$ of $\mathsf{S}_n^{F_0}$ and $\mathsf{S}_n^{F_1}$ such that

$$\mathsf{P}\left(\limsup_{n \to \infty} \frac{|\tilde{s}_0(n) - \tilde{s}_1(n)|}{a_n} \leq 2 \right) > 0.$$

The sets $C_0(F_0, F_1)$, $T(F_0, F_1)$ are also disjoint for any F_0, F_1, hence our conjecture means that $C_0(F_0, F_1) = C(F_0, F_1)$. Nevertheless, we can not prove any statement of this type.

In particular, we cannot answer the following question. Let $\mathscr{F}$ be the set of all distributions F such that for any G we can test whether the sample-distribution is F or G if the error is bounded. Can we estimate the sample-distribution in $\mathscr{F}$ if the error is bounded?

3. THE PROHOROV DISTANCE

Theorem 3. *If* $F \in \mathscr{F}_2 \cap \mathscr{F}_\infty$ *(cf.* (1.1) *and* (2.4)*), then there are positive constants* C_0, C_1 *such that for all* $n > 1$

$$C_0 \frac{\log n}{\sqrt{n}} \leq \rho(\mathsf{S}_n^F, \mathsf{W}) \leq C_1 \frac{\log n}{\sqrt{n}}. \tag{3.1}$$

Proof. Theorem A implies that if $F \in \mathscr{F}_2 \cap \mathscr{F}_\infty$, then

$$\rho(\mathsf{S}_n(F), \mathsf{W}) \leq \inf_{0 < \epsilon < 1} (\epsilon + Kn^C e^{-\lambda \epsilon \sqrt{n}}) \leq C_1 \frac{\log n}{\sqrt{n}},$$

which is the upper part of (3 1). Theorem D implis that there are positive constants Δ_0, C_0, n_0 such that if A_n is the subset of $C(0, 1)$ consisting of all functions f for which

$$\sup_{0 \leq t \leq 1 - \Delta_n} |f(t + \Delta_n) - f(t)| \geq C_0 \frac{\log n}{\sqrt{n}}, \tag{3.2}$$

where $\Delta_n = \Delta_0 \frac{\log n}{n}$, then the probability of A_n and $\bar{A}_n$ is greater than 3/4 with respect to S_n^F and W, respectively, for any $n > n_0$ (or conversely, the probability of A_n is large with respect to W and the probability of $\bar{A}_n$ is large with respect to S_n^F). This yields the lower part of (3.1).

Theorem 4. *If* $r > 2$, $F \in \mathscr{F}_r$ *(cf.* (1.1)*), then*

$$\rho(\mathsf{S}_n^F, \mathsf{W}) = o\left(n^{-\frac{r-2}{2(r+1)}}\right). \tag{3.3}$$

On the other hand, for any sequence ω_n *tending to* ∞ *with* $n \to \infty$ *there is an* $F \in \mathscr{F}_r$ *such that*

$$\limsup_{n\to\infty} \omega_n n^{-\frac{r-2}{2(r+1)}} \rho(\mathsf{S}_n^F, \mathsf{W}) = \infty. \tag{3.4}$$

Proof. For $2 < r \leqslant 3$ (3.3) was proved by B o r o v k o v [3]. If $r > 3$ and $F \in \mathscr{F}_r$, Theorem B implies that

$$\rho(\mathsf{S}_n^F, \mathsf{W}) \leqslant \inf_{0<\epsilon<1} \left(\epsilon + \frac{n\epsilon_n}{(\epsilon\sqrt{n})^r}\right) \leqslant K\epsilon_n^{\frac{1}{r+1}} n^{-\frac{r-2}{2(r+1)}}$$

with some positive constant K. So the first part is proved.

Given any sequences ω_n, x_n tending to ∞ with $n \to \infty$ there is an $F \in \mathscr{F}_r$ such that

$$\limsup_{n\to\infty} \omega_n x_n^r (1 - F(x_n)) = \infty.$$

Hence if $X_1, X_2, \ldots$ are i.i.d.r.v.-s with distribution F, then

$$\limsup_{n\to\infty} \omega_n n^{\frac{r-2}{2(r+1)}} \mathsf{P}\left(\max(X_1, \ldots, X_n) \geqslant n^{\frac{3}{2(r+1)}}\right) = \infty.$$

This yields (3.4).

Theorem 5. *There are positive constants* C_0, C_1 *such that for every* $n > 1$

$$C_0 \frac{\log n}{\sqrt{n}} \leqslant \rho(\mathsf{Z}_n, \mathsf{B}) \leqslant C_1 \frac{\log n}{\sqrt{n}}. \tag{3.5}$$

Proof. The metric d_0 of $D(0, 1)$ is majorated by the metric $C(0, 1)$, hence Theorem C implies that

$$\rho(\mathsf{Z}_n, \mathsf{B}) \leqslant \inf_{0<\epsilon<1} (\epsilon + \mathsf{P}(d_0(z_n, b) \geqslant \epsilon) \leqslant$$

$$\leqslant \inf_{0<\epsilon<1} (\epsilon + \mathsf{P}(d(z_n, b) \geqslant \epsilon) \leqslant C_1 \frac{\log n}{\sqrt{n}}$$

with some positive constant C_1 where (z_n, b) is the coupling given by Theorem C.

For proving the lower part of (3.5) we shall apply again Theorem D, now for Poisson variables. If $X_1, X_2, \ldots$ are independent Poisson variables with parameter 1, then the moment generating function of $(X_1 - 1)$ is $R(t) = \exp\{e^t - 1 - t\}$, hence

$$\pi(x) = 1 + (x + 1)(\log(x + 1) - 1)\,. \tag{3.6}$$

Let $y(t, \lambda)$ be a Poisson process on the plane with parameter 1, and let $Y_\lambda(\Delta)$ be defined by

$$Y_\lambda(\Delta) = \sup_{0\leqslant t\leqslant 1-\Delta} (\tilde{y}(t + \Delta, \lambda) - \tilde{y}(t, \lambda))\,, \tag{3.7}$$

where $\tilde{y}(t, \lambda) = (y(1, \lambda))^{-1/2}(y(t, \lambda) - ty(1, \lambda))$. In the same way, as Theorem D was proved, one can prove that

$$\mathsf{P}\Big(\lim_{\lambda\to\infty} \frac{\sqrt{\lambda}}{\log\lambda}\, Y_\lambda\Big(\frac{\log\lambda}{\lambda\pi(x)}\Big) = \frac{x}{\pi(x)}\Big) = 1\,. \tag{3.8}$$

It is well known that if $w(x)$ is a Wiener process and $W(\Delta)$ is defined by

$$W(\Delta) = \sup_{0<\delta\leqslant\Delta}\ \sup_{0\leqslant t\leqslant 1-\delta} (w(t + \delta) - w(t))\,, \tag{3.9}$$

then

$$\mathsf{P}\Big(\lim_{\lambda\to\infty} \frac{\sqrt{\lambda}}{\log\lambda}\, W\Big(\frac{\log\lambda}{\lambda\pi(x)}\Big) = \sqrt{\frac{2}{\pi(x)}}\Big) = 1\,. \tag{3.10}$$

For the function π defined by (3.6)

$$\lim_{x\to\infty} \left(\frac{x}{\pi(x)} - \sqrt{\frac{2}{\pi(x)}}\right) = \frac{1}{3}$$

holds true, hence it is enough to prove that (3.8) holds true if we substitute $Y_\lambda(\Delta)$ in it with

$$Z_n(\Delta) = \sup_{0\le t\le 1-\delta} (z_n(t+\Delta) - z_n(t)) ,$$

where $z_n(t)$ is defined by (1.3), i.e. if we prove that

$$\text{(3.11)} \qquad \mathsf{P}\left(\lim_{n\to\infty} \frac{\sqrt{n}}{\log n} Z_n\left(\frac{\log n}{n\pi(x)}\right) = \frac{x}{\pi(x)}\right) = 1 ,$$

where $\pi(x)$ is the same function as in (3.8). Let $\nu(x)$ be a Poisson process on the real line, and let the processes $\nu(\lambda)$, $\{z_n(t),\ n = 1, 2, \ldots\}$ be independent. Then the processes

$$\frac{\sqrt{\nu(\lambda)}}{\log \nu(\lambda)} Z_{\nu(\lambda)}\left(\frac{\log \nu(\lambda)}{\nu(\lambda)\pi(x)}\right), \quad \frac{\sqrt{\lambda}}{\log \lambda} Y_\lambda\left(\frac{\log \lambda}{\lambda\pi(x)}\right)$$

are equivalent (they generate the same probability measure), hence

$$\text{(3.12)} \qquad \mathsf{P}\left(\lim_{\lambda\to\infty} \frac{\sqrt{\nu(\lambda)}}{\log \nu(\lambda)} Z_{\nu(\lambda)}\left(\frac{\log \nu(\lambda)}{\nu(\lambda)\pi(x)}\right) = \frac{x}{\pi(x)}\right) = 1 .$$

This implies (3.11), and thus the proof is complete.

Remark. The statement of Theorem 5 remains valid if we use the metric d of the space $C(0, 1)$ instead of d_0 in the definition of $\rho(\mathsf{Z}_n, \mathsf{B})$. In fact the two versions of $\rho(\mathsf{Z}_n, \mathsf{B})$ are asymptotically equal.

4. APPLICATIONS

(a) *The Wasserstein metric.* Inequalities (3.1) and (3.5) remain valid if we substitute the Prohorov metric ρ by the Wasserstein metric ρ_0 defined by (1.12). The coupling given by Theorem B depends on the level x, hence it is not applicable for the estimation of the Wasserstein distance. It seems us, however, that there is no difficulty in getting rid of the effect of the level x in the construction, and taking so, to estimate the Wasserstein distance of S_n^F and W if $F \in \mathcal{F}_r$.

(b) *Embedding of functionals.* Let us say that the random variables ξ_n have a limit distribution F of rate $\frac{1}{\sqrt{n}}$ if the limit

$$\lim_{n \to \infty} \sqrt{n}\,(\mathsf{P}(\xi_n < x) - F(x)) = F_1(x)$$

exists for any continuity point of F. All the known functionals on the empirical process $z_n(t)$ defined by (1.3) have a limit distribution of rate $\frac{1}{\sqrt{n}}$, nevertheless there is no general theorem ensuring a limit distribution of rate for a whole class of functionals. As it was stated in [13], Theorem C have a Corollary on functionals fulfilling a Lipschitzian condition, but this Corollary gives only an estimation of rate $\frac{\log n}{\sqrt{n}}$. So it is an open question, whether all the Lipschitzian functionals on $z_n(t)$ have a limit distribution of rate $\frac{1}{\sqrt{n}}$, or not.

(c) *The law of iterated logarithm.* Strassen applied the Skorohod embedding for proving the extension of the law of iterated logarithm. The law of iterated logarithm holds true for any distribution having a finite second moment, hence our improvement of the Skorohod embedding for distributions having higher moments does not yield any improvement of the law of iterated logarithm. This holds true even for the law of iterated logarithm on the empirical process $z_n(t)$ made by Finkelstein [11]. One may expect improvements concerning the tail-behavior of $z_n(t)$, i.e. the investigation of the supremum $\sup_{\epsilon_n < t < 1 - \epsilon_n} \frac{z_n(t)}{\sqrt{t(1-t)}}$. In connection with this problem we refer to the paper of Csörgő and Révész [5]. Another possible application of the new embedding scheme would be the investigation of the law of iterated logarithm in the multidimensional case. This is hampered by the fact that our embedding is extended only to two dimensions yet.

(d) *The estimation of the density function.* Bickel and Rosenblatt [2] extended the heuristic approach of Doob to the Kolmogorov theorem for investigating the estimation of the density function. Our new embedding yields only a minor extension of their theorem, so we do not state it here explicitely. A real extension of their theorem would be the investigation of the multidimensional case, hence again the multidimensional embedding is needed.

(e) *Goodness-of-fit in the presence of nuisance parameters.* Durbin [9] extended the heuristic approach of Doob to the Kolmogorov theorem for investigating the case when some parameters of the distribution were estimated. Csörgő, Révész and the present authors applied Theorem C for this problem in [6].

REFERENCES

[1] P. Bártfai, Die Bestimmung der zu einem wiederkehrenden Prozess gehörenden Verteilungsfunktion aus den mit Fehlern behafteten Daten einer einzigen Realisation, *Studia Sci. Math. Hung.*, 1 (1966), 161-168.

[2] P.I. Bickel – M. Rosenblatt, On some global measures of deviations of density function estimates, *Ann. Statist.*, 1 (1973), 1071-1095.

[3] A.A. Borovkov, On the rate of convergence for the invariance principle, (in Russian), *Teorija Verojatn. i Primenen.*, 18 (1973), 217-235.

[4] M. Csörgő – P. Révész, A new method to prove laws of iterated logarithm of Strassen's type, I-II, *Z. Wahrscheinlichkeitstheorie verw. Geb.*, (to appear).

[5] M. Csörgő – P. Révész, Some notes on the empirical distribution function and the quantile process, (this volume).

[6] M. Csörgő – J. Komlós – P. Major – P. Révész – G. Tusnády, On the empirical process when parameters are estimated, *Transactions of the seventh Prague Conference*, 1974, (to appear).

[7] R. M. Dudley, Distances of probability measures and random variables, *Ann. Math. Statist.*, 39 (1968), 1563-1572.

[8] R. M. Dudley, Speeds of metric probability convergence, *Z. Wahrscheinlichkeitstheorie verw. Geb.*, 22 (1972), 323-332.

[9] J. Durbin, Weak convergence of the sample distribution function when parameters are estimated, *Ann. Statist.*, 1 (1973), 279-290.

[10] P. Erdős – A. Rényi, On a new law of large numbers, *Jour. Analyse Mathématique*, 23 (1970), 103-111.

[11] H. Finkelstein, The law of iterated logarithm for empirical distribution, *Ann. Math. Statist.*, 42 (1971), 607-615.

[12] G. Halász – P. Major, On the geyser problem with bounded errors, *Ann. of Prob.*, (to appear).

[13] J. Komlós – P. Major – G. Tusnády, An approximation of partial sums of independent RV'-s, and the sample DF., I-II., *Z. Wahrscheinlichkeitstheorie verw. Geb.*, (to appear).

[14] S. Sawyer, Rates of convergence for some functionals in probability, *Ann. Math. Statist.*, 43 (1972), 273-284.

[15] V. Strassen, Almost sure behaviour of sums of independent random variables and martingales, *Proc. 5th Berkeley Sympos. Math. Statist. Probab.*, II. (part 1), 315-343. Univ. of Calif. Press, Berkeley, 1967.

COLLOQUIA MATHEMATICA SOCIETATIS JÁNOS BOLYAI
11. LIMIT THEOREMS OF PROBABILITY THEORY, KESZTHELY (HUNGARY), 1974.

THE METHOD OF PERTURBATION ON THE SPECTRUM OF LINEAR OPERATORS IN ASYMPTOTIC PROBLEMS OF PROBABILITY THEORY

V.S. KOROLJUK – A.F. TURBIN

This talk offers a survey of some results concerning the method of perturbation on the spectrum of linear operators as applied to asymptotic problems in the theory of Markov and semi-Markov processes. At the present time these results can be used for describing the action of complex stochastic systems in queueing theory, reliability theory, the theory of stochastic automata, the theory of branching processes, the theory of storage control systems, etc.

The method developed by us enables one to obtain limit theorems and asymptotic expansions according to the powers of a small parameter.

The parameter with respect to which the limit is taken can be either the time parameter $(t \to \infty)$, or the corresponding parameter of the Laplace transformation over time $(\lambda \to 0)$, or the parameter that characterizes the scheme of series $(n \to \infty$ or $\epsilon \to 0)$.

Accordingly, we distinguish *two basic types of problems.*

(1) The study of the asymptotic behaviour of non-stationary characteristics for indefinitely increasing time parameter $t \to \infty$.

A classical example of a problem of this type is the convergence, for $t \to \infty$, of the transition probabilities of an ergodic Markov process to the ergodic distribution.

(2) The study of the asymptotic behaviour of non-stationary and stationary characteristics in the scheme of series if the original process depends on some, for convenience we assume, small parameter $\epsilon \to 0$.

As a simple example of a problem of the second type we mention the behaviour of the sojourn time of the process in the set of states before absorption, assuming that the probability of absorption tends to zero.

§1.

The initial subject in all problems considered by us is a linear equation in a Banach space, where the operator defining the equation depends on some parameter: $A_\lambda u_\lambda = \varphi_\lambda$. The essential feature of the equations under investigation consists of the fact that for $\lambda = 0$ the operator A_0 is *non-invertible,* i.e., the point zero belongs to the spectrum of the limit operator A_0.

The asymptotic behaviour of the inverse operator A_λ^{-1} (or of the solution u_λ of the equation) for $\lambda \to 0$ is extensively treated in the literature on the theory of perturbation on the spectrum of operators. There are various algorithms for constructing asymptotic expansions of the solution u_λ into powers of the small parameter λ. In that form, however, which is the most natural in probabilistic problems, we could not find any algorithm in the literature. Therefore the algorithm developed by us (in the essential part by A.F. Turbin) for the inversion of linear operators perturbed on the spectrum is interesting also by itself.

§2.

Let us turn to the specific description of the initial setting of probabilistic problems which lead to equations of the type indicated above.

(1) In the theory of semi-Markov processes the basic subjects are the so-called *Markov renewal equations.*

As it is well-known (see e.g. [1]), a semi-Markov process can be given by a semi-Markov matrix* $Q(x) = \{Q_{ij}(x);\ i, j \in E\}$ satisfying the following conditions

(1) the $Q_{ij}(x)$ are non-decreasing non-negative measurable functions of x;

(2) $\sum_{j \in E} Q_{ij}(\infty) = 1$ for all $i \in E$;

(3) $Q_{ij}(x) = 0$ if $x < 0$ for all $i, j \in E$.

The semi-Markov matrix $Q(x)$ specifies the transition probabilities of a two-dimensional Markov process $\{\xi_n, \theta_n;\ n \geq 0\}$, which is called Markov renewal process

$$Q_{ij}(x) = \mathsf{P}\{\xi_{n+1} = j;\ \theta_{n+1} \leq x \mid \xi_n = i\}\,.$$

The embedded Markov chain $\{\xi_n,\ n \geq 0\}$ is defined by the transition probabilities $p_{ij} = Q_{ij}(\infty)$

$$p_{ij} = \mathsf{P}\{\xi_{n+1} = j \mid \xi_n = i\}\,.$$

Set

$$\tau_n = \sum_{k=0}^{n} \theta_k\,,\quad \nu(t) = \sup\{n\colon\ \tau_n \leq t\}\,,$$

$$\tau_-(t) = t - \tau_{\nu(t)}\,,\quad \tau_+(t) = \tau_{\nu(t)+1} - t\,.$$

The linear stochastic processes $\tau_-(t)$ and $\tau_+(t)$, respectively, determine the value of non-reaching and exceeding the level t by the sequence of

*In the general case, a semi-Markov process is given by a semi-Markov kernel $Q(t, x, \Gamma)$ $t \in [0, \infty)$, $x \in E$, $\Gamma \in \mathscr{E}$, defined on a measurable space $(E, \mathscr{E})$ and satisfying certain conditions analogous to those listed above for a semi-Markov matrix [2].

The results considered in this talk are valid also for semi-Markov processes given by semi-Markov kernels. For the sake of clarity and simplicity of the presentation we restrict ourselves mostly to the case of a discrete, countable phase space E.

random variables $\{\tau_n, n \geq 0\}$. *The process* $\xi(t) = \xi_{\nu(t)}$ *is called a semi-Markov process.* The Markov chain ξ_n is said to be embedded in the semi-Markov process. τ_n are the moments of transition; θ_n denote the sojourn times of the semi-Markov process in the separate states. The semi-Markov process can also be defined as the discrete component of the two-dimensional Markov process $\{\xi(t), \tau_-(t)\}$ or $\{\xi(t), \tau_+(t)\}$ [3].

Introduce the transition probabilities of the semi-Markov process

$$u_{ij}(t) = \mathsf{P}\{\xi(t) = j \mid \xi(0) = i\} .$$

It is well known that they satisfy the following system of integral relations

$$u_{ij}(t) = G_{ij}(t) + \sum_{k\in E} \int_0^t Q_{ik}(ds)\, u_{kj}(t-s) . \tag{1}$$

These relations are called Markov renewal equations (MRE). Here

$$G_{ij}(t) = \delta_{ij}(1 - P_i(t)) .$$

It is possible to give examples for other characteristics of a semi-Markov process which also satisfy equations of type MRE (see [4]).

Let, for instance, f be a bounded measurable function on $E \times [0, \infty)$. Set

$$\varphi(t) = \sum_{n=0}^{\nu(t)} f(\xi_n, t - \tau_n) ,$$

$$u_i(t) = \mathsf{E}[\varphi(t) \mid \xi(0) = i] .$$

Then the $u_i(t)$ satisfy MRE with $G_i(t) = f(i, t)$. In fact, for $\varphi_i(t)$ we have the stochastic relation

$$\varphi_i(t) = f(i, t) + \mathscr{I}(\theta_1 < t) \sum_{j\in E} \mathscr{I}_{ij}(\theta_1)\varphi_j(t - \theta_1) ,$$

where $\mathscr{I}_{ij}(\theta_1)$ are the transition indicators of the semi-Markov process. Passing to mathematical expectations we obtain MRE.

The natural way of investigating the asymptotic behaviour, for $t \to \infty$, of the solutions of equation (1) consists of studying the behaviour of their

Laplace – Stieltjes transforms in the point zero and using tauberian theorems. If we take Laplace – Stieltjes transforms in (1), we obtain an equation which can be written in operator form as follows

(2) $$(I - Q_\lambda)\mu_\lambda = g_\lambda \,.$$

Here

$$g_\lambda = \{\delta_{ij}(1 - P_i(\lambda))\}, \quad P_i(\lambda) = \int_0^\infty e^{-\lambda t}\, dP_i(t)\,,$$

$$Q_\lambda u \equiv \Big\{\sum_{j \in E} q_{ij}(\lambda) u_j,\ i \in E\Big\}, \quad q_{ij}(\lambda) = \int_0^\infty e^{-\lambda t}\, dQ_{ij}(t)\,.$$

Note that $Q_0 = P_0$ is the matrix of transition probabilities of the embedded Markov chain and, clearly, if the corresponding chain is returning, then $I - P_0$ is non-invertible.

(2) Another group of problems under consideration is related to the study of the *asymptotic enlargement of semi-Markov processes.* The phase space E of the processes in question has an asymptotic decomposition $E = \bigcup_{k=1}^{m} E_k$ in the sense that the transition probabilities, depending on a small parameter ϵ, of the embedded chain between state classes tend to zero together with ϵ; for example,

(3) $$p_{ij}^{\epsilon} = \begin{cases} p_{ij}^{(k)} - \epsilon b_{ij}^{(k)}; & i, j \in E_k\,, \\ \epsilon b_{ij}^{(kr)}; & i \in E_k,\ j \in E_r\,, \end{cases}$$

where $\sum_{j \in E_k} p_{ij}^{(k)} = 1$. We shall assume that the Markov chains given by the transition probability matrices $p^{(k)} = \{p_{ij}^{(k)};\ i, j \in E_k\}$ are ergodic and have stationary distributions $\rho_k = \{\rho_i^{(k)},\ i \in E_k\}$.

For the same characteristics as in the first group of problems we obtain an equation of the form

(4) $$[I - Q_\epsilon(\lambda)]\, u_\epsilon(\lambda) = G_\epsilon(\lambda)\,,$$

where the matrix $Q_\epsilon(\lambda)$ admits the asymptotic representation

$$(5) \qquad Q_\epsilon(\lambda) = P_0 + \epsilon B + \epsilon\lambda C + o(\epsilon\lambda) .$$

(3) Finally, the third group of problems is concerned with the asymptotic enlargement of Markov chains and with the description of the stationary measure of the asymptotically enlarged chain.

Let us be given a homogeneous Markov chain $\{\xi_n^\epsilon, n \geqslant 1\}$ in the phase space $(E, \mathscr{E})$ with transition probabilities

$$(6) \qquad P_\epsilon(x, \Gamma) = P_0(x, \Gamma) + \epsilon Q(x, \Gamma) ,$$

where $P_0(x, \Gamma)$ are the transition probabilities of the "unperturbed" chain $\{\xi_n^0, n \geqslant 1\}$ having more than one class of ergodic states.

One has to establish the connection between the stationary measure of the perturbed chain ξ_n^ϵ and the ergodic distributions of the unperturbed chain ξ_n^0.

We introduce $\mathfrak{B}$, the Banach space of bounded measurable functions on E with the supremum norm. Then, as it is well known, the kernel $P_\epsilon(x, \Gamma)$ induces an operator P_ϵ in $\mathfrak{B}$:

$$P_\epsilon f(x) = \int_E P_\epsilon(x, dy) f(y) .$$

It turns out that the problem of asymptotic enlargement of the perturbed chain formulated above can be reduced to the study of the "eigenoperator" Λ_ϵ and the "eigenprojector" Π_ϵ which satisfy the relations

$$(7) \qquad \begin{cases} (I - P_\epsilon)\Pi_\epsilon = \Lambda_\epsilon \Pi_\epsilon , \\ \Pi_\epsilon(I - P_\epsilon) = \Pi_\epsilon \Lambda_\epsilon . \end{cases}$$

§3.

The problems mentioned above have been treated in a number of papers (e.g. in the works of R. Pyke [1], [5], Kshirsagar and Gupta [6], J. Keilson [7], R. Howard [8], E. Çinlar [4],

Čistjakov and Sevast'janov [9], G.N. Cercvadze [10], V. Anisimov [11], etc.).

The methods used by these authors rely on the results of matrix theory; the corresponding asymptotic expansions are hard to interpret in the language of probability theory. The utilization of the methods of matrix theory is difficult in the case of asymptotic enlargement problems, as indicated, for instance, by the papers of Cercvadze and others. And, what is perhaps the most important, this approach does not carry over to the case of an arbitrary phase space.

The present authors propose a new approach to problems of this kind, namely the inversion of operators perturbed on the spectrum. The new approach originates from the paper [12] of V.S. Koroljuk published in 1969, where problems of type (2) were solved by the aid of the well-known Višik – Ljusternik algorithm.

Let us mention those results from the inversion theory of linear operators perturbed on the spectrum which are employed for solving the problems considered.

Let A be a closed, normally solvable, densely defined operator acting in the space $\mathfrak{B}$ and satisfying the (a)-conditions below

(a_1) zero is an isolated point of the spectrum of the operator in the sense that exist $\alpha_- > 0$ and $\alpha_+ > 0$ with $\lambda \in \rho(A)$ for every $-\alpha_- < \operatorname{Re} \lambda < \alpha_+$, $\lambda \neq 0$;

(a_2) the null-space $N(A)$ of A coincides with the corresponding root space. Further, let B be a bounded operator in $\mathfrak{B}$. Let Π denote the operator of projection onto $N(A)$ parallel to $R(A)$ (the range of A), and let $\overline{\Pi B \Pi}$ be the restriction of the operator $\Pi B \Pi$ to $N(A)$.

Theorem 1. *If* $\overline{\Pi B \Pi}^{-1}$ *exists as a bounded operator, then for every* $0 < |\lambda| < \frac{1}{\| T_0 \|} \frac{1}{\| B \|}$ *we have*

$$(8) \qquad (A - \lambda B)^{-1} = -\frac{1}{\lambda} \Pi_B^{(-1)} + T_0 (I - \lambda B T_0)^{-1} ,$$

where $\Pi_B^{(-1)} = \Pi B^{(-1)}\Pi$, $B^{(-1)}$ *is the invariant extension of* $\overline{\Pi B \Pi}^{-1}$ *to all of* $\mathfrak{B}$,

$$T_0 = (I - \Pi_B^{(-1)} B) R_0 (I - B \Pi_B^{(-1)}) , \tag{9}$$

and

$$R_0 = (A + \Pi)^{-1} - \Pi . \tag{10}$$

Theorem 1 can be generalized to the case where

(a) the perturbation is non-linear,

(b) also the operator B is unbounded, but is subordinate to the operator A.

We are going to apply Theorem 1 for the study of $\lim_{\lambda \to 0} \lambda(I - Q_\lambda)^{-1}$ (see equation (2)).

Theorem 2. *If the states in* E *form one class of returning states,*

(1) $\lim_{n\to\infty} \frac{1}{n} \sum_0^{n-1} P^m = \Pi$ *exists and* $\|\Pi\| < \infty$,

(2) $\sup_{k\in E} \int_0^\infty t\, dP_k(t) < \infty$, *then*

$$\lim \lambda(I - Q_\lambda)^{-1} = \frac{1}{\pi}\Pi , \tag{11}$$

where

$$\pi = \sum_{k\in E} \rho_k a_k ,$$

ρ_k *stand for the stationary probabilities of the embedded Markov chain,*

$$a_k = \int_0^\infty t\, dP_k(t)$$

denotes the average sojourn time of the semi-Markov process in the k*-th state.*

The application of this theorem, in turn, obviously enables one to examine $\lim_{t \to \infty} u_t$, if this limit exists. As to the asymptotic expansion of u_λ for λ near zero, we can simply make use of the analogue of Theorem 1 relating to nonlinear perturbations and having a form close to the representation (8). Note that, as a consequence of (8), the operator R_0 plays a fundamental role in the asymptotic expansions. In probabilistic applications, usually, R_0 is the potential of the embedded Markov chain.

§4.

The results obtainable in problems of asymptotic enlargement are of a somewhat different nature. First we mention a result from the inversion theory of linear operators perturbed on the spectrum. As in the previous case, we restrict ourselves to the simplest case of linear perturbation.

Let A and B satisfy the conditions of Theorem 1.

Theorem 3. *If λ belongs to the resolvent set of the operator $\overline{\Pi B \Pi}$, then for sufficiently small values of $\epsilon > 0$ we have*

$$(12) \qquad (A - \epsilon\lambda I + \epsilon B)^{-1} = \frac{1}{\epsilon}\Pi_B^{(-1)}(\lambda) + T_\lambda(I + (B - \lambda I)T_\lambda)^{-1} ,$$

where

$$\Pi_B^{(-1)}(\lambda) = \Pi(\Pi B \Pi - \lambda I)^{-1} ,$$

$$T_\lambda = (I - \Pi_B^{(-1)}(\lambda)(B - \lambda I))R_0(I - (B - \lambda I)\Pi_B^{(-1)}(\lambda)) .$$

Let e.g. $A = I - P$, where P has the block structure

$$P = \begin{bmatrix} P^{(1)} & 0 & 0 \dots \\ 0 & P^{(2)} & 0 \dots \\ 0 & 0 & P^{(3)} \\ \vdots & \vdots & \ddots \end{bmatrix} ,$$

and $N(I - P)$ is the m-dimensional subspace generated by the vectors

$$1_k = (0, \ldots, 0; \underbrace{1, \ldots, 1}_{E_k}; 0, \ldots, 0) \qquad (k = 1, \ldots, m)$$

which induce a decomposition $E = \sum\limits_{k=1}^{m} E_k$ of the initial phase space. The perturbation is given by the matrix $B = \{b_{ij}^{(kr)}; \; i, j \in E\}$. The (a)-conditions assure the existence of the projector $\Pi = \lim\limits_{n \to \infty} \dfrac{1}{n} \sum\limits_{k=1}^{n} P^n$ describing all stationary distributions of the Markov chain with transition operator P. The projector Π is defined by the relation $\Pi = \sum\limits_{k=1}^{m} 1_k \otimes \rho_k$, where

$$1_k \otimes \rho_k = \left.\begin{bmatrix} 0 & \cdots & 0 & \overset{\displaystyle\overbrace{\hspace{2em}}^{\displaystyle E_k}}{0} & \cdots & 0 & \cdots & 0 \\ \multicolumn{8}{c}{\cdots\cdots\cdots\cdots} \\ 0 & \cdots & \rho_1^{(k)} & \rho_2^{(k)} & \cdots & \rho_{m_k}^{(k)} & \cdots & 0 \\ \multicolumn{8}{c}{\cdots\cdots\cdots\cdots\cdots} \\ 0 & \cdots & \rho_1^{(k)} & \rho_2^{(k)} & \cdots & \rho_{m_k}^{(k)} & \cdots & 0 \\ \multicolumn{8}{c}{\cdots\cdots\cdots\cdots} \\ 0 & \multicolumn{7}{c}{\cdots\cdots\cdots\cdots\cdots\cdots\cdots\cdots\cdots\;\; 0} \end{bmatrix}\right\} E_k$$

Further we have $\Pi B \Pi = \sum\limits_{k,r}' b_{kr} 1_k \otimes \rho_r$, where $b_{kr} = \rho_k B 1_k$, i.e.,

$$b_{kr} = \sum_{s \in E_k} \rho_s^{(k)} \sum_{t \in E_r}' b_{st}^{(kr)}.$$

Finally, restriction of $\Pi B \Pi$ to $N(I - P)$ yields

$$\overline{\Pi B \Pi} = \{b_{kr}; \; k, r = 1, \ldots, m\}.$$

Note that $\overline{\Pi B \Pi}$ is the generating Q-matrix of some Markov chain, since by assumption (see (3)) $b_{ij}^{(kk)} = b_{ij}^{(k)} \leqslant 0$; $b_{ij}^{(kr)} \geqslant 0$. On the other hand, it is natural to suppose that

$$\sum_{j \in E_k} \rho_j^{(k)} \sum_{i \in E_k} b_{ji}^{(k)} = q_k < 0.$$

Then, obviously,

$$b_{kk} = q_k < 0, \; b_{rk} = \sum_{s \in E_r} \rho_s^{(r)} \sum_{i \in E_k} b_{si}^{(rk)} \geqslant 0 \,,$$

and

$$\sum_{k \neq r} b_{rk} = \sum_{s \in E_k} \rho_s^{(r)} \sum_{k \neq r} \sum_{i \in E_k} b_{si}^{(rk)} = - b_{rr} \,.$$

Theorem 3 has an immediate probabilistic analogue which consists in the following.

Let a Markov process, defined on $(E, \mathscr{E})$, have an infinitesimal operator of the form $\frac{1}{\epsilon} A + B$, where A, in turn, is the infinitesimal operator of an "unperturbed" Markov process. Then

$$\epsilon(A - \epsilon\lambda I + \epsilon B)^{-1}$$

is the resolvent of the operator $\frac{1}{\epsilon} A + B$. From Theorem 3 it follows that for the operator of transition probabilities we have

Theorem 4.

(13) $$\lim_{\epsilon \to 0} P_\epsilon(t) = \Pi e^{\Pi B \Pi t} \,,$$

where

$$\Pi = \lim_{n \to \infty} \frac{1}{n} \sum_{0}^{n-1} P^m \,,$$

P being the operator of transition probabilities of the embedded Markov chain.

The latter result admits a probabilistic interpretation: the right-hand side of (13) corresponds to the transition probabilities of the process $\eta_{\bar{\xi}(t)}$, where $\eta_i(t)$ are processes with independent values whose transitions are defined by the restriction of Π to E_i $(i = 1, \ldots, n)$, and $\bar{\xi}(t)$ is a Markov chain with resolvent operator $\overline{\Pi(\Pi B \Pi - \lambda I)^{-1}}$.

A second result which can be obtained by applying Theorem 2 to the Markov process in question is the construction of an asymptotic expansion for $P_\epsilon(t)$.

Theorem 5. *For every finite* $t > 0$ *we have*

$$(14)\qquad \begin{aligned} P_\epsilon(t) &= \Pi e^{\Pi B \Pi t} + \epsilon R_1(t) + \epsilon^2 R_2(t) + \ldots \\ &\ldots + W_0\left(\frac{t}{\epsilon}\right) + \epsilon W_1\left(\frac{t}{\epsilon}\right) + \ldots, \end{aligned}$$

where $R_i(t)$ *and* $W_i\left(\frac{t}{\epsilon}\right)$ *are operator-valued functions that can be determined explicitly, and* $W_i\left(\frac{t}{\epsilon}\right)$ *satisfies the inequality*

$$\left\| W_i\left(\frac{t}{\epsilon}\right) \right\| \leqslant e^{-\alpha \frac{t}{\epsilon}} g_i\left(\frac{t}{\epsilon}\right)$$

with $g_i\left(\frac{t}{\epsilon}\right)$ *a polynomial of* $\frac{t}{\epsilon}$ *of degree* $i-1$,

$$\alpha \in (0, \alpha_-), \quad -\alpha_- = \sup_{\lambda \in \sigma(A) \setminus \{0\}} \operatorname{Re} \lambda .$$

Theorem 3 can easily be generalized to the following cases:

(a) The expression in (12) has the form

$$(A - \epsilon^k \lambda I + \epsilon B_1 + \epsilon^2 B_2 + \ldots)^{-1},$$

which corresponds to Markov processes where the transitions between states of different classes are of order ϵ^l $(l = 1, 2, \ldots)$ and the norming $\frac{t}{\epsilon^k}$ of time is introduced;

(b) $A - \epsilon^k \lambda G_1 + \epsilon B_1 + \epsilon^2 B_2 + \ldots + \epsilon^{k+1} D(\lambda, \epsilon)$.

So, if the Laplace – Stieltjes transform in t of the operator generated by the semi-Markov kernel $Q_\epsilon(t, x, \Gamma)$ in Problem 2 is of the form

$$(15)\qquad Q_\epsilon(\lambda) = P - \epsilon B - \lambda G_1 + \sigma(\epsilon\lambda),$$

and the operator

$$\Pi = \lim_{n\to\infty} \frac{1}{n} \sum_{0}^{n-1} P^m$$

is a bounded projector, then we have

Theorem 6. *For the semi-Markov process* $\xi_\epsilon(t)$ *with kernel* $Q_\epsilon(t, x, \Gamma)$ *satisfying* (15) *the relation*

$$\lim_{\epsilon\to 0} \mathsf{P}\left\{\xi_\epsilon\left(\frac{t}{\epsilon}\right) \in \Gamma \mid \xi(0) = x\right\} = \Pi e^{\Pi C^{(-1)}\Pi t} \chi_\Gamma(x)$$

is valid, where $C^{(-1)}$ *stands for the invariant extension of the operator* $-\overline{\Pi G_1 \Pi}^{-1}\,\overline{\Pi B \Pi}$, *the bars denoting restriction to the subspace* $N(I-P)$.

Thus we have found a result similar to Theorem 4.

§5.

To finish with, consider the solution of the problem (7).

Let

$$\Pi_0 = \lim_{n\to\infty} \frac{1}{n} \sum_{k=1}^{n} P_0^k$$

exist as a bounded projector and let $I - P_0$ satisfy the (a)-conditions. Introduce the operator $B = \Pi_0 Q \Pi_0$ and suppose that its restriction $\overline{B}$ to the subspace $N(I-P_0)$ also satisfies the (a)-conditions. Then the corresponding projector Π_B onto the subspace $N(B)$ exists, and we have $\Pi_B \mathfrak{B} \subset N(I-P_0)$, $\Pi_B \Pi_0 = \Pi_0 \Pi_B = \Pi_B$.

As we have already mentioned, the operator $\overline{B}$ defines an enlarged Markov chain on the "sewn" state space E_1 generated by the decomposition of the initial phase space E corresponding to the projector Π_0. The restriction of the operator $\overline{\Pi}_B$ to $N(I-P)$ defines the stationary distributions of the Markov chain with transition operator $\overline{B}$.

Under the assumptions formulated above the following result holds:

Theorem 7. *For* $0 < \epsilon < \frac{1}{\|R_0\|} \frac{1}{\|Q\|}$ *we have the relations*

$$(16)\qquad \begin{aligned} &(P_0 - I + \epsilon Q)\Pi_\epsilon = \Lambda_\epsilon \Pi_\epsilon\,, \\ &\Pi_\epsilon (P_0 - I + \epsilon Q) = \Pi_\epsilon \Lambda_\epsilon\,, \end{aligned}$$

where

$$(17)\qquad \Lambda_\epsilon = \epsilon \Pi_0 Q (I + \epsilon R_0 Q)^{-1} \Pi_0\,,$$

$$(18)\qquad \Pi_\epsilon^2 = \Pi_\epsilon = \sum_{k=0}^{\infty} (-\epsilon)^k \Pi_k\,,$$

$$(19)\qquad \Pi_k = (R_0 Q)^k \Pi_0 + \Pi_0 (Q R_0)^k + \sum_{i=1}^{k-1} (R_0 Q)^{k-i} \Pi_0 (B R_0)^i\,.$$

Moreover, if $\Lambda_\epsilon \equiv 0$ *in* (16), *then*

$$(20)\qquad \Pi_\epsilon = \sum_{k=0}^{\infty} (-\epsilon)^k \Pi_k^{(B)}\,,$$

where

$$(21)\qquad \begin{aligned} \Pi_0^{(B)} = \Pi_B\,,\ \Pi_k^{(B)} &= (R_0 Q)^k \Pi_B + \Pi_B (Q R_0)^k + \\ &+ \sum_{i=1}^{k-1} (R_0 Q)^{k-i} \Pi_B (Q R_0)^i\,. \end{aligned}$$

In particular, from Theorem 7 it follows that the stationary measure of the Markov chain with transition operator $P_0 + \epsilon Q$, provided it is unique, can be represented in the form

$$(22)\qquad \rho_\epsilon(\Gamma) = \sum_{k=1}^{m} P_k^0 \int_{E_k} \rho_k(dx) R_\epsilon(x, \Gamma)\,,$$

where $\{P_k^0;\ 1 \leqslant k \leqslant m\}$ is the stationary distribution of the enlarged Markov chain with transition operator $\bar{B} = \overline{\Pi_0 Q \Pi_0}$, further $\{\rho_k(\Gamma);$ $1 \leqslant k \leqslant m\}$ is the stationary measure of the chain with operator P_0, and $R_\epsilon(x, \Gamma)$ stands for the kernel of the operator $(I + \epsilon Q R_0)^{-1}$.

REFERENCES

[1] R. Pyke, Markov renewal processes: definitions and preliminary properties, *Ann. Math. Statist.*, 32 (1961), 1231-1242.

[2] E. Çinlar, Semi-Markov processes on arbitrary spaces, *Proc. Cambridge Philos. Soc.*, 66 (1969), 381-392.

[3] R. Pyke – R. Shaufelle, Limit theorems for Markov renewal processes, *Ann. Math. Statist.*, 35 (1964).

[4] E. Çinlar, Some joint distributions for Markov renewal processes, *Austral. J. Statist.*, 10 (1968), 8-20.

[5] R. Pyke, Markov renewal processes with finitely many states, *Ann. Math. Statist.*, 32 (1961), 1243-1259.

[6] Y.P. Gupta – A.M. Kshirsagar, Asymptotic values of the first two moments in Markov renewal processes, *Biometrika*, 54 (1967), 597-604.

[7] J. Keilson, On the matrix renewal function for Markov renewal processes, *Ann. Math. Statist.*, 40 (1969), 1901-1907.

[8] R.A. Howard, System analysis of semi-Markov processes, *IEEE Trans. Computers*, 8 (1964), 114-124.

[9] B.A. Sevast'janov – V.P. Čistjakov, Multidimensional renewal equations and moments of branching processes, (in Russian), *Teorija Verojatn. i Primenen.*, 16 (1971), 201-217.

[10] G.N. Cercvadze, Asymptotic enlargement of states in Markov chains and automata with stochastic input effects, (in Russian), Doctor's dissertation, Tbilisi, 1971.

[11] V.V. Anisimov, Asymptotic enlargement of stochastic processes, (in Russian), *Kibernetika*, 3 (1973), 109-117.

[12] V.S. Koroljuk, On the asymptotic behaviour of the sojourn time of a semi-Markov process in a subset of states, (in Russian), *Ukrainskiĭ Matematičeskiĭ Žurnal*, 21 (1969), 842-845.

[13] A.F. Turbin, Application of the inversion of linear operators perturbed on the spectrum to some asymptotic problems connected with Markov chains and semi-Markov processes, (in Russian), *Teorija, Verojatnosteĭ i Matematičeskaja Statistika,* Kiev, 1972.

COLLOQUIA MATHEMATICA SOCIETATIS JÁNOS BOLYAI
11. LIMIT THEOREMS OF PROBABILITY THEORY, KESZTHELY (HUNGARY), 1974.

EQUIVALENCE-ORTHOGONALITY DICHOTOMIES OF PROBABILITY MEASURES*

T. NEMETZ

1. INTRODUCTION

In 1948 S. Kakutani [6] proved the following famous

Theorem K. *Let* P_i *and* Q_i *be equivalent probability measures on* $\{X_i, \mathscr{X}_i\}$ $(i = 1, 2, \ldots)$ *and denote the Cartesian product measures of the product spaces* $\{X_1^n, \mathscr{X}_1^n\} = \mathop{\times}\limits_{i=1}^{n-1} \{X_i, \mathscr{X}_i\}$ *by* P_1^n *and* Q_1^n. *Then the probability measures* P_1^∞ *and* Q_1^∞ *are either orthogonal or equivalent on* $\{X_1^\infty, \mathscr{X}_1^\infty\}$ *depending on whether the infinite product*

$$(1) \qquad \prod_{i=1}^{\infty} \int \sqrt{p_i(x) \cdot q_i(x)}\, \mu(dx)$$

converges to zero or not, where $p_i(x)$ *and* $q_i(x)$ *denotes the Radon – Nykodim derivatives of* P_i *and* Q_i *with respect to the dominating* σ*-finite measure* μ.

*An earlier version of this paper was presented at the Math. Dept. of the University of Guelph, in 1972.

What is really fascinating in this theorem is that the two probability measures generated by the Cartesian products of two pairwise equivalent probability measure-sequences are either orthogonal or equivalent. This fascinating dichotomy attracted many mathematicians, e.g. Hájek [4], Feldman [3], Révész [10], Arató [1]. It has got a special attention in literature of the reproducing kernel Hilbert spaces. In this contribution we will use some properties of the Hellinger integrals to establish a little more general theorem in this direction.

Definition 1. Let P and Q be two probability measures on $\{X, \mathscr{X}\}$, μ be a σ-finite measure dominating both P and Q, and let $p(x)$ and $q(x)$ denote the Radon – Nykodim derivatives of P and Q with respect to μ. Then the Hellinger-integral of order α, $0 < \alpha < 1$ is defined by

$$H_\alpha(\mathrm{P}, \mathrm{Q}) = \int_X p^\alpha(x) q^{1-\alpha}(x) d\mu \,. \tag{2}$$

Remark 1. The integral is named after Hellinger, who investigated the case $\alpha = \frac{1}{2}$ in 1909, see [5]. Note, that the same integral $\left(\alpha = \frac{1}{2}\right)$ appears in Kakutani's original proof.

Remark 2. The Hellinger-integral of order α $(0 < \alpha < 1)$ is a useful tool in estimating error probability in statistical hypotheses-testing problems, since the error-probability can be both upper and lower-estimated by Hellinger integrals. On the other hand, in the case of an infinite sequence of observations the error probability tends to zero iff the corresponding measures on the infinite dimensional product space are pairwise orthogonal. This coincidence had lead A. Rényi to attack Kakutani's problem by the help of the Hellinger integrals. For earlier results see also Nemetz [8], [9].

The main result of this paper is a generalization of Kakutani's theorem, which we state now in the following theorem:

Theorem 1. *Let there be given two probability measures* P *and* Q *on the infinite dimensional product space* $\{X_1^\infty, \mathscr{X}_1^\infty\}$ *and let us denote* *the restrictions of* P *and* Q *to* $\{X_n^m, \mathscr{X}_n^m\} = \mathop{\times}\limits_{i=n}^{m-1} \{X_i, \mathscr{X}_i\}$ *by* P_n^m *and* Q_n^m. *Then*

(i) P *and* Q *are orthogonal on* $\{X_1^\infty, \mathscr{X}_1^\infty\}$ *iff*

$$\lim_{n\to\infty} H_\alpha(\mathsf{P}_1^n, \mathsf{Q}_1^n) \to 0 \qquad (0 < \alpha < 1), \tag{3}$$

(ii) Q *is absolutely continuous with respect to* P *on* $\{X_1^\infty, \mathscr{X}_1^\infty\}$ *iff for every preassigned* $\epsilon > 0$ *there exists* $\alpha_0 = \alpha(\epsilon)$ *such that*

$$H_\alpha(\mathsf{P}_1^n, \mathsf{Q}_1^n) \geqslant 1 - \epsilon, \quad \text{if} \quad 0 < \alpha \leqslant \alpha_0 . \tag{4}$$

2. PROPERTIES OF THE HELLINGER INTEGRALS

In this section we will list some properties of the Hellinger integrals, which will be used to prove Theorem 1. First of all, it is interesting to note, that the amount $-H_\alpha(\mathsf{P}, \mathsf{Q})$ is a particular f-divergence introduced by I. Csiszár [2]. This remark allows us to omit the proof of properties P9 and P10 below. On the other hand, the proof of the first four properties and that of property P6 is a routine work, therefore we state them without proof, as well.

P1. $H_\alpha(\mathsf{P}, \mathsf{Q})$ *does not depend on the choice of* μ.

P2. $H_\alpha(\mathsf{P}, \mathsf{Q}) \geqslant 0$ *with equality iff* P *and* Q *are orthogonal* $(\mathsf{P} \perp \mathsf{Q})$.

P3. $H_\alpha(\mathsf{P}, \mathsf{Q}) \leqslant 1$ *with equality iff* P *and* Q *are identical* $(\mathsf{P} \equiv \mathsf{Q})$.

P4. $H_\alpha(\mathsf{P}, \mathsf{Q}) = H_{1-\alpha}(\mathsf{Q}, \mathsf{P}) \quad (0 < \alpha < 1)$.

P5. $H_\alpha(\mathsf{P}, \mathsf{Q})$ *is a continuous convex function of* α $(0 < \alpha < 1)$, *for every fixed* P *and* Q.

Hint. The convexity follows from the fact, that t^α is a convex function of α $(0 < \alpha < 1)$ for every fixed $t \geqslant 0$. The continuity is a consequence of the convexity.

P6. *The Hellinger integrals are multiplicative on independent experiments, i.e. let* P_1 *and* Q_1 *be given on* $\{X_1, \mathscr{X}_1\}$ *and* P_2 *and* Q_2 *be given on* $\{X_2, \mathscr{X}_2\}$ *and let* $\mathsf{P}_1 * \mathsf{P}_2$ *and* $\mathsf{Q}_1 * \mathsf{Q}_2$ *be the Cartesian product measures on the product space* $\{X_1 \times X_2, \mathscr{X}_1 \times \mathscr{X}_2\}$, *then*

$$H_\alpha(\mathsf{P}_1 * \mathsf{P}_2, \mathsf{Q}_1 * \mathsf{Q}_2) = H_\alpha(\mathsf{P}_1, \mathsf{Q}_1) \cdot H_\alpha(\mathsf{P}_2, \mathsf{Q}_2) \quad (0 < \alpha < 1).$$

P7. $[H_{\frac{1}{2}}(\mathsf{P}, \mathsf{Q})]^2 \leqslant H_\alpha(\mathsf{P}, \mathsf{Q}) \quad (0 < \alpha < 1)$.

It can be seen from property P3, that this is a particular case of the inequiality

(5) $$H_{\frac{1}{2}}(\mathsf{P}, \mathsf{Q}) \leqslant \sqrt{H_\alpha(\mathsf{P}, \mathsf{Q})} \cdot \sqrt{H_{1-\alpha}(\mathsf{P}, \mathsf{Q})}\,.$$

This formula, in turn, follows from the Schwartz inequality:

$$\int_X \sqrt{p(x)q(x)}\, d\mu = \int_X \sqrt{p^\alpha(x) q^{1-\alpha}(x)} \cdot \sqrt{p^{1-\alpha}(x) q^\alpha(x)}\, d\mu \leqslant$$

$$\leqslant \sqrt{\int_X p^\alpha(x) q^{1-\alpha}(x)\, d\mu} \cdot \sqrt{\int_X p^{1-\alpha}(x) q^\alpha(x)\, d\mu}\,.$$

P8. $\lim\limits_{\alpha \to 0} H_\alpha(\mathsf{P}, \mathsf{Q}) = \int_A q(x)\mu(dx) = \mathsf{Q}(A)$

and

$$\lim_{\alpha \to 1} H_\alpha(\mathsf{P}, \mathsf{Q}) = \int_B p(x)\mu(dx) = \mathsf{P}(B)$$

where

$$A = \{x\colon p(x) > 0\} \quad \text{and} \quad B = \{x\colon q(x) > 0\}\,.$$

Proof. Choose $\mu = \mathsf{P} + \mathsf{Q}$ in order to ensure that $0 \leqslant p(x), q(x) \leqslant 1$. Let $A_\epsilon = \{x\colon p(x) > \epsilon\}$. Then for all $\delta > 0$, $\epsilon > 0$ there exists a number $\alpha(\delta, \epsilon)$ such that

$$1 \geqslant p^\alpha(x) \geqslant 1 - \delta \quad \text{if} \quad 0 \leqslant \alpha \leqslant \alpha(\delta, \epsilon), \qquad x \in A_\epsilon\,.$$

Obviously

$$H_\alpha(\mathsf{P},\mathsf{Q}) \geqslant \int_{A_\epsilon} p^\alpha(x) q^{1-\alpha}(x) d\mu \geqslant (1-\delta) \int_{A_\epsilon} q^{1-\alpha}(x) d\mu$$

$$(0 < \alpha \leqslant \alpha(\delta, \epsilon)) .$$

Thus

$$\liminf_{\alpha \to 0} H_\alpha(\mathsf{P},\mathsf{Q}) \geqslant (1-\delta) \lim_{\alpha \to 0} \int_{A_\epsilon} q^{1-\alpha}(x) d\mu = (1-\delta)\mathsf{Q}(A_\epsilon)$$

for all $\epsilon > 0$, and therefore

$$\liminf_{\alpha \to 0} H_\alpha(\mathsf{P},\mathsf{Q}) \geqslant (1-\delta)\mathsf{Q}(A) .$$

From here, δ being arbitrarily small, we have

$$\liminf_{\alpha \to 0} H_\alpha(\mathsf{P},\mathsf{Q}) \geqslant \mathsf{Q}(A) .$$

On the other hand

$$H_\alpha(\mathsf{P},\mathsf{Q}) \leqslant \int_A q^{1-\alpha}(x) d\mu$$

implying that

$$\limsup_{\alpha \to 0} H_\alpha(\mathsf{P},\mathsf{Q}) \leqslant \lim_{\alpha \to 0} \int_A q^{1-\alpha}(x) d\mu = \mathsf{Q}(A)$$

which completes the proof of the first relation of P8. The second one follows from P4.

Remark 3. Defining $H_0(\mathsf{P},\mathsf{Q})$ and $H_1(\mathsf{P},\mathsf{Q})$ as the limit values of $H_\alpha(\mathsf{P},\mathsf{Q})$ as $\alpha \to 0$ and $\alpha \to 1$ respectively, one can see that properties P2, P4, P5, P6 are valid in the whole closed interval $0 \leqslant \alpha \leqslant 1$. The following Corollary emphasizes the difference in property P3.

Corollary 1. $H_0(\mathsf{P},\mathsf{Q}) \leqslant 1$ *with equality iff* Q *is absolutely continuous with respect to* P.

P9. *Let* $\widetilde{\mathscr{X}}$ *be a sub-σ-algebra of* $\mathscr{X}$, *and* $\widetilde{\mathsf{P}}, \widetilde{\mathsf{Q}}$ *denote the restriction of* P *and* Q *to* $\widetilde{\mathscr{X}}$. *Then it holds*

$$H_\alpha(\widetilde{\mathsf{P}},\widetilde{\mathsf{Q}}) \geqslant H_\alpha(\mathsf{P},\mathsf{Q}) .$$

P10. *Suppose, that the sequence of sub-σ-algebras* $\mathcal{X}_1 \subset \mathcal{X}_2 \subset \dots$ $(\mathcal{X}_i \subset \mathcal{X})$ *generates* $\mathcal{X}$, *and let* P_n *and* Q_n *denote the restriction of* P *and* Q *to* $\mathcal{X}_n$. *Then*

$$\lim_{n\to\infty} H_\alpha(\mathsf{P}_n, \mathsf{Q}_n) = H_\alpha(\mathsf{P}, \mathsf{Q}) .$$

3. DEDUCTION OF KAKUTANI'S THEOREM FROM THEOREM 1

The orthogonality-part is obvious from the equality

$$H_\alpha(\mathsf{P}_1^n, \mathsf{Q}_1^n) = \prod_{i=1}^{n-1} H_\alpha(\mathsf{P}_i, \mathsf{Q}_i)$$

valid in the independent case (property P6). On the other hand, if

$$\prod_{i=1}^{\infty} H_{\frac{1}{2}}(\mathsf{P}_i, \mathsf{Q}_i) > 0$$

then

$$\prod_{i=N}^{\infty} H_{\frac{1}{2}}(\mathsf{P}_i, \mathsf{Q}_i) \to 1 \quad \text{if} \quad N \to \infty .$$

Thus by P7 there exists a number $N = N(\epsilon)$ such that

$$\prod_{i=N}^{\infty} H_\alpha(\mathsf{P}_i, \mathsf{Q}_i) > 1 - \frac{\epsilon}{3} \quad \text{for every} \quad 0 < \alpha < 1 .$$

And, since P_i and Q_i are equivalent for every i, by P8 there exists a number $\alpha_0 = \alpha(\epsilon, N)$ such that

$$H_\alpha(\mathsf{P}_1^n, \mathsf{Q}_1^n) = \prod_{i=1}^{n-1} H_\alpha(\mathsf{P}_i, \mathsf{Q}_i) > 1 - \frac{\epsilon}{3} \text{ if } 0 < \alpha \leqslant \alpha_0,\ n \leqslant N .$$

Furthermore, P9 implies $\prod_{i=N}^{n} H_\alpha(\mathsf{P}_i, \mathsf{Q}_i) \geqslant \prod_{i=N}^{\infty} H_\alpha(\mathsf{P}_i, \mathsf{Q}_i)$ if $n > N$,

therefore

$$\prod_{i=1}^{n} H_\alpha(\mathsf{P}_i, \mathsf{Q}_i) > \left(1 - \frac{\epsilon}{3}\right)^2 > 1 - \epsilon \quad \text{for all} \quad n \geq 1$$

$$\text{if} \quad 0 < \alpha \leq \alpha_0(\epsilon) ,$$

and, by (ii) of Theorem 1, Q is absolutely continuous with respect to P. Interchangeability of Q and P implies their equivalence.

4. PROOF OF THEOREM 1

P and Q are orthogonal on $\{X_1^\infty, \mathscr{X}_1^\infty\}$ iff $H_\alpha(\mathsf{P}, \mathsf{Q}) = 0$ for all $0 < \alpha < 1$ by the property P2. This, together with property P10 proves the part (i).

In order to prove part (ii) it suffices to show that (4) is equivalent to $H_0(\mathsf{P}, \mathsf{Q}) = 1$. (See Corollary 1.) However, according to Remark 3, $H_\alpha(\mathsf{P}, \mathsf{Q})$ is a continuous function of α in the closed interval $0 \leq \alpha \leq 1$. Therefore, for every $\epsilon > 0$ there exists $\alpha_0 = \alpha(\epsilon)$ such that

$$H_\alpha(\mathsf{P}, \mathsf{Q}) \geq 1 - \epsilon \quad \text{if} \quad 0 < \alpha \leq \alpha(\epsilon)$$

iff $H_0(\mathsf{P}, \mathsf{Q}) = 1$. Since P_1^n and Q_1^n are the restrictions of P and Q to $\{X_1^n, \mathscr{X}_1^n\}$, by property P9

$$H_\alpha(\mathsf{P}_1^n, \mathsf{Q}_1^n) \geq H_\alpha(\mathsf{P}, \mathsf{Q}) \geq 1 - \epsilon .$$

On the other hand, if (4) is fulfilled then by P10 for every $\epsilon > 0$ there is a number $\alpha_0 = \alpha(\epsilon)$ such that

$$H_\alpha(\mathsf{P}, \mathsf{Q}) \geq 1 - \epsilon \quad \text{if} \quad 0 < \alpha \leq \alpha_0$$

and the continuity of $H_\alpha(\mathsf{P}, \mathsf{Q})$ ensures that $H_0(\mathsf{P}, \mathsf{Q}) = 1$.

The following example shows that the equivalence of P_1^n and Q_1^n for every finite n does not imply, in general, that P and Q are either orthogonal or equivalent.

Example. Let P and Q be orthogonal measures on the infinite dimensional product space with equivalent finite dimensional restrictions P_1^n and Q_1^n $(n = 1, 2, \ldots)$. Let $\bar{\mathsf{Q}} = \frac{1}{2}(\mathsf{P} + \mathsf{Q})$. Obviously, the finite dimensional restrictions P_1^n and $\bar{\mathsf{Q}}_1^n$ are equivalent for all n, while P and $\bar{\mathsf{Q}}$ are neither orthogonal nor equivalent.

However, if the zero-one law holds true for a Markov-chain under both possible hypotheses, then the dichotomy takes place. More precisely

Theorem 2. *Let the observations* $\xi_1, \xi_2, \ldots$ *form a non-homogeneous Markov chain obeying the zero-one law under two possible hypotheses* H_1, H_2. *Denote the probability measures, associated with* $\xi_n^m = \{\xi_i, n \leqslant i < m\}$ *by* P_n^m *and* Q_n^m. *Suppose that* P_1^n *and* Q_1^n *are equivalent for every finite* n. *Then* $\mathsf{P} = \mathsf{P}_1^\infty$ *and* $\mathsf{Q} = \mathsf{Q}_1^\infty$ *are either orthogonal or equivalent depending on whether the limit value of the Hellinger-integrals of order* $\alpha = \frac{1}{2}$

$$\lim_{n \to \infty} H_{\frac{1}{2}}(\mathsf{P}_1^n, \mathsf{Q}_1^n)$$

is zero or not.

This theorem can be easily deduced from Theorem 1. We do not present a proof here, however, since it follows, as a particular case, from the paper [7].

REFERENCES

[1] M. Arató, Some remarks on the absolute-continuity of measures, *MTA Mat. Kut. Int. Közl.*, 6 (1961), 123-126 (in Russian).

[2] I. Csiszár, Information-type measures of divergence of probability distributions and indirect observations, *Studia Sci. Math. Hung.*, 2 (1967), 299-318.

[3] J. Feldman, Equivalence and perpendicularity of Gaussian processes, *Pacific J. Math.*, 8 (1958), 699-708.

[4] J. Hájek, On a property of Gaussian measures of stochastic processes, *Czech. Math. Journ.*, 8 (1958), 610-619.

[5] E. Hellinger, Neue Begründung der Theorie quadratischer Formen von unendlichen Veränderlichen, *Journ. für reine und angew. Math.*, 13 (1909), 210-271.

[6] S. Kakutani, On equivalence of infinite product measures, *Ann. of Math.*, 49 (1948), 214-226.

[7] R.D. Le Page – V. Mandrekar, Equivalence-singularity dichotomies from zero-one laws, *Proc. Amer. Math. Soc.*, 31 (1972), 251-254.

[8] T. Nemetz, Information theory and testing hypotheses, *Proc. of the Colloquium on Inf. Theory*, Debrecen, 1967, Colloquia Math. Societatis János Bolyai, Budapest, 1969, 283-293.

[9] T. Nemetz, On the orthogonality of probability measures, *Studia Sci. Math. Hung.*, 7 (1972), 111-115.

[10] P. Révész, A limit distribution theorem for sums of dependent random variables, *Acta Math. Acad. Sci. Hung.*, 10 (1959), 125-131.

COLLOQUIA MATHEMATICA SOCIETATIS JÁNOS BOLYAI

11. LIMIT THEOREMS OF PROBABILITY THEORY, KESZTHELY (HUNGARY), 1974.

ON SOME ASYMPTOTICAL PROPERTIES OF RECURSIVE ESTIMATES

M.B. NEVEL'SON

1. INTRODUCTION AND SUMMARY

Let $f(x)$ $(-\infty < x < \infty)$ be an unknown function, which is negative on the interval $(-\infty, x_0)$ and positive on (x_0, ∞). Suppose that we can measure the value of $f(x)$ everywhere with some random error $\xi(t)$, i.e. the value

$$Z(t, x) = f(x) + \xi(t) \tag{1.1}$$

for every $t = 1, 2, \ldots$ and x can be obtained by an experiment. Here $\xi(t)$ $(t = 1, 2, \ldots)$ denotes a sequence of independent and identically distributed random variables with distribution function $F(y)$.

Our aim is to determine the value x_0. In order to determine the value x_0 it must have some apriori informations about $\xi(t)$. If, for example, we know that $\mathsf{E}\,\xi(t) = 0$, then to estimate x_0 one can apply the Robbins – Monro process [1]

$$(1.2)\qquad \begin{aligned} &X(0) = x\,, \\ &X(t+1) - X(t) = -\frac{\alpha}{1+t}\, Z(t+1, X(t))\,. \end{aligned}$$

This process tends to x_0 and under some conditions $\sqrt{t}\,(X(t) - x_0)$ is asymptotically normal. It is well-known, that the optimal constant α has of the form $\alpha = \dfrac{1}{f'(x_0)}$ and the procedure (1.1) can be modified so that, with unknown $f'(x_0)$, it has the same asymptotic properties as the original procedure with the optimal constant α. This modification of the Robbins – Monro method was introduced by Venter [2] which requires the knowledge on an interval containing $f'(x_0)$ and not containing 0. Later Fabian [3] proved that this requirement can be omitted (see also [4], [5]).

However the assumption $\mathsf{E}\,\xi(t) = 0$ may be rather specific. But in some situations it is known other important parameters of the distribution $F(y)$ (for example the median m, or the moment $\sigma_k = \mathsf{E}\,\xi^k(t)$ of order k). That is why the problem of the estimation of the value x_0 arises to a more general problem than the case of knowing apriori information σ_1.

We shall confine our study to the case when random variables $\xi(t)$ are not necessarily identically distributed random variables and may depend on the point x, in which we measure the value of $f(x)$. Then

$$(1.3)\qquad Z(t, x) = f(x) + \xi(t, x)\,.$$

In addition let us assume that we know the expectation $S_0(t, x) = \mathsf{E}\,S(\xi(t, x))$ where $S(z)$ is a non-decreasing function of the variable z. This assumption holds in the case of observation (1.1), if we know the median* m or any moment denoted by σ_k of order k, where k is an odd number (in the first case we can take $S(z) = \operatorname{sign}(z - m)$ and in the second case $S(z) = z^k$).

Section 2 contains some notations.

In Section 3 we construct recursive estimates $X(t)$ of the value x_0.

*In this case we assume, that $\mathsf{P}\{\xi(t) = m\} = 0$.

If the function $S(z)$ is bounded, we use the Robbins – Monro process (3.2), (3.3) with, in general, non-stationary regression function. This process converges to x_0 (when time grows) under rather broad assumptions. If the function $S(z)$ is not bounded, one needs an additional apriori information on the growth of $|f(x)|$ for $|x| \to \infty$, which makes sure the convergence of this procedure. Therefore in the case, when $S(z)$ is not bounded, we construct a new procedure (3.11), (3.12), which tends to x_0 for any rate of growth of $|f(x)|$ when $|x| \to \infty$. The procedures were proposed in [6], [7], [8] to estimate the root x_0 of regression equation when $S(z) \equiv z$, $S_0(t, x) \equiv 0$ which also converges for any rate of growth of $|f(x)|$ when $|x| \to \infty$. These procedures can surely be applied also in the case $S(z) \neq z$. However this case needs some restrictions on the behavior of $|f(x)|$ for large value of $|x|$ (see in details in Section 3).

In Section 4 we construct under mild conditions asymptotically normal procedure, which has optimal limit variance in the same sense, as procedure described in [2], [3]. If the function $S(z)$ is bounded, we consider procedure (4.4), similar to the Fabian procedure [3]. This procedure has limit variance defined by formula (4.6). If $S(z)$ is unbounded, then procedure (4.14) constructed using the idea of [9] possesses the same property. Here as in Section 2 we do not require any restriction on behavior of $|f(x)|$ when $|x| \to \infty$.

Moreover, in Section 4 we investigate the properties of finite-dimensional distributions of estimates. Firstly such an investigation was carried out for the procedures of stochastic approximation by Has' minski [10]. To be precise in [10] it has been shown, that under suitable normalization in an appropriate time scale, the finite-dimensional distributions of the Robbins – Monro and Kiefer – Wolfowitz processes in the case of continuous time converges to the finite-dimensional distributions of some stationary Gaussian Markov process. Analogous result was established [11] for the discrete Robbins – Monro process too under additional assumption that the "error" satisfies Helder condition in mean-square sense in some neighbourhood of the point x_0. Furthermore we will show that this rather restrictive condition can be weakened.

2. BASIC NOTATIONS

All random variables are supposed to be defined on a probability space $(\Omega, \mathfrak{A}, P)$. Relations between random variables, including convergence, are in the sense probability one. The real line is denoted by R, and the indicator function of a set A by χ_A and $\mathfrak{B}$ denotes the class of all Borel subset of R.

We shall write $Y(t) \sim N(0, \sigma^2)$, if $Y(t)$ is asymptotically normal with mean value 0 and variance σ^2.

Let us denote by $\mathscr{S}_l(z_1, z_2)$ where $l \geqslant 0$, $-\infty \leqslant z_1 \leqslant z_2 \leqslant \infty$, a class of non-decreasing function $S(z)$, which satisfies the following conditions:

(a) if $z_1 \neq -\infty$, then $S(z_1 + 0) > S(z)$ for $z_1 > z$,

(b) if $z_2 \neq \infty$, then $S(z_2 - 0) < S(z)$ for $z_2 < z$,

(c) if $S(z) \equiv \text{Const.}$ on the interval $(z_1', z_2') \subset (z_1, z_2)$, then $|z_1' - z_2'| < l$.

Let $\mathscr{Q}(S)$ be the class of functions $q(z)$ such that

(a) $q(z)$ is non-negative, bounded and

$$\inf_{q_1 < z < q_2} q(z) > 0$$

for every q_1 and q_2,

(b) function $S(z)q(z)$ is non-decreasing.

We will say, that the function $B(t, x)$, which is defined for all t in some neighbourhood of x_0, is continuous at the point $t = \infty$, $x = x_0$, if the limit $\lim_{t \to \infty} B(t, x_0)$ exists and

$$\lim_{t \to \infty} [B(t, x) - B(t, x_0)] = 0 .$$

Let us introduce the following notations.

Let $a(t), b(t)$ be sequences with relation $a(t) < b(t)$ $(t = 0, 1, 2, \ldots)$. Let us denote

$$[x]_{a(t)}^{b(t)} = \begin{cases} x & \text{if} \quad a(t) \leqslant x \leqslant b(t)\,, \\ a(t) & \text{if} \quad a(t) > x\,, \\ b(t) & \text{if} \quad b(t) < x\,. \end{cases}$$

For every function $\varphi(x)$ let

$$\underline{\varphi}_\epsilon = \inf_{-\frac{1}{\epsilon} < x - x_0 < -\epsilon} |\varphi(x)|\,, \quad \bar{\varphi}_\epsilon = \inf_{\epsilon < x - x_0 < \frac{1}{\epsilon}} |\varphi(x)|\,,$$

$$\varphi_0 = \inf_{x \neq x_0} |\varphi(x)|\,.$$

3. CONVERGENCE

Let $\mathfrak{A}_t$ is σ-algebra generated by the family of random variables $\{\xi(t,x),\ x \in R\}$ and $\mathscr{F}_t$ the σ-algebra generated by the famility $\{\xi(u,x),\ u \leqslant t,\ x \in R\}$.

Henceforth we will assume that $\xi(t,x)$ is $\mathfrak{A}_t \times \mathfrak{B}$-measurable and the family $\{\xi(t,x), x \in R\}$ is independent of $\mathscr{F}_{t-1}$.

We list some assumptions for later references.

Assumption 3.1. $f(x)$ is a Borel-measurable function and

(a) $f(x)(x - x_0) \geqslant 0$ for every $x \in R$,

(b) for every $\epsilon \in (0,1)$

$$\inf_{\epsilon < |x - x_0| < \frac{1}{\epsilon}} |f(x)| > 0\,.$$

Assumption 3.1′. Assumption 3.1 holds and

$$\sup_{\epsilon < |x - x_0| < \frac{1}{\epsilon}} |f(x)| < \infty$$

for every $\epsilon \in (0,1)$.

Assumption 3.2. For some $\delta > 0$

$$\mathsf{E}\,|S(\xi(t,x))|^{1+\delta} \leqslant k(t)(1 + r(x)) \tag{3.1}$$

where $r(x)$ is a non-negative measurable locally bounded function, $k(t)$ is a positive sequence.

Denote

$$Y(t, x) = S(Z(t, x)) - S_0(t, x), \quad R(t, x) = \mathsf{E}\, Y(t, x), \tag{3.2}$$
$$\Phi(t, x) = Y(t, x) - R(t, x).$$

Let us consider the Robbins – Monro procedure

$$X(0) = x, \tag{3.3}$$
$$X(t+1) - X(t) = -\alpha(t+1) Y(t+1, X(t))$$

where $\alpha(t) \geqslant 0$, $x \in R$.

Theorem 3.1. *If* $S(z)$ *is non-increasing, Assumption* 3.1 *holds and*

(a) *for every* $\epsilon \in (0, 1)$

$$\sum_{t=1}^{\infty} \alpha(t) r_{\epsilon}(t) = \infty, \tag{3.4}$$

where

$$r_{\epsilon}(t) = \inf_{\epsilon < |x - x_0| < \frac{1}{\epsilon}} |R(t, x)|,$$

(b) $|R(t, x)| \leqslant \varphi(t)(1 + |x|)$,

(c) *for some* $\delta \in (0, 1)$

$$\mathsf{E}\, |\Phi(t, x)|^{1+\delta} \leqslant k(t)(1 + |x|^{1+\delta}),$$

(d) $\sum_{t=1}^{\infty} \alpha^{1+\delta}(t)[\varphi^{1+\delta}(t) + k(t)] < \infty$,

then for process (3.2), (3.3) *we have*

$$\lim_{t \to \infty} X(t) = x_0. \tag{3.5}$$

This theorem follows from Theorem A.1 (see Appendix).

The question arise naturally: under which conditions holds the assumption (3.4)?

For the sake of simplicity we assume that the observation $Z(t,x)$ is defined on the same manner as (1.1) where $\xi(t)$ $(t = 1, 2, \dots)$ denotes a sequence of independent and identically distributed random variables. We will show that then (3.4) holds if in addition the function $S(z)$ is decreasing within an interval $A \in \mathfrak{B}$ and $\mathsf{P}\{\xi(t) \in A\} > 0$. However, it can happen, that $S(z)$ is constant in an interval $A' \subset \mathfrak{B}$ and $\mathsf{P}\{\xi(t) \in A'\} = 1$. If in this case $f(x)$ is continuous at the point x_0 (so that $f_0 = 0$) then, of course, $r_\epsilon(t) \equiv 0$ for all $\epsilon > 0$ small enough. But in such a case we generally cannot estimate x_0 by observation (1.1) at all*. But if $f_0 \neq 0$ then condition (3.4) is satisfied even then $\mathsf{P}\{\xi(t) \in (z_1, z_2)\} > 0$ and $S(z) \in \mathscr{S}_{f_0}(z_1, z_2)$ (see Lemma 3.1 and Lemma 3.2).

The formulated consideration lead to the following conditions.

Conditions (α). For every $\epsilon \in (0, 1)$

(α.1) there exist sets C_ϵ, D_ϵ such that

$$\inf_{z \in C_\epsilon} [S(\bar{f}_\epsilon + z) - S(z)] = \bar{\delta}_\epsilon > 0\,,$$

$$\inf_{z \in D_\epsilon} [S(z) - S(z - \underline{f}_\epsilon)[= \underline{\delta}_\epsilon > 0\,;$$

(α.2) the following inequalities hold

$$\inf_{\epsilon < x - x_0 < \frac{1}{\epsilon}} \mathsf{P}\{\xi(t, x) \in C_\epsilon\} \geqslant g_\epsilon(t)\,,$$

$$\inf_{-\frac{1}{\epsilon} < x - x_0 < -\epsilon} \mathsf{P}\{\xi(t, x) \in D_\epsilon\} \geqslant g_\epsilon(t)$$

and at the same time

*Indeed, in this case $Z(t,x) = \tilde{f}(x) + \tilde{\xi}(t)$ where $\tilde{f}(x) = f(x) - a$, $\tilde{\xi}(t) = \xi(t) + a$ and $\mathsf{E}S(\tilde{\xi}(t)) = \mathsf{E}S(\xi(t))$, $\tilde{f}(x) = 0$ if $x \neq x_0$ for all small $a \neq 0$.

$$(3.6) \qquad g_\epsilon(t) \geqslant 0\,, \quad \sum_{t=1}^{\infty} \alpha(t) g_\epsilon(t) = \infty\,.$$

Lemma 3.1. *In order to the Conditions* (α) *be satisfied it is sufficient that either* (a) *or* (b) *holds:*

(a) $S(z) \in \mathscr{S}_{f_0}(-\infty, \infty)$ *and for every* $\epsilon \in (0, 1)$ *there exists* K_ϵ *such that*

$$\inf_{\epsilon < |x - x_0| < \frac{1}{\epsilon}} \mathsf{P}\{|\xi(t, x)| < K_\epsilon\} \geqslant g_\epsilon(t)$$

or

(b) $S(z) \in \mathscr{S}_{f_0}(z_1, z_2)$ $(-\infty < z_1 \leqslant z_2 < \infty)$ *and for every* $\epsilon \in (0, 1)$

$$\inf_{\epsilon < x - x_0 < \frac{1}{\epsilon}} \mathsf{P}\{z_1 - \bar{f}_\epsilon < \xi(t, x) < z_2\} \geqslant g_\epsilon(t)\,,$$

$$\inf_{-\frac{1}{\epsilon} < x - x_0 < -\epsilon} \mathsf{P}\{z_1 < \xi(t, x) < z_2 + \underline{f}_\epsilon\} \geqslant g_\epsilon(t)\,,$$

where the sequence $g_\epsilon(t)$ *satisfies* (3.6).

Lemma 3.2. *If assumption* (3.1) *and Conditions* (α) *hold then* (3.4) *is satisfied.*

Further the conditions (b) and (c) included in the formulation of the Theorem 3.1 needs in general an additional apriori information concerning $f(x)$ and $\xi(t, x)$. But these conditions are satisfied, if $S(z)$ is a bounded function. Therefore Theorem 3.1 and Lemma 3.1 implies

Theorem 3.2. *If* $S(z)$ *is bounded, the Assumption* 3.1 *and Conditions* (α) *are fulfilled and*

$$\sum_{t=1}^{\infty} \alpha^2(t) < \infty$$

then the process (3.2), (3.3) *satisfies* (3.5).

Example 3.1. Let the observation $Z(t, x)$ be defined by the formula (1.1), where $\xi(t)$ is a sequence of independent random variables with common distribution $F(y)$. Suppose that we know the value of function $F(y)$ at certain point $y = k$. Let

$$(3.7) \qquad S_1(z) = \begin{cases} F(k), & \text{if} \quad y \geqslant k \\ F(k) - 1, & \text{if} \quad y < k. \end{cases}$$

We have $\mathsf{E} S_1(\xi(t)) = 0$. In addition we mention $S(z) \in \mathscr{S}_0(k, k)$. Thus from Theorem 3.2 and Lemma 3.2 it follows, that the procedure

$$X(0) = x ,$$

$$X(t+1) - X(t) = -\frac{\alpha}{1+t} S_1(Z(t+1, X(t))) \qquad (\alpha > 0)$$

satisfies (3.5) if Assumption 3.1 and the inequalities

$$(3.8) \qquad \begin{aligned} &\mathsf{P}\{k - \bar{f}_\epsilon < \xi(1) < k\} > 0 \\ &\mathsf{P}\{k < \xi(1) < k + \underline{f}_\epsilon\} > 0 \end{aligned}$$

for every $\epsilon \in (0, 1)$ hold. Inequalities (3.8) hold, if, for example, the function $F(y)$ is decreasing in some neighbourhood of the point $y = k$.

Now let the function $S(z)$ be unbounded. Then the process (3.2), (3.3) with $\alpha(t) = \frac{\alpha}{t}$ $(\alpha > 0)$ tends to x_0 a.s., if Conditions (α) and inequalities

$$(3.9) \qquad |\mathsf{E}[S(f(x) + \xi(t, x)) - S(\xi(t, x))]| \leqslant K(1 + |x|)$$

$$(3.10) \qquad \mathsf{E}[S(f(x) + \xi(t, x)) - \mathsf{E}S(f(x) + \xi(t, x))]^2 \leqslant K(1 + x^2)$$

hold. If we apply the ideas of the modification of the Robbins – Monro method from [6]-[8] to (3.2), (3.3), then it permits us to avoide only the condition (3.9). The procedure constructed in follows permits us not only to avoide (3.9) but change (3.10) to

$$\mathsf{E}S^2(\xi(t, x)) \leqslant K(1 + x^2)$$

(or to the even more general condition (3.1)), which does not include the unknown function $f(x)$.

Let

$$(3.11) \qquad A_t(z) = \frac{S(z)q(z)}{q(z) + \beta(t)},$$

where $q(z) \in \mathcal{Q}(S)$, $\beta(t) \geqslant 0$. Consider the process

$$(3.12) \qquad \begin{aligned} &X(0) = x, \\ &X(t+1) - X(t) = \\ &\quad = -\frac{\alpha(t+1)}{1 + r(X(t))}\,[A_{t+1}(Z(t+1, X(t))) - S_0(t+1, X(t))]. \end{aligned}$$

Theorem 3.3. *Let us assume, that the Assumptions* 3.1′, 3.2 *and Conditions* (α) *hold furthermore the inequalities*

$$\sum_{t=1}^{\infty} \left\{\alpha(t)\beta^{\delta}(t)k(t) + \left[\frac{\alpha(t)}{\beta(t)}\right]^2\right\} < \infty, \qquad \sup_{t>0} \beta(t) < \infty$$

are satisfied. Then the process (3.11), (3.12) *satisfies* (3.5).

We note, that if $S(z) \in \mathcal{S}_{f_0}(-\infty, \infty)$,

$$(3.13) \qquad \lim_{|z| \to \infty} |S(z)| = \infty$$

and inequality (3.1) holds with $k(t) = \text{const}$, then the condition (a) of Lemma 3.1 holds too. Therefore, from the Theorem 3.3 we get the

Consequence. *Let Assumptions* 3.1′ *and* 3.2 *with* $k(t) = \text{const}$. *hold,* $S(z)$ *is increasing function and* (3.13) *is satisfied. Then process* (3.11), (3.12) *where* $\alpha(t) = \frac{\alpha}{t}$ $(\alpha > 0)$, $\beta(t) = \beta t^{-\mu}$ $\left(\beta > 0,\ 0 < \mu < \frac{1}{2}\right)$, *tends a.s. to* x_0 *when* $t \to \infty$.

Example 3.2. Let $Z(t, x)$ be defined as in Example 3.1 and let the expectation $\sigma_k = \mathsf{E}\xi^k(1)$ be known for some odd k. Consider the process

$$X(0) = x,$$

$$X(t+1) - X(t) =$$

$$= -\frac{\alpha}{1+t}\left[\frac{\operatorname{arct} Z^k(t+1, X(t))}{\dfrac{\operatorname{arctg} Z^k(t+1, X(t))}{Z^k(t+1, X(t))} + b(1+t)^{-\mu}} - \sigma_k\right],$$

where $\alpha > 0$, $\beta > 0$, $0 < \mu < \frac{1}{2}$. From the Consequence we have, that this process tends to x_0 as $t \to \infty$, if Assumption 3.1′ holds and $\mathsf{E}\,|\,\xi(1)\,|^{k(1+\delta)} < \infty$ for some $\delta > 0$.

4. ASYMPTOTIC NORMALITY AND CONVERGENCE OF THE FINITE-DIMENSIONAL DISTRIBUTIONS

Let us introduce the following assumptions.

Assumption 4.1. The function $R(t, x) = \mathsf{E}\,Y(t, x)$ is finite for all $t = 1, 2, \ldots$ and for all x lying in some ν-neighbourhood of x_0; for these values of t and x the derivative $\dfrac{\partial R(t, x)}{\partial x} = R'(t, x)$ exists and it is continuous at the point $t = \infty$, $x = x_0$.

Assumption 4.2. The inequality

$$\sup_{t>0,\ |x-x_0|<\nu} \mathsf{E}\,\Phi^2(t, x) < \infty,$$

where $\Phi(t, x) = Y(t, x) - R(t, x)$, holds.

Assumption 4.3. Assumption 4.2 holds and the function $A(t, x) = \mathsf{E}\,\Phi^2(t, x)$ is continuous at the point $t = \infty$, $x = x_0$.

Assumption 4.4. Assumption 4.2 holds and

$$\lim_{R\to\infty} \sup_{|x-x_0|<\nu} \sup_{t>0} \mathsf{E}\{\Phi^2(t, x)\chi_{|\Phi(t,x)|>R}\} = 0.$$

Assumption 4.5. For any $\epsilon > 0$

$$\lim_{t\to\infty,\ x\to x_0} \mathsf{P}\{|\,\Phi(t, x) - \Phi(t, x_0)\,| > \epsilon\} = 0$$

and $A(t, x_0)$ has a finite limit as $t \to \infty$.

Assumption 4.6. For some $\delta > 0$

$$\sup_{t>0} \mathsf{E}|\Phi(t,x_0)|^{2+\delta} < \infty .$$

As always we need an estimation of the value

$$\lambda = \lim_{t\to\infty} R'(t,x_0) .$$

In order to obtain such an estimation, we introduce according to [2] and [8] the following construction. Let $X(t)$ be some $\mathscr{F}_t$-measurable random process, t_j is a sequence of positive numbers, satisfying the conditions

$$t_{j+1} > t_j \quad (j = 1, 2, \dots), \quad \lim_{j\to\infty} t_j = \infty . \tag{4.1}$$

$$\begin{aligned} W(t) &\equiv W(t;\ t_j, X(t_j - 1), c(j),\ j = 1, \dots, q(t)) = \\ &= \frac{1}{q(t)} \sum_{j=1}^{q(t)} Y_{0j}(t_j, X(t_j - 1)) , \end{aligned} \tag{4.2}$$

where

$$Y_{0j}(t,x) = \frac{Y(t, x + c(j)) - Y(t, x - c(j))}{2c(j)} ,$$

$q(t)$ is the number of t_j's which do not exceed t and $c(j)$ is an arbitrary sequence.

It is easy to see, that the value of the process $W(t)$ at the moment t can be obtained by the following recursive formulae:

$$\begin{aligned} W(t) &= \begin{cases} 0 & \text{if} \quad 0 \leqslant t < t_i \\ W(t_i) & \text{if} \quad t_i \leqslant t < t_{i+1} \quad (i = 1, 2, \dots) \end{cases} \\ W(t_{i+1}) - W(t_i) &= \\ &= \frac{1}{1+i} [- W(t_i) + Y_{0\,i+1}(t_{i+1}, X(t_{i+1} - 1))] \\ &\qquad (t_0 = 0,\ i = 0, 1, 2, \dots) . \end{aligned} \tag{4.3}$$

Lemma 4.1. *Let Assumptions* 4.1, 4.2 *holds and* $X(t_j - 1) \to 0$ *a.s. when* $j \to \infty$. *Then* $W(t) \to \lambda$ *if*

$$\sum_{j=1}^{\infty} \frac{1}{j^2 c^2(j)} < \infty , \qquad \lim_{j \to \infty} c(j) = 0 .$$

The proof is similar to that of Lemma 1.1 of [2] and Lemma 5.1 of [11], Ch. 7.

Consider, according to [3], the procedure

$$X(0) = x ,$$

$$X(t+1) - X(t) = - \frac{Y(t+1, X(t))}{(1+t)\widetilde{W}(t)} , \tag{4.4}$$

$$\widetilde{W}(t) = [W(t)]_{a(t)}^{b(t)} .$$

Here $W(t) = W(t;\ t_j, X(t_j - 1), c(j),\ j = 1, \ldots, q(t))$ is process defined by the formula (4.2) (or (4.3)), $a(t), b(t), c(t)$ are some sequence of positive numbers, $x \in R$ and t_j satisfies the conditions (4.1).

The following theorem shows that in the case when $S(z)$ is bounded we can choose under rather weak conditions sequences $a(t), b(t), c(t)$ so that the procedure (4.4) converges to x_0 a.s. and it is asymptotically normal with optimal variance (in the sense mentioned above).

Theorem 4.1. *Let the function* $S(z)$ *be bounded, Assumptions* 3.1, 4.1, 4.3 *and Conditions* (α) *for* $\alpha(t) = \dfrac{1}{tb(t-1)}$ *hold and*

$$a(t) \to 0, \quad b(t) \to \infty, \quad c(t) \to 0$$

$$\sum_{t=1}^{\infty} \frac{1}{(1+t)^2} \left[\frac{1}{a^2(t)} + \frac{1}{c^2(t)}\right] < \infty . \tag{4.5}$$

Then we have for the process (4.4) *the relation*

$$X(t) \to x_0, \quad \sqrt{t}\,(X(t) - x_0) \sim N\left(0, \frac{\sigma^2}{\lambda^2}\right) , \tag{4.6}$$

where

$$\sigma^2 = \lim_{t \to \infty,\ x \to x_0} A(t,x) , \quad \lambda = \lim_{t \to \infty} R'(t, x_0) .$$

Remark 4.1. The number of observations which was used for the consturction of the process (4.4) is $n(t) = t + 2q(t)$. If t_j satisfies the condition

$$\lim_{j\to\infty} \frac{t_j}{j} = 0\,, \tag{4.7}$$

then

$$\lim_{t\to\infty} \frac{q(t)}{t} = 0\,.$$

Hence for such a choice of t_j in the conditions of Theorem 4.1 we have

$$\sqrt{n(t)}(X(t) - x_0) \sim N\left(0, \frac{\sigma^2}{\lambda^2}\right).$$

Theorem 4.2. *Let the function* $S(z)$ *be bounded, Assumptions* 3.1, 4.1, 4.5 *Conditions* (α) *for* $\alpha(t) = \frac{1}{tb(t-1)}$, (4.5) *hold and the process* $X(t)$ *be defined by the formulae* (4.4). *Let further* $T_1, \ldots, T_n$ *be a sequence of positive integers such that*

$$t < T_1 < \ldots < T_n\,, \qquad \lim_{t\to\infty} \log \frac{T_i}{t} = \widetilde{T}_i \qquad (i = 1, \ldots, n)\,. \tag{4.8}$$

Then $X(t) \to x_0$ *when* $t \to \infty$ *and the distribution of the random vector*

$$(\sqrt{T_1}\,(X(T_1) - x_0), \ldots, \sqrt{T_n}\,(X(T_n) - x_0)) \tag{4.9}$$

converges to the distribution with density function

$$p(x_1, \ldots, x_n) = \prod_{i=1}^{n} \sqrt{\frac{Q_i}{(Q_i - Q_{i-1})2\pi\sigma_0^2}} \exp\left\{-\sum_{i=1}^{n} \frac{(\sqrt{Q_i}\,x_i - \sqrt{Q_{i-1}}\,x_{i-1})^2}{2(Q_i - Q_{i-1})\sigma_0^2}\right\} \tag{4.10}$$

when $t \to \infty$. *Here* $Q_0 = 0$, $x_0 = 0$, $Q_i = e^{\widetilde{T}_i}$ $(i = 1, \ldots, n)$, $\sigma_0^2 = \frac{\sigma^2}{\lambda^2}$, $\sigma^2 = \lim_{t\to\infty} A(t, x_0)$.

Remark 4.2. From the formula (A.26) (see Appendix) and from the proving method of [12] it follows that in the case of the Theorems 4.1, 4.2 the law of the iterated logarithm holds for the process $\sqrt{t}\,(X(t)-x_0)$, i.e.

$$\text{(4.11)}\qquad \overline{\lim_{t\to\infty}}\ \frac{\sqrt{t}\,(X(t)-x_0)}{\sqrt{2\log\log t}} = |\sigma_0|\,,\qquad \underline{\lim_{t\to\infty}}\ \frac{\sqrt{t}\,(X(t)-x_0)}{\sqrt{2\log\log t}} = -|\sigma_0|\,.$$

Example 4.1. Let $Z(t, x)$ be defined as in Example 3.1 and let the value of the function $F(y)$ at the point $y = k$ be known. Consider the function (3.7). Then

$$R(x) = \mathsf{E}S_1(f(x) + \xi(1)) = q - F(k - f(x))\,,$$

$$A(x) = \mathsf{E}[S_1(f(x) + \xi(1)) - R(x)]^2 =$$

$$= F(k - f(x))(1 - F(k - f(x)))\,.$$

Moreover, $S_1(z) \in \mathscr{S}_0(k, k)$. Hence from Theorem 4.1 it follows for the process

$$X(0) = x\,,$$

$$\text{(4.12)}\qquad X(t+1) - X(t) = -\frac{S(Z(t+1, X(t)))}{(1+t)\widetilde{W}(t)}\,,$$

$$\widetilde{W}(t) = [W(t)]_{t^{-\gamma}}^{\log(1+t)}\,,$$

where $W(t) = W(t;\ t_j, X(t_j - 1), j^{-\gamma},\ j = 1, 2, \ldots, q(t))$ $\left(0 < \gamma < \frac{1}{2}\right)$, that

$$X(t) \to x_0\,,$$

$$\sqrt{t}\,(X(t) - x_0) \sim N\left(0, \frac{q(1-q)}{[F'(k)f'(x_0)]^2}\right),$$

if

(1°) $f(x)$ satisfies Assumption 3.1 and has a derivative in a neighbourhood of x_0, which is continuous at x_0,

(2°) $F(y)$ has a derivative in a neighbourhood of the point k, which is continuous at this point and $F(k) > 0$.

Further, it is easy to calculate, that

$$\varphi(x) = \mathrm{E}[\Phi(x) - \Phi(x_0)]^2 =$$

$$= |q - F(k - f(x))| - |q - F(k - f(x))|^2 ,$$

where $\Phi(x) = S(f(x) + \xi(1)) - R(x)$. Therefore, if the condition (1°), (2°) hold then $\varphi(x) \leqslant c|f(x)|$ in some neighbourhood of x_0. Hence, for every $n, T_1, \ldots, T_n$, which satisfy (4.8), the distribution of the vector (4.9) converges to the distribution with density (4.10) when $t \to \infty$. The process (4.12) also satisfies (4.11).

Now let us consider the case, when the function $S(z)$ is unbounded. Define the process $X_0(t)$ by the formula

$$X_0(t) = \begin{cases} \tilde{x} & \text{for} \quad 0 \leqslant t < t_i \quad (\tilde{x} \in R), \\ X_0(t_i) & \text{for} \quad t_i \leqslant t < t_{i+1} , \end{cases}$$

(4.13) $$X_0(t_{i+1}) - X_0(t_i) =$$

$$= -\frac{\alpha}{(1+i)(1+r(X(t_i)))}[A_{i+1}(Z(i+1, X_0(t_i))) -$$

$$- S_0(i+1, X_0(t_i))] .$$

Consider the procedure

$$X(0) = x ,$$

(4.14) $$X(t+1) = \Big[X(t) - \frac{Y(t+1, X(t))}{(1+t)\widetilde{W}(t)}\Big]_{X_0(t)-\epsilon}^{X_0(t)+\epsilon} ,$$

$$\widetilde{W}(t) = [W(t)]_{a(t)}^{b(t)} .$$

Here, as above, $W(t) = W(t;\ t_j, X(t_j - 1), c(j),\ j = 1, \ldots, q(t))$, $0 < a(t) < b(t)$, $c(t) > 0$, $\epsilon > 0$.

Theorem 4.3. *Suppose that the Assumptions* 3.1′, 3.2, 4.1, 4.3, 4.4, *and Conditions* (α) *hold for* $\alpha(t) = \dfrac{1}{tb(t-1)}$ *and* $\epsilon < \dfrac{\nu}{2}$. *Let the relations* (4.5) *and*

$$(4.15) \qquad \sum_{t=1}^{\infty} \left[\frac{\beta^{\delta}(t)k(t)}{1+t} + \frac{1}{(1+t)^2\beta^2(t)}\right] < \infty$$

be satisfied, too. Then the process (4.14) *satisfies* (4.6).

Theorem 4.4. *Suppose that Assumptions* 3.1′, 3.2, 4.1, 4.4-4.6, *Conditions* (α) *for* $\alpha(t) = \dfrac{1}{tb(t-1)}$ *and* (4.5), (4.15) *hold and* $\epsilon < \dfrac{\nu}{2}$. *Then for the process* (4.14) *the conclusion of Theorem* 4.2 *holds.*

Example 4.2. Let $Z(t, x)$ be defined in the same manner as in Example 3.1 and let us assume that t_j satisfies the conditions (4.1), (4.7), and that $q(z) \in \mathscr{Q}(z^k)$, where k is some positive odd number. Assume that we know the moment $\sigma_k = \mathsf{E}\xi^k(1)$.

Let the process $X_0(t)$ be defined by (4.13) and $W(t)$ by the formulae

$$W(t) = \begin{cases} 0 & \text{if} \quad 0 \leqslant t < t_i \\ W(t_i) & \text{if} \quad t_i \leqslant t < t_{i+1}, \end{cases}$$

$$W(t_{i+1}) - W(t_i) =$$

$$= \frac{1}{1+i}\Big[- W(t_i) +$$

$$+ i^{\gamma} \frac{Z^k(t_{i+1}, X(t_{i+1} - 1) + i^{-\gamma})}{2} -$$

$$- i^{\gamma} \frac{Z^k(t_{i+1}, X(t_{i+1} - 1) - i^{-\gamma})}{2}\Big].$$

Consider the procedure

$$X(0) = x,$$

$$(4.16) \qquad X(t+1) = \left[X(t) - \frac{Z^k(t+1, X(t)) - \sigma_k}{(1+t)\widetilde{W}(t)}\right]_{X_0(t)-1}^{X_0(t)+1},$$

$$\widetilde{W}(t) = [W(t)]_{t^{-\gamma}}^{\ln(1+t)} \qquad \left(0 < \gamma < \frac{1}{2}\right).$$

Let

$$R(x) = \mathsf{E}[f(x) + \xi(1)]^k - \sigma_k ,$$

$$A(x) = \mathsf{E}\{[f(x) + \xi(1)]^k - \mathsf{E}[f(x) + \xi(1)]^k\}^2 ,$$

$$\Phi(x) = [f(x) + \xi(1)]^k - R(x) .$$

Let $f(x)$ satisfy Assumption 3.1 and has a derivative in a neighbourhood of x_0, which is continuous at x_0 and $\mathsf{E}|\xi(1)|^{2k(1+\delta)} < \infty$ for some $\delta > 0$. Then

$$R(x) = f(x) \sum_{j=0}^{k-1} C_k^j f^{k-1-j}(x)\sigma_j$$

and

$$\mathsf{E}[\Phi(x) - \Phi(x_0)]^2 \leqslant Cf^2(x)$$

for all x in some neighbourhood of the point x_0. Thus from Theorems 4.3, 4.4 it follows that

$$X(t) \to x_0 , \qquad \sqrt{t}\,(X(t) - x_0) \sim N(0, \sigma_0^2) ,$$

where

$$\sigma_0^2 = \frac{\sigma_{2k} - \sigma_k^2}{[kf'(x_0)\sigma_{k-1}]^2}$$

and for every $T_1, \ldots, T_n$ which satisfy (4.8), the distribution of the vector $(\sqrt{T_1}\,(X(T_1) - x_0), \ldots, \sqrt{T_n}\,(X(T_n) - x_0))$ converges to the distribution with density (4.10) when $t \to \infty$.

APPENDIX

I.

Let $Y(t, x)$ $(t = 1, 2, \ldots, -\infty < x < \infty)$ be a family of random variables with $R(t, x) = \mathsf{E}\,Y(t, x)$, $\sigma(t, x) = \mathsf{E}|\Phi(t, x)|^{1+\delta} < \infty$, where $\Phi(t, x) = Y(t, x) - R(t, x)$ and $\delta \leqslant 1$ is some positive number. Starting with an arbitrary $X(0) = x$ we define the Robbins – Monro process by

$$X(t+1) - X(t) = -\alpha(t+1)Y(t+1) \tag{A.1}$$

where $\alpha(t)$ is a non-negative sequence, and conditioned by $X(1), \ldots, X(t)$ the random variable $Y(t+1)$ has the distribution of $Y(t+1, X(t))$. We assume that the functions $R(t,x)$ and $\sigma(t,x)$ are measurable for $t = 1, 2, \ldots$.

The following theorem is a simple generalization of the corresponding results of [13], [14], [15].

Theorem A.1. *Let* $R(t,x) = R_1(t,x) + R_2(t,x)$, *where* $R_1(t,x)$ *and* $R_2(t,x)$ *satisfy the conditions:*

(a) *there exist a point* x_0 *such that*

$$R_1(t,x)(x - x_0) \geqslant 0$$

for all t, x,

(b) *for each* $\epsilon > 0$

$$\sum_{t=1}^{\infty} \alpha(t) r_\epsilon(t) = \infty\,, \tag{A.2}$$

where

$$r_\epsilon(t) = \inf_{\epsilon < |x - x_0| < \frac{1}{\epsilon}} |R_1(t,x)|\,,$$

(c) *the following inequalities hold*

$$|R_1(t,x)\alpha(t)|^{1+\delta} \leqslant \varphi(t)(1 + |x|^{1+\delta}) + A|x|^\delta |R_1(t,x)|\alpha(t)\,, \tag{A.3}$$

$$R_2(t,x) \leqslant \psi(t)(1 + |x|)\,, \tag{A.4}$$

where δ, A *are positive numbers* $(\delta \leqslant 1,\ 2A \leqslant 1)$ *and* $\varphi(t), \psi(t)$ *are sequences such that*

$$\sum_{t=1}^{\infty} \varphi(t) < \infty\,, \tag{A.5}$$

$$\sum_{t=1}^{\infty} \alpha(t)\psi(t) < \infty\,. \tag{A.6}$$

Let moreover

$$\text{(A.7)} \qquad \mathsf{E}\,|\,\Phi(t,x)|^{1+\delta} \leqslant k(t)(1 + |x|^{1+\delta}) ,$$

where

$$\text{(A.8)} \qquad \sum_{t=1}^{\infty} \alpha^{1+\delta}(t)k(t) < \infty .$$

Then $\lim_{t\to\infty} X(t) = x_0$ *with probability one.*

Proof. Without loss of generality we may assume that $x_0 = 0$; then

$$\begin{aligned}
L(t) &= \mathsf{E}\{|X(t+1)|^{1+\delta}\,|\,X(1),\ldots,X(t)\} - |X(t)|^{1+\delta} = \\
&= -(1+\delta)\alpha(t+1)R(t+1,X(t))|X(t)|^{\delta} \operatorname{sign} X(t) - \\
&\quad -(1+\delta)\,\mathsf{E}\{[|X(t) - \eta\alpha(t+1)Y(t+1)|^{\delta} \times \\
&\quad \times \operatorname{sign}[X(t) - \eta\alpha(t+1)Y(t+1)] - \\
&\quad - |X(t)|^{\delta} \operatorname{sign} X(t)]\alpha(t+1)Y(t+1)\,|\,X(1),\ldots,X(t)\} \\
&\qquad (0 < \eta = \eta(t,x) < 1) .
\end{aligned} \tag{A.9}$$

By using the conditions (a), (A.3), (A.4), (A.7) and the inequality

$$||z|^{\delta} \operatorname{sign} z - |y|^{\delta} \operatorname{sign} y| < 2^{1-\delta}|y - z|^{\delta} ,$$

we have from (A.9)

$$\begin{aligned}
L(t) &\leqslant -(1+\delta)\alpha(t+1)|R_1(t+1,X(t))||X(t)|^{\delta} + \\
&\quad + \alpha^{1+\delta}(t+1)[2(1+\delta)R_1(t+1,X(t)) + \\
&\quad + c_1\psi^{1+\delta}(t+1)(1 + |X(t)|^{1+\delta}) + c_1\sigma(t+1,X(t))] \leqslant \\
&\leqslant -p|R_1(t+1,X(t))||X(t)|^{\delta} + c_2[\alpha(t)\psi(t) + \varphi(t)] \times \\
&\quad \times [1 + |X(t)|^{\delta}] + c_2\alpha^{1+\delta}(t)k(t)[1 + |X(t)|^{\delta}] \qquad (p > 0) .
\end{aligned} \tag{A.10}$$

(Here and below c_i are positive constants.) We see from (A.10), (A.5), (A.6), (A.8) that $\lim_{t\to\infty} |X(t)| = \zeta$ exists and is finite furthermore

$$\sum_{t=1}^{\infty} \alpha(t+1)|R_1(t+1, X(t))||X(t)|^{\delta} < \infty .$$

Hence $\lim_{t\to\infty} X(t) = x_0$ a.s.

Proof of Lemma 3.1. It is sufficient to notice that Conditions (α) are satisfied in the case (a) for $C_\epsilon = D_\epsilon = (-K_\epsilon, K_\epsilon)$ and in the case (b) for $C_\epsilon = (z_1 - \bar{f}_\epsilon, z_2)$, $D_\epsilon = (z_1, z_2 + \underline{f}_\epsilon)$.

Proof of Lemma 3.2. From the Condition (α.1) and from the Assumption 3.1 we have, that

$$\text{(A.11)} \qquad \inf_{\substack{\epsilon < x - x_0 < \frac{1}{\epsilon} \\ z \in C_\epsilon}} [S(f(x)+z) - S(z)] \geqslant \bar{\delta}_\epsilon ,$$

$$\text{(A.12)} \qquad \inf_{\substack{-\frac{1}{\epsilon} < x - x_0 < -\epsilon \\ z \in D_\epsilon}} [S(z) - S(f(x)+z)] \geqslant \underline{\delta}_\epsilon .$$

Moreover

$$\text{(A.13)} \qquad \begin{aligned} \bar{r}_\epsilon(t) &= \inf_{\epsilon < x - x_0 < \frac{1}{\epsilon}} \mathrm{E}[S(f(x) + \xi(t,x)) - S(\xi(t,x))] \geqslant \\ &\geqslant \inf_{\epsilon < x - x_0 < \frac{1}{\epsilon}} \mathrm{E}[S(f(x) + \xi(t,x)) - S(\xi(t,x))]\chi_{\{\xi(t,x)\in C_\epsilon\}} , \end{aligned}$$

$$\text{(A.14)} \qquad \begin{aligned} \underline{r}_\epsilon(t) &= \inf_{-\frac{1}{\epsilon} < x - x_0 < -\epsilon} \mathrm{E}[S(\xi(t,x)) - S(f(x) + \xi(t,x))] \geqslant \\ &\geqslant \inf_{-\frac{1}{\epsilon} < x - x_0 < -\epsilon} \mathrm{E}[S(\xi(t,x)) - S(f(x) + \xi(t,x))]\chi_{\{\xi(t,x)\in D_\epsilon\}} . \end{aligned}$$

From (A.11)-(A.14) and from the Condition (α.2) it follows

$$\text{(A.15)} \qquad \bar{r}_\epsilon(t) \geqslant \bar{\delta}_\epsilon g_\epsilon(t), \quad \underline{r}_\epsilon(t) \geqslant \underline{\delta}_\epsilon g_\epsilon(t) .$$

From (A.15) we obtain

$$r_\epsilon(t) = \inf_{\epsilon < |x - x_0| < \frac{1}{\epsilon}} |\, \mathsf{E}[S(f(x) + \xi(t,x)) - S(\xi(t,x))] \geqslant \delta_\epsilon g_\epsilon(t)$$

where $\delta_\epsilon = \min(\underline{\delta}_\epsilon, \overline{\delta}_\epsilon)$.

Proof of Theorem 3.3. Set

$$Y(t,x) = A_t(Z(t,x)) - S_0(t,x)\,,$$

$$R(t,x) = \mathsf{E}A_t(Z(t,x)) - S_0(t,x)\,,$$

$$\Phi(t,x) = A_t(Z(t,x)) - \mathsf{E}A_t(Z(t,x))\,.$$

We shall show that the conditions of the Theorem A.1 are satisfied.

Let

$$R(t,x) = R_1(t,x) + R_2(t,x)\,,$$

where

$$R_1(t,x) = \mathsf{E}A_t(f(x) + \xi(t,x)) - A_t(\xi(t,x))\,,$$

$$R_2(t,x) = -\beta(t)\,\mathsf{E}\frac{S(\xi(t,x))}{q(\xi(t,x)) + \beta(t)}\,.$$

Further $R_1(t,x) = R_1^{(1)}(t,x) + R_1^{(2)}(t,x)$, where

$$R_1^{(1)}(t,x) = $$

$$= \mathsf{E}\frac{[S(\xi_1(t,x)) - S(\xi(t,x))]\,q(\xi_1(t,x))q(\xi(t,x))}{[q(\xi_1(t,x)) + \beta(t)][q(\xi(t,x)) + \beta(t)]}\,,$$

$$R_1^{(2)}(t,x) = $$

$$= \beta(t)\,\mathsf{E}\frac{S(\xi_1(t,x))q(\xi_1(t,x)) - S(\xi(t,x))q(\xi(t,x))}{[q(\xi_1(t,x)) + \beta(t)][q(\xi(t,x)) + \beta(t)]}\,,$$

$$\xi_1(t,x) = \xi(t,x) + f(x)\,.$$

Hence $S(z)q(z)$ and $S(z)$ are non-decreasing and $f(x)(x - x_0) \geqslant 0$, it follows that

$$R_1^{(1)}(t,x)(x-x_0) \geqslant 0$$

(A.16)

$$R_1^{(2)}(t,x)(x-x_0) \geqslant 0$$

for all t, x. Hence, condition (a) of Theorem A.1 is satisfied.

From (A.16) (see the proof of Lemma 3.2, too) we have

$$r_\epsilon(t) = \inf_{\epsilon < |x-x_0| < \frac{1}{\epsilon}} |R(t,x)| \geqslant \inf_{\epsilon < |x-x_0| > \frac{1}{\epsilon}} |R_1^{(1)}(t,x)| \geqslant$$

$$\geqslant c_3 \inf_{\epsilon < |x-x_0| < \frac{1}{\epsilon}} \mathsf{E}\,|S(f(x)+\xi(t,x)) - \tag{A.17}$$

$$- S(\xi(t,x))|\, q(f(x)+\xi(t,x))q(\xi(t,x)) \geqslant c g_\epsilon(t) \qquad (c > 0)\,.$$

From (A.17) follows that condition (b) of Theorem A.1 is satisfied.

If the function $S(z)q(z)$ is bounded, then

$$[R_1(t,x)\alpha(t)]^2 \leqslant c_4 \left[\frac{\alpha(t)}{\beta(t)}\right]^2, \quad \mathsf{E}\Phi^2(t,x) \leqslant c_4 \left[\frac{\alpha(t)}{\beta(t)}\right]^2.$$

Hence, the conditions (A.3), (A.5), (A.7), (A.8) are also satisfied for $\delta = 1,\ A = 0,\ \varphi(t) = k(t) = c_4 \left[\frac{\alpha(t)}{\beta(t)}\right]^2$.

From the inequality

$$q(z) + \beta(t) \geqslant q^\delta(z)\beta^{1-\delta}(t)$$

we have, that

$$|R_2(t,x)| \leqslant \beta^\delta(t)\, \mathsf{E} \frac{|S(\xi(t,x))|}{q^\delta(\xi(t,x))}\,.$$

By virtue of the assumptions on the functions $q(z)$, $S(z)q(z)$ there exist a constant c_5 for which

$$1 \leqslant c_5[q^\delta(z) + |S(z)q(z)|^\delta]\,.$$

From this relation and (3.1) we have

$$|R_2(t,x)| \leqslant c_5 \beta^\delta(t)\, \mathsf{E}[|S(\xi(t,x))| + |S(\xi(t,x))|^{1+\delta}] \leqslant$$
$$\leqslant c_6 \beta^\delta(t) k(t)(1+|x|)\,.$$

Therefore the conditions (A.4), (A.5) are satisfied for $\psi(t) = c_6 \beta^\delta(t) k(t)$.

II. PROOF OF THEOREMS 4.1 AND 4.2

1. Let the Assumptions 3.1, 4.1 and the Conditions (α) for $\alpha(t) = \dfrac{1}{tb(t-1)}$ and (4.5) holds. Similar computation show that

$$\mathsf{E}\{[X(t+1)-x_0]^2 \,|\, X(1),\dots,X(t)\} \leqslant$$
$$\leqslant (X(t)-x_0)^2 - \frac{2R(t+1,X(t))(X(t)-x_0)}{(1+t)b(t)} + \frac{c_7}{(1+t)a^2(t)}\,.$$

As $S(z)$ non-decreasing and $f(x)(x-x_0) \geqslant 0$, then $R(t,x)(x-x_0) \geqslant 0$. Therefore as usually we have that $\lim_{t\to\infty} |X(t)|$ exists and is finite, further

$$\text{(A.18)} \qquad \sum_{t=1}^{\infty} \frac{R(t+1,X(t))(X(t)-x_0)}{(1+t)b(t)} < \infty\,.$$

Moreover, from the Lemma 3.2 it follows that for any $\epsilon \in (0,1)$

$$\text{(A.19)} \qquad \sum_{t=1}^{\infty} \frac{r_\epsilon(t+1)}{(1+t)b(t)} = \infty\,,$$

where

$$r_\epsilon(t) = \inf_{\epsilon < |x-x_0| < \frac{1}{\epsilon}} |R(t,x)|\,.$$

From (A.18), (A.19) we have

$$\text{(A.20)} \qquad \lim_{t\to\infty} X(t) = x_0\,.$$

Using the Lemma 4.1 and (A.10) it gives

$$\text{(A.21)} \qquad \lim_{t\to\infty} \widetilde{W}(t) = \lambda\,.$$

By Assumption 4.1 and (A.20)

$$R(t+1, X(t)) = \gamma(t)[X(t) - x_0]$$

where

$$\lim_{t\to\infty} \gamma(t) = \lambda . \tag{A.22}$$

Hence

$$X(t+1) - x_0 = \Big[1 - \frac{\widetilde{\gamma}(t)}{1+t}\Big](X(t) - x_0) - \frac{\Phi(t+1, X(t))}{(1+t)\widetilde{W}(t)} .$$

Here $\widetilde{\gamma}(t) = \gamma(t)\widetilde{W}^{-1}(t)$ and by virtue of (A.21), (A.22)

$$\lim_{t\to\infty} \widetilde{\gamma}(t) = 1 . \tag{A.23}$$

Let

$$\widetilde{\gamma}(t) = \begin{cases} \widetilde{\gamma}(t) & \text{if} \quad \frac{1}{2} < \widetilde{\gamma}(t) < 2 , \\ 1 & \text{if} \quad \widetilde{\gamma}(t) \leqslant \frac{1}{2} \quad \text{or} \quad \widetilde{\gamma}(t) \geqslant 2 , \end{cases} \tag{A.24}$$

$$\hat{W}(t) = \begin{cases} \widetilde{W}(t) & \text{if} \quad \widetilde{W}(t) > \frac{\lambda}{2} , \\ 1 & \text{if} \quad \widetilde{W}(t) \leqslant \frac{\lambda}{2} . \end{cases} \tag{A.25}$$

Consider the new process $\hat{X}(t) = \hat{X}^{s,\zeta}(t)$, and let us define it by the formulae

$$\begin{aligned} &\hat{X}(s) = \zeta , \\ &\hat{X}(t+1) - x_0 = \Big[1 - \frac{\widetilde{\gamma}(t)}{1+t}\Big](\hat{X}(t) - x_0) - \frac{\Phi(t+1, X(t))}{(1+t)\hat{W}(t)} \end{aligned} \tag{A.26}$$

where $s \geqslant 0$, ζ is $\mathscr{F}_s$-measurable random variables with finite variance.

As usually it can be show that

$$\mathsf{E}\,|\hat{X}(t) - x_0| = O\Big(\frac{1}{\sqrt{t}}\Big) \qquad (t \to \infty) . \tag{A.27}$$

Introducing $V(t) = \sqrt{t}\,(\hat{X}(t) - x_0)$ we obtain from (A.26)

$$(A.28)\qquad \begin{aligned} V(t+1) &= A_{ss-1}\sqrt{s}\,(\zeta - x_0) + \\ &+ \sum_{k=s}^{t} \frac{A_{kt}}{\sqrt{k+1}}\,\psi(t)(\hat{X}(t) - x_0) - \sum_{k=s}^{t} \frac{A_{kt}}{\sqrt{k+1}}\,\frac{\Phi(k+1, \hat{X}(k))}{\hat{W}(k)}\,. \end{aligned}$$

Here

$$A_{kt} = \begin{cases} \prod_{m=k+1}^{t} \left(1 - \frac{1}{2(m+1)}\right) & \text{for} \quad 1 \leqslant k < t \\ 1 & \text{for} \quad k = t\,. \end{cases}$$

$$(A.29)\qquad \psi(t) \to 0 \quad \text{a.s., when} \quad t \to \infty\,, \quad \sup_{t \geqslant 0} |\,\psi(t)| < \infty\,.$$

Notice, that

$$(A.30)\qquad A_{kt} = (1 + \Theta_{kt})\left(\frac{k+1}{t+1}\right)^{1/2},$$

where $\Theta_{kt} \to 0$ when $k \to \infty$ uniformly in t.

By virtue of (A.30) the first member of the right hand side of (A.28) tends to 0 a.s. when $t \to \infty$. From (A.27), (A.29) it follows that the second term tends to 0 in probability. Hence

$$(A.31)\qquad V(t+1) + \sum_{k=s}^{t} \frac{A_{kt}}{\sqrt{k+1}}\,\frac{\Phi(k+1, \hat{X}(k))}{\hat{W}(k)} \to 0$$

in probability when $t \to \infty$.

2. Let us assume that Assumption 4.3 holds. Then (A.21) implies

$$\mathsf{E}\left\{\left[\frac{\Phi(k+1, \hat{X}(k))}{\hat{W}(k)}\right]^2 \,\Big|\, \hat{X}(s), \ldots, \hat{X}(k)\right\} = \frac{A(k+1, \hat{X}(k))}{\hat{W}^2(k)} \to \frac{\sigma^2}{\lambda^2}\,.$$

From this relation and from (A.31) (see [16]) we obtain that

$$(A.32)\qquad V(t) \sim N\left(0, \frac{\sigma^2}{\lambda^2}\right).$$

From the definition of the process $\hat{X}(t)$ and from (A.21), (A.23) it can be derived that

$$\mathsf{P}\{X(t) = \hat{X}^{T,X(T)}(t) \ \text{for all} \ t \geqslant T\} > 1 - \delta \tag{A.33}$$

for any $\delta > 0$ and some $T = T(\delta)$. This statement with (A.32) proves the second assertion of Theorem 4.1.

3. Let Assumption 4.5 hold instead of Assumption 4.3.

Let

$$\psi(k, x) = \mathsf{E}[\Phi(k + 1, x) - \Phi(k + 1, x_0)]^2 .$$

Then by using the fact $\sup_{k \geqslant 1,\ x \in R} |\Phi(k, x)| < \infty$, we obtain that $\psi(k, x(k)) \to 0$ for any sequence $x(k)$ such that $x(k) \to x_0$ when $k \to \infty$. Hence

$$\tilde{\psi}(k) = \mathsf{E}[\Phi(k + 1, \hat{X}(k)) - \Phi(k + 1, x_0)]^2 \to 0 . \tag{A.34}$$

Let

$$\eta(t) = \sum_{k=s}^{t} \frac{A_{kt}}{\sqrt{k + 1}} \frac{[\Phi(k + 1, \hat{X}(k)) - \Phi(k + 1, x_0)]}{\hat{W}(k)} .$$

From (A.30), (A.34) we have

$$\mathsf{E}\eta^2(t) \leqslant \frac{c_8}{t} \sum_{k=s}^{t} \tilde{\psi}^2(k) \to 0 .$$

Hence $\eta(t) \to 0$ in probability. Therefore

$$V(t + 1) + \sum_{k=s}^{t} \frac{A_{kt}}{\sqrt{k + 1}} \frac{\Phi(k + 1, x_0)}{\hat{W}(k)} \to 0$$

in probability when $t \to \infty$.

The second assertion of Theorem 4.2 can be proved from this relation for the process $\hat{X}(t)$ (see the proof of Theorem 6.3 of [11], Ch. 6). This assertion follows easily from (A.33) for the process $X(t)$ (see also [17]).

III. PROOF OF THEOREMS 4.3, 4.4

1. Let Assumptions 3.1′, 3.2, 4.1, 4.2, Conditions (α) for $\alpha(t) = \dfrac{1}{tb(t-1)}$ and relations (4.5), (4.15) hold. From Theorem 3.3 it can be derived that $X_0(t) \to x_0$ a.s. when $t \to \infty$. Hence, $X_0(t) = x_0 + \psi(t)$, where $\psi(t) \to 0$ a.s. Let γ is arbitrary positive number and $T_1 = T_1(\gamma)$ such that

$$\mathsf{P}\{|\psi(t)| < \epsilon \text{ for all } t \geq T_1\} > 1 - \frac{\gamma}{3}.$$

Consider the new process

(A.35)
$$X_1(T_1) = X(T_1),$$
$$X_1(t+1) = \Big[X_1(t) - \frac{Y(t+1, X_1(t))}{(1+t)\hat{W}(t)}\Big]_{x_0 + [\psi(t)]_{-\epsilon}^{\epsilon} - \epsilon}^{x_0 + [\psi(t)]_{-\epsilon}^{\epsilon} + \epsilon}.$$

Then

(A.36)
$$\begin{aligned}
&\mathsf{E}\{[X_1(t+1) - x_0]^2 \mid X_1(T_1), \dots, X_1(t)\} \leq \\
&\leq \mathsf{E}\Big\{\Big[X_1(t) - \frac{Y(t+1, X_1(t))}{(1+t)\widetilde{W}(t)} - x_0\Big]^2 \Big| X_1(T_1), \dots, X_1(t)\Big\} \leq \\
&\leq (X_1(t) - x_0)^2 - \frac{2R(t+1, X_1(t))(X_1(t) - x_0)}{(1+t)\widetilde{W}(t)} + \\
&+ \frac{\mathsf{E}\{\Phi^2(t+1, X_1(t)) \mid X_1(T_1), \dots, X_1(t)\}}{(1+t)^2 a^2(t)}.
\end{aligned}$$

The inequality $|X_1(t) - x_0| \leq 2\epsilon < \nu$ for $t \geq T_1$ with Assumption 4.2 gives

$$\mathsf{E}\{\Phi^2(t+1, X_1(t)) \mid X_1(T_1), \dots, X_1(t)\} = A(t+1, X_1(t)) < c_9$$

for all $t \geq T_1$. From this relation and from (A.36) we obtain (see the proof of Theorem 4.1)

(A.37) $$\lim_{t\to\infty} X_1(t) = x_0.$$

As

$$\text{(A.38)} \qquad \mathsf{P}\{X(t) = X_1(t) \text{ for all } t \geqslant T_1\} > 1 - \frac{\gamma}{3}$$

and γ is arbitrary then from (A.37) we obtain the first assertion of the Theorems 4.3, 4.4.

From (A.35), (A.37) it follows that

$$\mathsf{P}\Big\{x_0 - 2\epsilon \leqslant X_1(t) - \frac{Y(t+1, X(t))}{(1+t)\widetilde{W}(t)} \leqslant x_0 + 2\epsilon \quad \text{for all } t \geqslant \tau\Big\} = 1$$

for some random variable τ. Hence, for some $T_2 = T_2(\gamma)$

$$\text{(A.39)} \qquad \mathsf{P}\{X_1(t) = X_2(t) \text{ for all } t \geqslant T_2(\gamma)\} > 1 - \frac{\gamma}{3},$$

where the process $X_2(t)$ defined for all $t \geqslant T_2$ by formulae

$$X_2(T_2) = X_1(T_2),$$

$$X_2(t+1) - X_2(t) = -\frac{\hat{Y}(t+1, X_2(t))}{(1+t)\widetilde{W}(t)},$$

$$\hat{Y}(t,x) = \hat{R}(t,x) + \hat{\Phi}(t,x),$$

$$\hat{R}(t,x) = \begin{cases} R(t,x) & \text{if } |x| \leqslant 2\epsilon, \\ \operatorname{sign} x & \text{if } |x| > 2\epsilon, \end{cases}$$

$$\hat{\Phi}(t,x) = \begin{cases} \Phi(t,x) & \text{if } |x| \leqslant 2\epsilon, \\ \Phi(t,x_0) & \text{if } |x| \geqslant 2\epsilon. \end{cases}$$

It is easy to verify that $X_2(t) \to x_0$ a.s. Therefore

$$X_2(t+1) - x_0 = \Big[1 - \frac{\widetilde{\gamma}(t)}{1+t}\Big](X_2(t) - x_0) - \frac{\hat{\Phi}(t+1, X_2(t))}{(1+t)\widetilde{W}(t)},$$

where $\widetilde{\gamma}(t) \to 1$ a.s. when $t \to \infty$.

Consider for $t \geqslant T_3$ the process

$$X_3(T_3) = X_2(T_3),$$

$$X_3(t+1) - x_0 = \left[1 - \frac{\hat{\gamma}(t)}{1+t}\right](X_3(t) - x_0) - \frac{\hat{\Phi}(t+1, X_3(t))}{(1+t)\hat{W}(t)},$$

where $T_3 \geqslant T_2$ and $\hat{\gamma}(t), \hat{W}(t)$ are defined by the formulae (A.24), (A.25). The constant T_3 can be choosen such that

(A.40) $\quad \mathsf{P}\{X_3(t) = X_2(t) \text{ for all } t \geqslant T_3\} > 1 - \frac{\gamma}{3}.$

As above it is not difficult to prove that

(A.41) $\quad \sqrt{t}(X_3(t) - x_0) + \sum_{k=T_3}^{t} \frac{A_{kt}}{\sqrt{k+1}} \frac{\hat{\Phi}(k+1, X_3(k))}{\hat{W}(k)} \to 0$

in probability when $t \to \infty$.

2. Let us assume that Assumptions 4.3 and 4.4 hold. Then

$$\lim_{k \to \infty} \mathsf{E}\left\{\left[\frac{\hat{\Phi}(k+1, X_3(k))}{\hat{W}(k)}\right]^2 \,\middle|\, X_3(T_3), \ldots, X_3(k)\right\} = \frac{\sigma^2}{\lambda^2}.$$

From this relation and from (A.41) we obtain, that $\sqrt{t}(X_3(t) - x_0) \sim$ $\sim N\left(0, \frac{\sigma^2}{\lambda^2}\right)$. The second assertion of Theorem 4.3 follows easily from (A.38)-(A.40).

3. Let Assumption 4.5 hold instead of the Assumption 4.3. Set

$$\tilde{\psi}(k) = \mathsf{E}[\hat{\Phi}(k+1, X_3(k)) - \hat{\Phi}(k+1, x_0)]^2.$$

Then

$$\tilde{\psi}(k) = \psi_{1R_0}(k+1, X_3(k)) + \psi_{2R_0}(k+1, X_3(k)) +$$
$$+ \psi_{3R_0}(k+1, X_3(k)) + \psi_{4R_0}(k+1, X_3(k)),$$

where

$$\psi_{1R_0}(k,x) = \mathsf{E}[\hat\Phi(k,x) - \hat\Phi(k,x_0)]^2 \chi_{\{|\hat\Phi(k,x)| > R_0,\, |\hat\Phi(k,x_0)| < R_0\}},$$

$$\psi_{2R_0}(k,x) = \mathsf{E}[\hat\Phi(k,x) - \hat\Phi(k,x_0)]^2 \chi_{\{|\hat\Phi(k,x)| < R_0,\, |\hat\Phi(k,x_0)| > R_0\}},$$

$$\psi_{3R_0}(k,x) = \mathsf{E}[\hat\Phi(k,x) - \hat\Phi(k,x_0)]^2 \chi_{\{|\hat\Phi(k,x)| > R_0,\, |\hat\Phi(k,x_0)| > R_0\}},$$

$$\psi_{4R_0}(k,x) = \mathsf{E}[\hat\Phi(k,x) - \hat\Phi(k,x_0)]^2 \chi_{\{|\hat\Phi(k,x)| \leqslant R_0,\, |\hat\Phi(k,x_0)| \leqslant R_0\}},$$

From Assumption 4.4 we have

$$\sup_{x\in R}\ \sup_{k\geqslant T_3} \psi_{iR_0}(k,x) \to 0 \quad \text{as} \quad R_0 \to \infty \qquad (i = 1, 2, 3)\,.$$

Hence for $i = 1, 2, 3$

$$\sup_{k\geqslant T_3} \psi_{iR_0}(k+1, \hat X_3(k)) \to 0 \qquad \text{a.s. when} \qquad R \to \infty\,.$$

Moreover by Assumption 4.5

$$\psi_{4R_0}(k, x(k)) \to 0 \qquad \text{a.s. when} \qquad k \to \infty$$

for any R_0 and for any sequence $x(k) \to x_0$ when $k \to \infty$. This with $X_3(k) \to x_0$ gives that $\widetilde\psi(k) \to 0$ when $k \to \infty$. Hence, the process

$$\eta(t) = \sum_{k=T_3}^{t} \frac{A_{kt}}{\sqrt{k+1}}\ \frac{[\hat\Phi(k+1, \hat X_3(k)) - \hat\Phi(k+1, x_0)]}{\hat W(k)}$$

tends to 0 in probability. Therefore

$$\sqrt{t}\,(X_3(t) - x_0) + \sum_{k=T_3}^{t} \frac{A_{kt}}{\sqrt{k+1}}\ \frac{\Phi(k+1, x_0)}{\hat W(k)} \to 0$$

in probability when $t \to \infty$. The second assertion of Theorem 4.3 can be proved from this relation and the fact that

$$\mathsf{P}\{X(t) \equiv X_3(t) \ \text{ for all } \ t \geqslant T_3\} > 1 - \gamma$$

for any $\gamma > 0$ (see the proof of Theorem 6.3 of [11], Ch. 6).

REFERENCES

[1] H. Robbins – S. Monro, A stochastic approximation method, *Ann. Math. Statist.*, 22 (1951), 400-407.

[2] J.H. Venter, An extension of the Robbins – Monro procedure, *Ann. Math. Statist.*,, 38 (1967), 181-190.

[3] V. Fabian, On asymptotic normality in stochastic approximation, *Ann. Math. Statist.*, 39 (1968), 1327-1332.

[4] R.L. Stratonovič, On optimal algorithms of type of stochastic approximation, *Tehn. Kibern.*, 1 (1970).

[5] M.B. Nevel'son – R.Z. Has'minskij, Adaptive procedure of Robbins – Monro, *Avtom. i Telemeh.*, 10 (1973), 71-83.

[6] H. Robbins – D. Siegmund, A convergence theorem for non-negative almost supermartingales and some applications, *Optimizing methods in statistics,* Academic Press, New York and London, 1971.

[7] J. Komlós – P. Révész, A modification of the Robbins – Monro process, *Studia Sci. Math. Hungar.*, 8 (1973), 329-340.

[8] V. Fabian, Asymptotically efficient stochastic approximation; the RM case, *Ann. Statist.*, 1 (1973), 486-495.

[9] R.Z. Has'minskij, Sequential estimation and recursive asymptotically optimal procedure of estimation and observation control, *Proceedings of the Prague Symposium on asymptotic statistics,* Prague, 1974.

[10] R.Z. Has'minskij, On behaviour of the stochastic approximation processes at large time values, *Probl. Peredači Inf.*, 8 (1972), 81-91.

[11] M.B. Nevel'son – R.Z. Has'minskij, *Stochastic approximation and recurrent estimations,* Nauka, Moscow, 1972.

[12] V.F. Gapoškin – T.P. Krasulina, On the law of iterated logarithm for stochastic approximation processes, *Teorija Verojatn. i Primenen.*, 19 (1974), 879-886.

[13] T.P. Krasulina, On the stochastic approximation processes with infinite variance, *Teorija Verojatn. i Primenen.*, 14 (1969), 546-551.

[14] D.L. Burkholder, On a class of stochastic approximation processes, *Ann. Math. Statist.*, 27 (1956), 1044-1059.

[15] S.N. Abdelhamid, Transformation of observation in stochastic approximation, *Ann. Math. Statist.*, 1 (1973), 1158-1174.

[16] J. Sacks, Asymptotic distribution of stochastic approximation procedures, *Ann. Math. Statist.*, 29 (1958), 373-405.

[17] I.A. Ibragimov – R.Z. Has'minskij, On the approximation of statistical estimates with sums of independent variables, *Doklady AN SSSR,* 210 (1973), 883-887.

COLLOQUIA MATHEMATICA SOCIETATIS JÁNOS BOLYAI
11. LIMIT THEOREMS OF PROBABILITY THEORY, KESZTHELY (HUNGARY), 1974.

ON THE PROPERTIES OF THE RECURSIVE ESTIMATES FOR A FUNCTIONAL OF AN UNKNOWN DISTRIBUTION FUNCTION

M.B. NEVEL'SON

1. Let $X_1, \ldots, X_n$ be independent observations with an unknown distribution function $F(y)$ and let $\psi(x, t)$ be a function* which is non-decreasing in t for arbitrary fixed x.

Let us assume that the integral

$$\lambda(t) = \int \psi(x, t)\, dF(x)$$

is finite for arbitrary t and the equation $\lambda(t) = 0$ has one and only one solution $t = t_0$.

The value $t_0 = t_0(F)$ is a functional of the unknown distribution function F. A number of important problems of mathematical statistics can be reduced to the estimation of this functional (see e.g. [1], [2]).

To estimate the value t_0 Huber suggested the so-called M-estimates in [1] which are defined by solution of the following equations

*$\psi(x, t)$ is Borel-measurable as a function of two variables.

$$(1.1)\qquad \sum_{i=1}^{n} \psi(X_i, T_n) = 0$$

or more generally [2]

$$(1.2)\qquad T_n = \inf \left\{ t\colon \sum_{i=1}^{n} \psi(X_i, t) \geq 0 \right\}.$$

The equations (1.1) and (1.2) are connected with the maximum likelihood estimates and the least square estimates (or their generalizations, see [3]).

It is well known [1] (see also [2]) that if the assumptions

(A) the function $\lambda(t)$ is continuously differentiable at t_0 and $\lambda'(t_0) \neq 0$,

(B) the function

$$\sigma^2(t) = \int \psi^2(x, t)\, dF(x)$$

is finite in any neighbourhood of t_0 and it is continuous at t_0,

are fulfilled, then the M-estimate T_n satisfies the following relation

$$(1.3)\qquad \sqrt{n}\,(T_n - t_0) \sim N(0, \sigma_0^2)$$

where

$$\sigma_0^2 = \frac{\sigma^2(t_0)}{[\lambda'(t_0)]^2}\,.$$

(Here $\xi_n \sim N(0, \sigma_0^2)$ means asymptotical normality with parameters $(0, \sigma_0^2)$.)

As Levitt showed [2] in (1.3) the normal limit distribution seems to be optimal in minimax sense.

The disadvantage of the M-estimates is that they can be computed with difficulty. Furthermore it is necessary to know all of earlier $X_1, \ldots, X_n$ in $(n+1)$-th step.

The question naturally arises to construct a more simplified procedure.

In Section 2 we prove, that if (A), (B) is fulfilled, and the next rather general assumption

(C) for some $\delta > 0,\ \Delta > 0$

$$\sup_{|t-t_0|<\delta} \int |\psi(x, t)|^{2+\Delta}\, dF(x) < \infty$$

is also fulfilled, then the estimation T_n (which is a type of stochastic approximation) is computable by recurrent formulas (2.1) and these also satisfy (1.3) with optimal variance σ_0^2.

The procedure (2.1) seems to be adaptive in that sense, that it constructs a W_n estimation for the unknown value of $\lambda_0 = \lambda'(t_0)$.

For the purpose of estimation of the roots of the regression equation this type of procedures was firstly introduced by Venter. He assumed that the statistics of the interval, containing the $\lambda_0 > 0$ is known. Later Fabian so simplified this assumption, that instead of the estimaticn W_n he introduced the truncated estimation $\widetilde{W}_n$.

$$\widetilde{W}_n = \begin{cases} W_n & \text{for} \quad n^{-\alpha} \leqslant W_n \leqslant \log(1+n), \quad 0 < \alpha < \frac{1}{2}, \\ n^{-\alpha} & \text{for} \quad W_n < n^{-\alpha}, \\ \log(1+n) & \text{for} \quad W_n > \log(1+n). \end{cases}$$

We will investigate the truncating ability of the W_n with the aid of the sequence $\mu_n \neq \log(1+n)$. In addition, analogously to [2] we introduce as well the truncation of the function $\psi(x, t)$ in the procedure (2.1).

The difference between M-estimation (1.1) and (1.2) is, that in order to compute the estimation T_{n+1} we use the estimation T_n and the value W_n, and it is unnecessary to use the observations $X_1, \ldots, X_n$.

The question arises to construct esumations T_n to satisfy (1.3) and the convergence of the moments of value $\sqrt{n}(T_n - t_0)$ to the suitable moments of the Gaussian random variables with the parameters $(0, \sigma_0^2)$. In [2] it is proved, that this convergence exists, if T_n is some truncated modification of the M-estimates.

In Section 3 we prove, that if conditions (A)-(C) are satisfied then analogous connections are true also for the procedure (2.1), where the sequences a_n, b_n, ν_n, μ_n (for the moments of order $p < 2 + \Delta$) are chosen especially.

In order to prove the convergence of the moments of procedure (2.1) we used the idea of Komlós and Révész, [6].

In Section 4 we give two examples.

2. Let us introduce the following notation

$$[t]_a^b = \begin{cases} t & \text{for} \quad a \leqslant t \leqslant b\,, \\ a & \text{for} \quad t < a\,, \\ b & \text{for} \quad t > b\,. \end{cases}$$

Let a_n, b_n, ν_n, μ_n be sequences of positive numbers. Let us regard the algorithm

$$T_{n+1} - T_n = \frac{[\psi(X_{n+1}, T_n)]_{-a_n}^{a_n}}{n[W_n]_{\nu_n}^{\mu_n}}\,,$$

$$\text{(2.1)} \qquad W_{n+1} - W_n = -\frac{1}{n+1} W_n +$$

$$+ \frac{[\psi(X_{n+1}, T_n + b_{n+1})]_{-a_n}^{a_n} - [\psi(X_{n+1}, T_n - b_{n+1})]_{-a_n}^{a_n}}{2(n+1)b_{n+1}}$$

with initial conditions $T_1 = t$, $W_0 = 0$ (t is an arbitrary number).

Theorem 2.1. *Let us assume that conditions* (A)-(C) *are fulfilled and the sequences* a_n, b_n, ν_n, μ_n *are chosen as follows:* $a_n \to \infty$, $b_n \to 0$, $\nu_n \to 0$, $\mu_n \to \infty$

$$\text{(2.2)} \qquad \sum_{n=1}^{\infty} \frac{a_n^2}{n^2 \nu_n^2} < \infty\,,$$

$$\text{(2.3)} \qquad \sqrt{n} = o(a_n^{1+\Delta} \nu_n) \qquad \textit{for} \qquad n \to \infty\,,$$

$$(2.4)\qquad \sum_{n=1}^{\infty} \frac{1}{n\mu_n} = \infty ,$$

$$(2.5)\qquad \sum_{n=1}^{\infty} \frac{1}{n^2 b_n^2} < \infty ,$$

$$(2.6)\qquad \frac{1}{n} \sum_{i=1}^{n} \frac{1}{b_i a_i^{1+\Delta}} \to 0 \quad \text{for} \quad n \to \infty ,$$

then

$$(2.7)\qquad T_n \to t_0 \quad \text{a.s. for} \quad n \to \infty$$

and

$$\sqrt{n}\,(T_n - t_0) \sim N(0, \sigma_0^2) ,$$

where

$$\sigma_0^2 = \frac{\sigma^2(t_0)}{[\lambda'(t_0)]^2} .$$

Proof.

1. Let us assume

$$\lambda_n(t) = \mathsf{E}[\psi(X_1, t)]_{-a_n}^{a_n} ,$$

obviously

$$(2.8)\qquad \begin{aligned} \lambda_n(t) &= \int_{|\psi(x,t)| \leq a_n} \psi(x, t)\, dF(x) + \\ &+ \int_{|\psi(x,t)| > a_n} a_n \operatorname{sign} \psi(x, t)\, dF(x) = \\ &= \lambda(t) - \int_{|\psi(x,t)| > a_n} \psi(x, t)\, dF(x) + \\ &+ \int_{|\psi(x,t)| > a_n} a_n \operatorname{sign} \psi(x, t)\, dF(x) . \end{aligned}$$

In the sense of condition (2)

$$\sup_{|t-t_0|\leqslant\delta} \int_{|\psi(x,t)|>a_n} |\psi(x,t)|\, dF(x) \leqslant \frac{c_1}{a_n^{1+\Delta}}$$

(here and in sequel c_i is a positive constant). Therefore

(2.9) $$\lambda_n(t) = \lambda(t) + c_n(t)$$

where

(2.10) $$\sup_{|t-t_0|\leqslant\delta} |c_n(t)| \leqslant \frac{2c_1}{a_n^{1+\Delta}} .$$

Because the function $\psi(x, t)$ is not decreasing for arbitrary fixed x, so the function $\lambda_n(t)$ is also non-decreasing in t. It means that $\lambda_n(t) > \lambda_n(t_0 + \delta)$ for $t - t_0 \geqslant \delta$ and $\lambda_n(t) < \lambda_n(t_0 - \delta)$ for $t - t_0 \leqslant - \delta$. In addition from (2.9) and (2.10) it follows, that for $n > n_0$

(2.11) $$\lambda_n(t_0 + \delta) \geqslant \frac{\lambda(t_0 + \delta)}{2} > 0 ,$$
$$\lambda_n(t_0 + \delta) \leqslant \frac{\lambda(t_0 - \delta)}{2} < 0$$

and consequently

(2.12) $$\inf_{\substack{|t-t_0|\geqslant\delta \\ n>n_0}} \lambda_n(t)(t - t_0) > 0 .$$

From (2.9), (2.10), (2.12) we obtain that to any fixed $\epsilon \in (0, 1)$ there exists $n_1 = n_1(\epsilon)$ for which

(2.13) $$\inf_{\substack{|t-t_0|>\epsilon \\ n>n_1}} \lambda_n(t)(t - t_0) > 0 .$$

Furthermore

(2.14) $$\mathsf{E}\{(T_{n+1} - t_0)^2 \mid T_1, \ldots, T_n\} \leqslant (T_n - t_0)^2 - \frac{2(T_n - t_0)\lambda_n(T_n)}{n[W_n]_{\nu_n}^{\mu_n}} + \frac{a_n^2}{n^2\nu_n^2} .$$

From this by (2.9), (2.10), (2.12) and $\lambda(t)(t-t_0) \geqslant 0$ we obtain

$$\mathsf{E}\{(T_{n+1}-t_0)^2 \mid T_1 \ldots T_n\} \leqslant \tag{2.15}$$
$$\leqslant (T_n - t_0)^2 + \frac{c_2 \mid T_n - t_0 \mid}{n\nu_n a_n^{1+\Delta}} + \frac{a_n^2}{n^2 \nu_n^2}.$$

From the convergence of series (2.2), $\sum_{n=1}^{\infty} [n\nu_n a_n^{1+\Delta}]^{-1}$ and from inequalities (2.14) and (2.15) we obtain the relations

$$\mid T_n - t_0 \mid \to \xi < \infty \qquad \text{a.s.},$$

$$\sum_{n=1}^{\infty} \frac{\lambda_n(T_n)(T_n - t_0)}{n[W_n]_{\nu_n}^{\mu_n}} < \infty \qquad \text{a.s.}$$

From these formulae with regard to (2.13) and (2.14) we obtain that $\xi \equiv 0$ almost everywhere. In such a way the first statement of the theorem is proved.

2. Obviously

$$T_{n+1} - T_n = -\frac{\lambda_n(T_n) + c_n(T_n)}{n[W_n]_{\nu_n}^{\mu_n}} - \frac{\tilde{\psi}_n}{n} \tag{2.16}$$

where

$$\tilde{\psi}_n = \frac{[\psi(X_{n+1}, T_n)]_{-a_n}^{a_n} - \lambda_n(T_n)}{[W_n]_{\nu_n}^{\mu_n}}.$$

In the sense (A) and (2.7)

$$\lambda(T_n) = \gamma_n(T_n - t_0) \tag{2.17}$$

where

$$\lim_{n\to\infty} \gamma_n = \lambda'(t_0) \qquad \text{a.s.} \tag{2.18}$$

Furthermore

$$W_n = \frac{1}{n} \sum_{i=1}^{n} \frac{[\psi(X_i, T_{i-1} + b_i)]_{-a_{i-1}}^{a_{i-1}} - [\psi(X_i, T_{i-1} - b_i)]_{-a_{i-1}}^{a_{i-1}}}{2b_i}$$

Using the condition (A) and the relations (2.5), (2.6), (2.7) it is easy to prove (see [4], [7, Ch. 7]) that

$$(2.19) \qquad \widetilde{W}_n \to \lambda'(t_0) \qquad \text{a.s. when} \qquad n \to \infty .$$

With regard to (2.17)-(2.19) we can write the equation (2.16) in the form

$$T_{n+1} - t_0 = \left(1 - \frac{\widetilde{\gamma}_n}{n}\right)(T_n - t_0) - \frac{\widetilde{c}_n}{n^{\frac{3}{2}}} - \frac{\widetilde{\psi}_n}{n} ,$$

where $\widetilde{\gamma}_n \to 1$ a.s., and

$$\widetilde{c}_n = \frac{c_n(T_n)\sqrt{n}}{[W_n]_{\nu_n}^{\mu_n}} .$$

It follows from (2.3), (2.7), (2.9) and (2.19) that

$$\widetilde{c}_n \to 0 \qquad \text{a.s. when} \qquad n \to \infty .$$

Furthermore with a simple computation we can prove

$$\mathsf{E}\{\widetilde{\psi}_n^2 \mid T_1, \ldots, T_n\} \to \sigma_0^2 \qquad \text{when} \qquad n \to \infty .$$

And so the second statement of the theorem is a consequence of the theorem (2.2) in [5].

Remark 2.1. The values of sequences a_n, b_n, ν_n, μ_n, playing a role in Theorem 2.1 can be chosen for example $a_n = an^{\frac{1}{2} - \alpha}$, $b_n = \nu_n = bn^{-\beta}$, $\mu_n = c \log^{\kappa}(1 + n)$ where $a > 0$, $b > 0$, $c > 0$, $1 \geqslant \kappa > 0$,

$$(2.20) \qquad \frac{\Delta - 2\beta}{2(1 + \Delta)} > \alpha > \beta > 0 .$$

It is easy to prove that the statement of Theorem 2.1 is true, if we substitute the second relation among the relations of (2.1) for the following relation

(2.21)
$$W_{n+1} - W_n = -\frac{1}{n+1} W_n + \\ + \frac{\psi(X_{n+1}, T_n + b_{n+1}) - \psi(X_{n+1}, T_n - b_{n+1})}{2(n+1)b_{n+1}}$$

If the function $\mathsf{E}\psi^2(X_1, t)$ is not so rapidly increasing, the truncation of the function $\psi(x, t)$ in the first equation of (2.1) can be omitted. More exactly, it is true the following theorem which can be easily proved analogously to the proof of Theorem 2.1.

Theorem 2.2 *Let*

$$\sup_{t \geq 0} \int \frac{\psi^2(x, t)\, dF(x)}{1 + t^2} < \infty$$

and let us assume that conditions (A)-(C) *are satisfied and that the sequences* a_n, ν_n, μ_n *are chosen as follows*

$$\sum_{n=1}^{\infty} \frac{1}{n^2} \left[\frac{1}{\nu_n^2} + \frac{1}{b_n^2}\right] < \infty, \quad \sum_{i=1}^{\infty} \frac{1}{n\mu_n} = \infty .$$

Then the algorithm

(2.22)
$$T_{n+1} - T_n = -\frac{\psi(X_{n+1}, T_n)}{n[W_n]_{\nu_n}^{\mu_n}}, \quad T_1 = t$$

and (2.21) *satisfy the last consequence of Theorem* 2.1.

Remark 2.1. Theorem 2.2 is true if the condition concerning with the monotonity of $\psi(x, t)$ is replaced by

$$\inf_{\frac{1}{\epsilon} > |t - t_0| > \epsilon, n} \lambda_n(t)(t - t_0) > 0 \quad \text{for arbitrary} \quad \epsilon \in (0, 1) .$$

3. Let us regard the question of the convergence of moments of the process $\sqrt{n}(T_n - t_0)$ to the moments of Gaussian random variables with parameters $(0, \sigma_0^2)$.

It is true the following

Theorem 3.1. *Let us assume that conditions* (A)-(C) *are fulfilled and the sequences* a_n, b_n, ν_n, μ_n *are chosen so, that* $a_n = a_n^{\frac{1}{2}-\alpha}$, $b_n = \nu_n = bn^{-\beta}$, $\mu_n = c_n \log^{\kappa}(1+n)$, $a > 0$, $b > 0$, $c > 0$, *and is true the inequality* (2.20), *and*

$$(3.1) \qquad (1-\kappa)\frac{4\gamma}{1-2\gamma} > \kappa \qquad (0 < \kappa < 1)$$

where $\gamma = \alpha - \beta$. *Then for arbitrary continuous function* $l(x)$, *for which* $|l(x)| \leqslant K(1 + |x|^r)$, $K = \text{const.}$, $r < 2 + \Delta$, *is true the next relation*

$$\mathsf{E}\, l(\sqrt{n}(T_n - t_0)) \to \frac{1}{\sqrt{2\pi}\,|\sigma_0|} \int_{-\infty}^{\infty} l(y) e^{-\frac{y^2}{2\sigma_0^2}} \, dy .$$

To the proof of the theorem we need some lemmas.

Lemma 3.1. *Let* $\eta_1, \eta_2, \ldots$ *be a sequence of random variables such that*

$$\mathsf{E}\{\eta_{n+1} \mid \eta_1, \ldots, \eta_n\} = 0, \qquad |\eta_n| \leqslant 1 \qquad a.s.$$

and d_n *is a monotone decreasing sequence of positive numbers, for which*

$$\sum_{i=1}^{\infty} d_i^2 < \infty ,$$

then

$$\mathsf{P}\Big\{\sum_{i=k}^{n} d_i \eta_i \geqslant R\Big\} \leqslant e^{-\frac{R}{2D_k}}, \qquad D_k = \sum_{i=k}^{\infty} d_i^2$$

if $1 \leqslant k \leqslant n$, $1 \leqslant \dfrac{D_k}{d_k} \log R$.

This lemma is a simple consequence of Lemma 1 in [6]. The key to the proof of the following lemma is the idea of the proof of Lemma 2 in [6].

Lemma 3.2. *Let the sequence of random variables* η_n *be such that the conditions of Lemma* 3.1 *are fulfilled and the constans* γ, κ *are defined by inequality* (3.1). *Then for arbitrary chosen* q, A *and* $B > 0$ *it is true*

$$\lim_{n\to\infty} n^q \mathsf{P}\Big\{\sum_{i=k}^{n} \frac{\eta_i}{i^{\frac{1}{2}+\gamma}} \leqslant A - B \sum_{i=k}^{n} \frac{1}{i \log^{\kappa} i}\Big\} = 0 \quad (1 < k \leqslant [\sqrt{n}]) .$$

Proof. Let us assume

$$k_n = [k^{\frac{1}{2}-\gamma} + Q(\log^{1-\kappa} n - \log^{1-\kappa} k)]^{\frac{1}{\frac{1}{2}-\gamma}}$$

where the constant $Q > 0$ will be chosen later. Obviously $k_n \geqslant k$, if $k \leqslant [\sqrt{n}]$. Moreover

$$\mathsf{P}\Big\{\sum_{i=k}^{n} \frac{\eta_i}{i^{\frac{1}{2}+\gamma}} \leqslant A - B \sum_{i=k}^{n} \frac{1}{i \log^{\kappa} i}\Big\} \leqslant P_{kn}^{(1)} + P_{kn}^{(2)} \tag{3.2}$$

where

$$P_{kn}^{(1)} = \mathsf{P}\Big\{\sum_{i=k}^{k_n} \frac{\eta_i}{i^{\frac{1}{2}+\gamma}} \leqslant A - \frac{B}{2} \sum_{i=k}^{n} \frac{1}{i \log^{\kappa} i}\Big\},$$

$$P_{kn}^{(2)} = \mathsf{P}\Big\{\sum_{i=k_n}^{n} \frac{\eta_i}{i^{\frac{1}{2}+\gamma}} \leqslant - \frac{B}{2} \sum_{i=k}^{n} \frac{1}{i \log^{\kappa} i}\Big\}. \tag{3.3}$$

Furthermore for certain $D_1 = D_1(\gamma)$ and $D_2 = D_2(\gamma)$

$$\sum_{i=k}^{k_n} \frac{1}{i^{\frac{1}{2}+\gamma}} \leqslant D_1 (k_n^{\frac{1}{2}-\gamma} - k^{\frac{1}{2}-\gamma}) = D_1 Q(\log^{1-\kappa} n - \log^{1-\kappa} k) ,$$

$$\sum_{i=k}^{n} \frac{1}{i \log^{\kappa} i} \geqslant D_2 (\log^{1-\kappa} n - \log^{1-\kappa} k) .$$

Then, if the event standing in brackets in (3.3) occurs, the inequality

$$-\sum_{i=k}^{k_n} \frac{1}{i^{\frac{1}{2}+\gamma}} \leqslant A - \frac{BD_2}{2}\,(\log^{1-\kappa} n - \log^{1-\kappa} k)$$

holds, and

$$(3.4)\qquad \left(\frac{BD_2}{2} - D_1 Q\right)(\log^{1-\kappa} n - \log^{1-\kappa} k) \leqslant A\,.$$

If we choose Q such that

$$\frac{BD_2}{2D_1} > Q\,,$$

then (3.4) is false from certain $n = n_0$. From this follows, that

$$(3.5)\qquad P_{kn}^{(1)} = 0 \qquad \text{for} \qquad n \geqslant n_0\,.$$

In order to estimate the probability $P_{kn}^{(2)}$ we apply Lemma 3.1 with $d_n = n^{-\left(\frac{1}{2}+\gamma\right)}$, $R = \frac{B}{2} \sum_{i=k}^{n} \frac{1}{i \log^{\kappa} i}$.

Since

$$k_n^{\frac{1}{2}+\gamma} \sum_{i=k_n}^{\infty} \frac{1}{i^{1+2\gamma}} \log R > 1$$

for sufficiently large n and $1 < k \leqslant [\sqrt{n}]$ so in sense of Lemma 3.1

$$(3.6)\qquad \begin{aligned} P_{kn}^{(2)} &\leqslant e^{-c_3 \sum_{i=k}^{n} \frac{1}{i \log^{\kappa} i} k_n^{2\gamma}} \leqslant \\ &\leqslant e^{-c_4 \log^{1-\kappa} n \log^{(1-\kappa)\frac{4\gamma}{1-2\gamma}} n} = \frac{1}{n^{c_4 \log^{d} n}}\,, \end{aligned}$$

where

$$d = \frac{(1-\kappa)4\gamma}{1-2\gamma} - \kappa\,.$$

The statement of Lemma 3.2 follows from (3.2), (3.5), (3.6).

Lemma 3.3. *Let us assume that condition* (A) *is fulfilled and the sequences* a_n, b_n, ν_n, μ_n *are chosen as in Theorem* 3.1. *Then for arbitrary* $q > 0$ *and* $\epsilon > 0$

$$\lim_{n \to \infty} n^q \mathsf{P}\{|T_n - t_0| > \epsilon\} = 0 .$$

Proof. Let $t_0 = 0$. It is sufficient to estimate the following probability

$$P_n = \mathsf{P}\{T_n > \epsilon\} .$$

Using [6] it is easy to prove, that for certain constants $A > 0$, $B > 0$, k_0 and for every sufficient large n the inequality

$$P_n \leqslant P_n^{(1)} + P_n^{(2)} + P_n^{(3)} \tag{3.7}$$

holds, where

$$P_n^{(1)} = \sum_{k=k_0+1}^{[\sqrt{n}]-1} \mathsf{P}\Big\{\sum_{i=k+1}^{n-1} \frac{\tilde{\psi}_i}{i\widetilde{W}_i} \leqslant -\frac{\epsilon}{4} - B \sum_{i=k+1}^{n-1} \frac{1}{i\widetilde{W}_i}\Big\},$$

$$P_n^{(2)} = \sum_{k=0}^{k_0} \mathsf{P}\Big\{\sum_{i=k+1}^{n-1} \frac{\tilde{\psi}_i}{i\widetilde{W}_i} \leqslant A - B \sum_{i=k+1}^{n-1} \frac{1}{i\widetilde{W}_i}\Big\},$$

$$P_n^{(3)} = \sum_{k=[\sqrt{n}]-1}^{n-2} \mathsf{P}\Big\{\sum_{i=k+1}^{n-1} \frac{\tilde{\psi}_i}{i\widetilde{W}_i} \leqslant -\frac{\epsilon}{4} - B \sum_{i=k+1}^{n-1} \frac{1}{i\widetilde{W}_i}\Big\},$$

$$\widetilde{W}_i = [W_i]_{\nu_i}^{\mu_i} .$$

Obviously

$$\frac{\tilde{\psi}_i}{i\widetilde{W}_i} = \frac{\eta_i}{\frac{1}{i^{2}}+\gamma}$$

where $\mathsf{E}\{\eta_{i+1} | \eta_1, \ldots, \eta_i\} = 0$, $|\eta_i| \leqslant 2$ a.s. In such a way according to Lemma 3.2

$$P_n^{(1)} \leqslant \sum_{k=k_0+1}^{[\sqrt{n}]-1} \mathsf{P}\Big\{\sum_{i=k+1}^{n-1} \frac{\eta_i}{i^{\frac{1}{2}+\gamma}} \leqslant -\frac{\epsilon}{4} - B \sum_{i=k+1}^{n-1} \frac{1}{i \log^{\kappa} i}\Big\} \leqslant \frac{c_5}{n^{1+q}} \tag{3.8}$$

and

$$P_n^{(2)} \leqslant \frac{c_6}{n^{1+q}} \,. \tag{3.9}$$

Finally from Lemma 3.1 for $[\sqrt{n}] - 1 \leqslant k \leqslant n$ we have

$$\begin{aligned} P_n^{(3)} &\leqslant \sum_{k=[n]-1}^{n} \mathsf{P}\Big\{\sum_{i=k+1}^{n-1} \frac{\eta_i}{i^{\frac{1}{2}+\gamma}} \leqslant -\frac{\epsilon}{4}\Big\} \leqslant \\ &\leqslant c_7 \sum_{k=[n]-1}^{n} e^{-c_8[\sqrt{n}\,]^{2\gamma}} . \end{aligned} \tag{3.10}$$

(3.7)-(3.10) prove the required result.

Lemma 3.4. *Let us assume that the conditions of Theorem 3.1 are fulfilled, then for arbitrary* q *and* $\epsilon > 0$

$$\lim_{n\to\infty} n^q \mathsf{P}\{|\,[W_n]_{\nu_n}^{\mu_n} - \lambda'(t_0)| > \epsilon\} = 0\,.$$

Proof. We will estimate the probability $P_n = \mathsf{P}\{\widetilde{W}_n - \lambda'(t_0) > \epsilon\}$, taking $t_0 = 0$ into consideration. Obviously

$$p_n \leqslant \mathsf{P}\{W_n - \lambda_0 > \epsilon\}, \qquad \lambda_0 = \lambda'(0)\,,$$

in this case

$$\mathsf{P}\{W_n - \lambda_0 > \epsilon\} \leqslant p_{n1} + p_{n2}$$

where

$$p_{n1} = \mathsf{P}\Big\{\frac{1}{n}\sum_{i=1}^{n} \frac{\lambda_{i-1}(T_{i-1}+b_i) - \lambda_{i-1}(T_{i-1}-b_i)}{2b_i} - \lambda_0 \geqslant \frac{\epsilon}{2}\Big\}\,,$$

$$p_{n2} = \mathsf{P}\Big\{\frac{1}{n}\sum_{i=1}^{n} \frac{\xi_i}{b_i} \geqslant \frac{\epsilon}{2}\Big\}\,,$$

and

$$\xi_i = \frac{[\psi(X_i, T_{i-1} + b_i)]_{-a_{i-1}}^{a_{i-1}} - [\psi(X_i, T_{i-1} - b_i)]_{-a_{i-1}}^{a_{i-1}}}{2} -$$

$$- \frac{\lambda_{i-1}(T_{i-1} + b_i) - \lambda(T_{i-1} - b_i)}{2}.$$

Furthermore

$$p_{n1} \leqslant p_{n1}^{(1)} + p_{n1}^{(2)}$$

where

$$p_{n1}^{(1)} = \mathsf{P}\Big\{\frac{1}{n} \sum_{i=1}^{[\sqrt{n}]} \frac{\lambda_{i-1}(T_i + b_{i-1}) - \lambda_i(T_i - b_{i-1})}{2b_{i-1}} - \lambda_0 \geqslant \frac{\epsilon}{4}\Big\}, \tag{3.11}$$

$$p_{n1}^{(2)} = \mathsf{P}\Big\{\frac{1}{n} \sum_{i=[\sqrt{n}]+1}^{n} \frac{\lambda_{i-1}(T_i + b_{i-1}) - \lambda_i(T_i - b_{i-1})}{2b_{i-1}} \geqslant \frac{\epsilon}{4}\Big\}.$$

But

$$\Big|\frac{1}{n} \sum_{i=1}^{[\sqrt{n}]} \frac{\lambda_{i-1}(T_i + b_{i-1}) - \lambda_{i-1}(T_i - b_{i-1})}{2b_{i-1}}\Big| \leqslant$$

$$\leqslant \frac{1}{n} \sum_{i=1}^{[\sqrt{n}]} \frac{a_i}{b_i} = \frac{1}{n} \sum_{i=1}^{[\sqrt{n}]} i^{\frac{1}{2}-\gamma} \to 0 \quad \text{for} \quad n \to \infty,$$

hence $p_{n1}^{(1)} \equiv 0$ for $n \geqslant n_0$. Now, let us choose a $\delta_1 < \delta$ according to the condition

$$|\lambda'(t) - \lambda_0| \leqslant \frac{\epsilon}{10} \quad \text{for} \quad |t| \leqslant \delta_1. \tag{3.12}$$

If we denote the event standing into brackets in the relation (3.11) by Γ_n, then

$$p_{n1}^{(2)} \leqslant \mathsf{P}\{\Gamma_n, |T_{[\sqrt{n}]+1} \pm b_{[\sqrt{n}]}| < \delta_1, \dots, |T_n \pm b_{n-1}| < \delta_1\} +$$

$$+ \sum_{k=[\sqrt{n}]+1}^{n-1} \mathsf{P}\{\Gamma_n, |T_k \pm b_{k-1}| > \delta_1, |T_{k+1} \pm b_k| < \tag{3.13}$$

$$< \delta_1, \dots, |T_n \pm b_{n+1}| < \delta_1\} + \mathsf{P}\{\Gamma_n, |T_n \pm b_{n-1}| > \delta_1\}.$$

It is easy to see, that

$$P\{\Gamma_n, |T_{[\sqrt{n}]+1} \pm b_{[\sqrt{n}]}| < \delta_1, \ldots, |T_n \pm b_{n-1}| < \delta_1\} \leqslant$$

$$\leqslant P\Big\{\frac{1}{n} \sum_{i=[\sqrt{n}]+1}^{n} \frac{\lambda(T_i + b_{i-1}) - \lambda(T_i - b_{i-1})}{2b_{i-1}} - \lambda_0 \geqslant \frac{\epsilon}{8},$$

$$|T_{[\sqrt{n}]+1} \pm b_{[\sqrt{n}]}| < \delta_1, \ldots, |T_n \pm b_{n-1}| < \delta_1\Big\} +$$

$$+ P\Big\{\frac{1}{n} \sum_{i=[\sqrt{n}]+1}^{n} \frac{c_{i-1}(T_i + b_{i-1}) - c_i(T_i - b_{i-1})}{2b_{i-1}} \geqslant \frac{\epsilon}{8},$$

$$|T_{[\sqrt{n}]+1} \pm b_{[\sqrt{n}]}| < \delta_1, \ldots, |T_n \pm b_{n-1}| < \delta_1\Big\}.$$

If $|T_i \pm b_{i-1}| < \delta_1$ for $[\sqrt{n}] + 1 \leqslant i \leqslant n$, then according to (3.12) an (2.10) we have the following inequality

$$\Big|\frac{1}{n} \sum_{i=[\sqrt{n}]+1}^{n} \frac{\lambda(T_i + b_{i-1}) - \lambda(T_i - b_{i-1})}{2b_{i-1}} - \lambda_0\Big| \leqslant$$

$$\leqslant \frac{1}{n} \sum_{[\sqrt{n}]+1}^{n} \frac{|\lambda'(T_i + \Theta_1 b_{i-1}) - \lambda_0| + |\lambda'(T_i + \Theta_2 b_{i-1}) - \lambda_0|}{2}$$

$$\leqslant \frac{\epsilon}{10} \; (|\Theta_j| < 1, \; j \leqslant 1, 2),$$

$$\Big|\frac{1}{n} \sum_{i=[\sqrt{n}]+1}^{n} \frac{c_{i-1}(T_i + b_{i-1}) - c_i(T_i - b_{i-1})}{2b_{i-1}}\Big| \leqslant$$

$$\leqslant \frac{2c_1}{n} \sum_{i=[\sqrt{n}]+1}^{n} \frac{1}{b_i a_i^{1+\Delta}} \to 0 \quad \text{when} \quad n \to \infty .$$

From these relations and using (3.13) it follows that the probability

$$P\{\Gamma_n, |T_{[\sqrt{n}]+1} \pm b_{[\sqrt{n}]}| < \delta_1, \ldots, |T_n \pm b_{n-1}| < \delta_1\}$$

equal to 0, for sufficient large $n > n_1$. From this and from (3.13) we o tain

$$p_{n1}^{(2)} \leqslant \sum_{k=[\sqrt{n}]+1}^{n} \mathsf{P}\{|T_k \pm b_{k-1}| > \delta_1\}$$

for $n > n_1$. It means according to Lemma 3.3, that

$$\lim_{n\to\infty} n^q p_{n1}^{(2)} = 0$$

for arbitrary q. And this simultaneously means, that

$$(3.14)\qquad \lim_{n\to\infty} n^q p_{n1} = 0$$

for arbitrary q. Finally

$$\frac{\xi_i}{b_i} = 2\eta_i i^{\frac{1}{2}-\gamma}$$

if $|\eta_i| \leqslant 1$, a.s. In such a way in the sense of Lemma 1 from [6]

$$(3.15)\qquad P_{n2} = \mathsf{P}\Big\{\sum_{i=1}^{n} \eta_i i^{\frac{1}{2}-\gamma} > \frac{\epsilon n}{4}\Big\} \leqslant e^{c_9 n^{2\gamma}} .$$

From (3.14) and (3.15) follows, that

$$\lim_{n\to\infty} n^q P_n = 0$$

for arbitrary chosen q. In the same way we can estimate the probability $\mathsf{P}\{\widetilde{W}_i - \lambda_0 < -\epsilon\}$.

Proof of Theorem 3.1. Let $t_0 = 0$. According to Theorem 2.1 $\sqrt{n}T_n \sim N(0, \sigma_0^2)$. And so it is sufficient to prove, that if $2p < 2 + \Delta$, $p \geqslant 1$, then

$$\sup_{n\geqslant 1} \mathsf{E}|\sqrt{n}\,T_n|^{2p} < \infty .$$

Using the following formula

$$|x+h|^{2p} = |x|^{2p} + 2p|x|^{2p-1} h \operatorname{sign} x +$$
$$+ p(2p-1)|x+\theta h|^{2p-2} \qquad (0<\theta<1)$$

we have the following estimation from (2.1)

$$
(3.16) \quad \begin{aligned} \mathsf{E}|T_{n+1}|^{2p} \leqslant \mathsf{E}|T_n|^{2p} - \frac{2p}{n}\,\mathsf{E}\,\frac{|T_n|^{2p-1}\lambda_n(T_n)\,\mathrm{sign}\,T_n}{\widetilde{W}_n} + \\ + c_{10}\,\mathsf{E}\,\frac{|T_n|^{2(p-1)}\varphi_n^{(1)}(T_n)}{n^2\,\widetilde{W}_n^2} + c_{10}\,\mathsf{E}\,\frac{\varphi_n^{(2)}(T_n)}{n^{2p}\,\widetilde{W}_n^{2p}} \end{aligned}
$$

where

$$
\varphi_n^{(1)}(t) = \mathsf{E}([\psi(X_{n+1}, t)_{-a_n}^{a_n})^2 ,
$$

$$
\varphi_n^{(2)}(t) = \mathsf{E}([\psi(X_{n+1}, t)_{-a_n}^{a_n})^{2p} .
$$

Choose $\epsilon > 0$ such that $\dfrac{\lambda_0 - \epsilon}{\lambda_0 + \epsilon} > \dfrac{1}{2}$, and δ_1 according to the condition $\lambda(t)t \geqslant (\lambda_0 - \epsilon)t^2$ for $|t| < \delta_1$. Denote $\delta_2 = \min(\delta, \delta_1)$. Then, for $n > n_0$ we have

$$
(3.17) \quad \begin{aligned} \mathsf{E}\,\frac{|T_n|^{2p-1}\lambda_n(T_n)\,\mathrm{sign}\,T_n}{\widetilde{W}_n} \geqslant \\ \geqslant \mathsf{E}\,\frac{|T_n|^{2p-1}\lambda_n(T_n)\,\mathrm{sign}\,T_n}{\widetilde{W}_n}\,\chi_{\{|T_n| \leqslant \delta_2\}} = I_n^{(1)} + I_n^{(2)} \end{aligned}
$$

where

$$
I_n^{(1)} = \mathsf{E}\,\frac{|T_n|^{2p-1}\,\lambda_n(T_n)\,\mathrm{sign}\,T_n}{\widetilde{W}_n}\,\chi_{\{|T_n| \leqslant \delta_2\}} ,
$$

$$
I_n^{(2)} = \mathsf{E}\,\frac{|T_n|^{2p-1}\,c_n(T_n)\,\mathrm{sign}\,T_n}{\widetilde{W}_n}\,\chi_{\{|T_n| \leqslant \delta_2\}} .
$$

Obviously

$$
(3.18) \quad \begin{aligned} I_n^{(1)} \geqslant (\lambda_0 - \epsilon)\mathsf{E}\,\frac{|T_n|^{2p}}{\widetilde{W}_n}\,\chi_{\{|T_n| \leqslant \delta_2\}} = \\ = (\lambda_0 - \epsilon)\mathsf{E}\,\frac{|T_n|^{2p}}{\widetilde{W}_n} - (\lambda_0 - \epsilon)\mathsf{E}\,\frac{|T_n|^{2p}}{\widetilde{W}_n}\,\chi_{\{|T_n| > \delta_2\}} \geqslant \end{aligned}
$$

$$\geq \frac{\lambda_0 - \epsilon}{\lambda_0 + \epsilon} \mathsf{E} \, | T_n |^{2p} \chi_{\{\widetilde{W}_n < \lambda_0 + \epsilon\}} -$$

$$- (\lambda_0 - \epsilon) \mathsf{E} \frac{| T_n |^{2p}}{\widetilde{W}_n} \chi_{\{| T_n | > \delta_2\}} =$$

$$= \frac{\lambda_0 - \epsilon}{\lambda_0 + \epsilon} \mathsf{E} \, | T_n |^{2p} - \frac{\lambda_0 - \epsilon}{\lambda_0 + \epsilon} \mathsf{E} \, | T_n |^{2p} \chi_{\{\widetilde{W}_n \geq \lambda_0 + \epsilon\}} -$$

$$- (\lambda_0 - \epsilon) \mathsf{E} \frac{| T_n |^{2p}}{\widetilde{W}_n} \chi_{\{| T_n | > \delta_2\}} \, .$$

Since

$$| T_n |^{2p} < cn^s, \qquad | T_n^{2p} \widetilde{W}_n^{-1} | \leq c_{11} n^s$$

for certain c_{11}, $s > 0$ and according to Lemmas 3.3 and 3.4

$$n^f [\mathsf{P}\{\widetilde{W}_n \geq \lambda_0 + \epsilon\} + \mathsf{P}\{| T_n | > \delta_2\} \to \infty \qquad \text{if} \quad n \to \infty$$

for arbitrary f. Then from (3.18) follows, that

$$\text{(3.19)} \qquad I_n^{(1)} \geq \frac{\lambda_0 - \epsilon}{\lambda_0 + \epsilon} \mathsf{E} \, | T_n |^{2p} + o\Big(\frac{1}{n^{2p}}\Big) \qquad (n \to \infty) \, .$$

Furthermore by (2.10)

$$\text{(3.20)} \qquad | I_n^{(2)} | \leq \frac{2c_1}{a_n^{1+\Delta} \nu_n} \mathsf{E} \, | T_n |^{2p-1} = \frac{2c_1}{n^g} \mathsf{E} \, | T_n |^{2p-1} \qquad \Big(g > \frac{1}{2}\Big) \, .$$

Hence from (3.17), (3.19) and (3.20) we have the estimation for all sufficiently large n

$$\text{(3.21)} \qquad \begin{aligned} &\mathsf{E} \frac{| T_n |^{2p-1} \lambda_n(T_n) \operatorname{sign} T_n}{\widetilde{W}_n} \geq \frac{\lambda_0 - \epsilon}{\lambda_0 + \epsilon} \mathsf{E} \, | T_n |^{2p} - \\ &- \frac{2c_1}{n^g} \mathsf{E} \, | T_n |^{2p-1} + o\Big(\frac{1}{n^{2p}}\Big) \qquad (n \to \infty) \, . \end{aligned}$$

Analogously, using* Lemmas 3.3 and 3.4,

*In order to prove (3.23) we must use condition (C) also.

(3.22) $$\mathsf{E}\,\frac{|T_n|^{2(p-1)}\varphi_n^{(1)}(T_n)}{\widetilde{W}_n^2} \leqslant c_{12}\,\mathsf{E}\,|T_n|^{2(p-1)} + o\left(\frac{1}{n^{2p}}\right) \quad (n \to \infty),$$

(3.23) $$\mathsf{E}\left|\frac{\varphi_n^{(2)}(T_n)}{\widetilde{W}_n^{2p}}\right| \leqslant c_{13}\,.$$

From (3.16), (3.21)-(3.23) finally we make the inequality

(3.24) $$\mathsf{E}\,|T_{n+1}|^{2p} \leqslant \mathsf{E}\,|T_n|^{2p} - \frac{2p\lambda}{n}\,\mathsf{E}\,|T_n|^{2p} + c_{14}\left[\frac{\mathsf{E}|T_n|^{2p-1}}{n^{1+g}} + \frac{\mathsf{E}|T_n|^{2(p-1)}}{n^2} + \frac{1}{n^{2p}}\right], \quad \left(\lambda > \frac{1}{2}\right)$$

for all sufficiently large n.

First of all we prove

(3.25) $$\mathsf{E}\,T_n^2 = O\left(\frac{1}{n}\right) \quad (n \to \infty).$$

From (3.24) for $p = 1$, we have

(3.26) $$\mathsf{E}\,T_{n+1}^2 \leqslant \mathsf{E}\,T_n^2 - \frac{2\lambda}{n}\,\mathsf{E}\,T_n^2 + c_{14}\left[\frac{\mathsf{E}|T_n|}{n^{1+g}} + \frac{1}{n^2}\right].$$

From (3.26) it follows, that $\mathsf{E}\,T_n^2 < c_{15}$. Then

$$\mathsf{E}\,T_{n+1}^2 \leqslant \mathsf{E}\,T_n^2 - \frac{2\lambda}{n}\,\mathsf{E}\,T_n^2 + c_{16}\left[\frac{1}{n^{1+g}} + \frac{1}{n^2}\right].$$

From the Chung's lemma and using the above inequality we have

(3.27) $$\mathsf{E}\,T_n^2 = O\left(\frac{1}{n^{\min(1,g)}}\right) \quad (n \to \infty).$$

If $g < 1$, then according to (3.27)

$$\mathsf{E}|T_n| = O\left(\frac{1}{n^{\frac{g}{2}}}\right) \quad (n \to \infty).$$

Thus from (3.26) we have

$$\mathsf{E}T_{n+1}^2 \leqslant \mathsf{E}T_n^2 - \frac{2\lambda}{n}\mathsf{E}T_n^2 + c_{17}\left[\frac{1}{n^{1+g+\frac{g}{2}}} + \frac{1}{n^2}\right],$$

and using the Chung's lemma we obtain

$$\mathsf{E}T_n^2 = O\left(\frac{1}{n^{\min\left(g+\frac{g}{2},1\right)}}\right) \qquad (n \to \infty).$$

If $g + \frac{g}{2} < 1$, then from (3.26) we get in the same manner that

$$\mathsf{E}T_n^2 = O\left(\frac{1}{n^{\min\left(g+\frac{g}{2}+\frac{g}{4},1\right)}}\right) \qquad (n \to \infty).$$

Since

$$\sum_{k=0}^{\infty} \frac{g}{2^k} = 2g > 1,$$

so this consideration proves (3.25).

Furthermore substituting $p = \frac{3}{2}$ in (3.24) we obtain from (3.25)

$$\mathsf{E}|T_n|^3 = O\left(\frac{1}{n^{\frac{3}{2}}}\right) \qquad (n \to \infty).$$

Firstly let be $p \leqslant 2$. Then

$$\mathsf{E}|T_n|^{2p-2} \leqslant (\mathsf{E}T_n^2)^{p-1} = O\left(\frac{1}{n^{p-1}}\right) \qquad (n \to \infty),$$

$$\mathsf{E}|T_n|^{2p-1} \leqslant (\mathsf{E}|T_n|^3)^{\frac{2p-1}{3}} = O\left(\frac{1}{n^{p-\frac{1}{2}}}\right) \qquad (n \to \infty).$$

From (3.24) and from the Chung's lemma it follows

$$\mathsf{E}T_n^{2p} = O\left(\frac{1}{n^p}\right) \qquad (n \to \infty). \tag{3.28}$$

Using the same consideration as in the proof of theorem of [9] we extend the validity of (3.28) for arbitrary chosen $p \leqslant 1 + \frac{\Delta}{2}$. Theorem 3.1 is proved.

From Theorem 3.1 it follows, that in the case when the function $\psi(x, t)$ is bounded, the procedure (2.1) (if the conditions of this theorem are assumed) satisfies the following relation

$$(3.29) \qquad \mathsf{E}[\sqrt{n}(T_n - t_0)]^N \to \frac{1}{\sqrt{2\pi}\,|\sigma_0|} \int_{-\infty}^{+\infty} y^N e^{-\frac{y^2}{2\sigma_0^2}} dy \qquad (n \to \infty)$$

for arbitrary $N = 1, 2, \ldots$.

The next theorem shows that in this case we can use also a more simplified procedure without truncation of the function $\psi(x, t)$.

Theorem 3.2. *If the function* $\psi(x, t)$ *is bounded and if we assume the conditions* (A)-(C), $b_n = \nu_n = bn^{-\beta}$, $\mu_n = c \log^\kappa(1 + n)$, $b > 0$, $c > 0$, *and*

$$(1 - \kappa)\frac{1 - 2\beta}{\beta} > \kappa \qquad (0 < \kappa < 1)$$

then for arbitrary $N = 1, 2, \ldots$ *the procedure* (2.21), (2.22) *satisfies the relation* (3.29).

In order to prove this, we must repeat almost exactly the proof of Theorem 3.1, with regard that $\gamma = \frac{1}{2} - \beta$.

4. Let us see two examples.

1. Let us assume that observations X_i are chosen in the following way: $X_i = t_0 + \xi_i$, where $\xi_1, \xi_2, \ldots$ is a sequence of independent, identically distributed random variables, and $\mathsf{E}\xi_1^k = 0$, $\mathsf{E}|\xi_1|^{k(2+\Delta)} < \infty$, for some odd k and for some $\Delta > 0$. Let $\psi(x, t) = (t - x)^k$. Then

$$\lambda(t) = \mathsf{E}\,\psi(X_1, t) = \sum_{j=0}^{k-1} C_k^j (t - t_0)^{k-j} m_j$$

$m_j = \mathsf{E}\xi_1^j$, and so $\lambda'(t_0) = km_{k-1}$. Furthermore the function $\sigma^2(t) = \mathsf{E}\,\psi^2(X_{1,t})$ is continuous in the point t_0, and $\sigma^2(t_0) = m_{2k}$. Consequently from [1] follows that the estimation T_n defined by the equation

$$(4.1) \qquad \sum_{i=1}^{n} (T_n - X_i)^k = 0$$

satisfies the relation

$$(4.2) \qquad \sqrt{n}\,(T_n - t_0) \sim N\Big(0, \frac{m_{2k}}{k^2 m_{k-1}^2}\Big) .$$

In order to find the estimation T_n in (4.1) it is necessary to solve an algebraic equation of order k.

From Theorems 2.1 and 3.1 it follows, that for a suitable choose of sequences a_n, b_n, ν_n, μ_n, relations (4.2) and (3.29) for $N < 2 + \Delta$ is satisfied by the estimation T_n which can be determined from the following recurrent relations

$$T_1 = t ,$$

$$T_{n+1} - T_n = - \frac{[T_n - X_{n+1}]_{-a_n}^{a_n}}{n[W_n]_{\nu_n}^{\mu_n}} ,$$

$$(4.3) \qquad W_0 = 0 ,$$

$$W_{n+1} - W_n = - \frac{1}{n+1} W_n +$$

$$+ \frac{[T_n + b_{n+1} - X_{n+1}]_{-a_n}^{a_n} - [T_n - b_{n+1} - X_{n+1}]_{-a_n}^{a_n}}{2(n+1)b_{n+1}} .$$

From the point of view of the computation (4.3) is much simpler then the M-estimate (4.1).

2. Let $F(y)$ be an unknown distribution function with a uniquely determined median m. Let us assume that we must estimate m, using the independent sequence of observations $X_1, \ldots, X_n$, (where X_i is distributed according to $F(y)$ for all i). Let $\psi(x, t) = \operatorname{sign}(t - x)$, then

$\lambda(t) = 2F(t) - 1$ and the solution to of equation $\lambda(t) = 0$ is identical with m.

Let us assume, that the function $F(y)$ is continuously differentiable at the point $y = m$, and $F'(m) \neq 0$. Then, from [1] and [2] it follows, that the estimation

$$T_n = \inf_t \left\{ t: \sum_{i=1}^{n} \operatorname{sign}(t - X_i) \geq 0 \right\}$$

satisfies the following two relations

$$\sqrt{n}\,(T_n - m) \sim N\left(0, \frac{1}{[F'(m)]^2}\right), \tag{4.4}$$

$$\mathsf{E}[\sqrt{n}\,(T_n - m)]^N \to \mathsf{E}\xi^N \qquad (n \to \infty) \tag{4.5}$$

where ξ is a Gaussian random variable with expectation 0, and with variance $[F'(m)]^{-2}$.

In order to compute this estimation we must use in the n-th step all observations $X_1, \ldots X_n$.

From Theorems 2.2, 3.2 it follows, that using the same condition for $F(y)$ as above, relations (4.4), (4.5) satisfy the recurrent estimation T_n, which is computable by the following simple formulae:

$$T_1 = t,$$

$$T_{n+1} - T_n = -\frac{\operatorname{sign}(T_n - X_{n+1})}{n[W_n]^{\sqrt{\log(1+n)}}_{n^{-\frac{1}{4}}}},$$

$$W_0 = 0,$$

$$W_{n+1} - W_n = -\frac{1}{n+1} W_n - \frac{\operatorname{sign}(T_n + n^{-\frac{1}{4}} - X_{n+1}) - \operatorname{sign}(T_n - n^{-\frac{1}{4}} - X_{n+1})}{2(n+1)^{\frac{3}{4}}}.$$

REFERENCES

[1] P.J. Huber, Robust estimation of a location parameter, *Ann. Math. Statist.*, 35 (1964), 73-101.

[2] B.Ja. Levit, On efficiency of a class of nonparametric statistics, *Teorija Verojatn. i Primenen.*, (to appear).

[3] J. Pfanzagl, On the measurability and consistency of minimum constrast estimates, *Metrika,* 14 (1969), 249-272.

[4] J.H. Venter, An extension of the Robbins – Monro procedure, *Ann. Math. Statist.*, 39 (1968), 181-190.

[5] V. Fabian, On asymptotic normality in stochastic approximation, *Ann. Math. Statist.*, 39 (1968), 1327-1332.

[6] J. Komlós – P. Révész, On the rate of convergence of the Robbins – Monro method, *Z. Warscheinlichkeitstheorie verw. Geb.*, 25 (1972), 39-47.

[7] M.B. Nevel'son – R.Z. Has'minskij, *Stochastic approximation and recursive estimations,* Nauka, Moskow, 1972.

[8] K.L. Chung, On stochastic approximation methods, *Ann. Math. Statist.*, 25 (1954), 463-483.

[9] M.B. Nevel'son – R.Z. Has'minskij, On the convergence of moments of Robbins – Monro processes, *Avtomat. i Telemeh.*, 1 (1973), 96-100.

COLLOQUIA MATHEMATICA SOCIETATIS JÁNOS BOLYAI
11. LIMIT THEOREMS OF PROBABILITY THEORY, KESZTHELY (HUNGARY), 1974.

SOME FUNCTIONAL LAWS OF THE ITERATED LOGARITHM FOR DEPENDENT RANDOM VARIABLES

H. OODAIRA

1. INTRODUCTION

The purpose of this paper is to discuss some extensions of the following theorems of V. Strassen [13] and of H. Finkelstein [6] to certain classes of dependent random variables.

Let $\{B(t),\ 0 \leqslant t < \infty\}$ be the Brownian motion and let $C[0, 1]$ denote the space of all continuous functions on $[0, 1]$ with the sup norm $\|\cdot\|_\infty$. Define the sequence of random functions $\{f_n(t)\}$ by

$$f_n(t) = \frac{B(nt)}{\sqrt{2n \log\log n}} \qquad (0 \leqslant t \leqslant 1,\ n = 3, 4, \ldots)$$

and let K_B be the set of all absolutely continuous functions h in $C[0, 1]$ such that $h(0) = 0$ and $\int_0^1 \left(\frac{dh}{dt}\right)^2 dt \leqslant 1$. Then

Theorem A (Strassen [13]). *$\{f_n(t)\}$ is relatively compact in $C[0, 1]$ and the set of its limit points is K_B almost surely (a.s.).*

Let ξ_j be independent identically distributed (i.i.d.) random variables with mean zero and variance one, and set $S_0 = 0$, $S_k = \sum_{j=0}^{k} \xi_j$. Define in $C[0, 1]$

$$f_n(t) = \begin{cases} \dfrac{S_k}{\sqrt{2n \log\log n}} & \text{for} \quad t = \dfrac{k}{n} \quad (k = 0, 1, \dots, n) \\ \text{linear} & \text{for} \quad t \in \left[\dfrac{k}{n}, \dfrac{k+1}{n}\right] \end{cases}$$

$$(k = 0, \dots, n-1).$$

Theorem B (Strassen [13]). *$\{f_n(t)\}$ is relatively compact and the set of its limit points is K_B a.s.*

Now let ξ_j be independent identically uniformly distributed over $[0, 1]$, and let $F_n(t)$ be the empirical distribution function at stage n. Let $E[0, 1]$ denote the space of functions on $[0, 1]$ which are right continuous and have left limits everywhere, with the sup norm $\| \cdot \|_\infty$. Define in $E[0, 1]$

$$f_n(t) = \sqrt{\frac{n}{2 \log\log n}} \, (F_n(t) - t) \qquad (0 \leqslant t \leqslant 1, \ n = 3, 4, \dots),$$

and let K_{BB} be the set of all absolutely continuous functions h in $E[0, 1]$ such that $h(0) = h(1) = 0$ and $\int_0^1 \left(\frac{dh}{dt}\right)^2 dt \leqslant 1$. Then

Theorem C (Finkelstein [6]). *$\{f_n(t)\}$ is relatively compact in $E[0, 1]$ and the set of its limit points is K_{BB} a.s.*

Theorem A has been extended to a class of Gaussian processes in [9], [10], and Theorem B to various classes of dependent random variables by several authors, e.g., to some classes of stationary sequences satisfying certain mixing conditions in [7], [12]. In this paper we shall give a further extension of Theorem A by weakening the conditions imposed in [10], and also we shall extend Theorem C to so-called m-dependent random variables. We are mainly interested in characterizing the set of limit points of $\{f_n(t)\}$ defined suitably for dependent random variables. Notice that the sets K_B and K_{BB} are the unit balls of the reproducing kernel Hilbert spaces (RKHS) associated with the Brownian motion and the Brownian bridge, respectively. These processes are the limit Gaussian processes of the sequences of random functions $\{f_n(t)\sqrt{2 \log \log n}\}$ in the sense of weak convergence of the corresponding probability measures. In exactly the same way, for all cases considered in this paper, the sets of limit points of $\{f_n(t)\}$ will be shown to be the unit balls of the RKHS associated with some appropriate limit Gaussian processes. The characterization of the set of limit points in terms of RKHS appears to be natural and most convenient for dependent random variables.

Some simple but basic propositions are given in Section 2, and in Section 3 a generalization of our earlier result for Gaussian processes is proved basing on the approach described in Section 2. Some earlier results for dependent random sequences are briefly discussed in Section 4, and an extension of Theorem C to m-dependent random variables is given in Section 5.

2. BASIC PROPOSITIONS

A standard method of proving the weak convergence of a sequence of random functions X_n in $C[0, 1]$ to a random function X is to show that the probability measures induced by X_n are uniformly tight and that all the finite dimensional distributions of X_n converge weakly to the corresponding finite dimensional distributions of X (cf. e.g., [2]). It appears convenient to have a similar formulation for functional (Strassen-type) laws of the iterated logarithm.

Let $\{f_n(t, \omega)\}$ be a sequence of random functions in $C[0, 1]$ with $f_n(0) = 0$, defined on a probability space $(\Omega, \mathscr{F}, \mathrm{P})$. Let $\{T_m\}$ be a monotone increasing sequence of finite subsets of $[0, 1]$ such that $\bigcup_{m=1}^{\infty} T_m$ is dense in $[0, 1]$, e.g., $T_m = \left\{\frac{k}{2^m},\ k = 1, 2, \ldots, 2^m\right\}$. For simplicity, we shall write $T = T_m = \{t_1, \ldots, t_m\}$, $t_i \in (0, 1]$. Denote by $\varphi^T = (\varphi(t_1), \ldots, \varphi(t_m))$ the restriction of φ in $C[0, 1]$ to T, and, for any subset A of $C[0, 1]$, denote by A^T its restriction to T, i.e., $A^T = \{\varphi^T \mid \varphi \in A\}$.

Proposition 1. *If*

(a) $\{f_n(t)\}$ *is relatively compact a.s., and*

(b) *for any* $T \in \{T_m\}$, *the set of limit points of random vectors* $\{f_n^T\}$ *is* K^T *a.s., where* K *is a compact set in* $C[0, 1]$,

then the set of limit points of $\{f_n(t)\}$ *is* K *a.s.*

Remark 1. Here the norm of a finite dimensional space R^m is $\|\varphi\|_\infty = \max_{1 \leq j \leq m} |\varphi_j|$ for $\varphi = (\varphi_1, \ldots, \varphi_m) \in R^m$.

Proof. Let $L(\omega)$ be the set of limit points of $\{f_n(\cdot, \omega)\}$, and let $\Omega_0 = \{\omega \mid \{f_n(\cdot, \omega)\}$ is relatively compact$\}$, $\Omega_m = \{\omega \mid$ the set of limit points of $\{f_n^T(\omega)\}$ is K^T for $T = T_m\}$ and $\Omega^* = \bigcap_{m=0}^{\infty} \Omega_m$. It suffices to show that if $\omega \in \Omega^*$, then, for any $\epsilon > 0$, $L(\omega) \subset K_{2\epsilon}$ and $K \subset L_{2\epsilon}(\omega)$, where $K_{2\epsilon}$ and $L_{2\epsilon}(\omega)$ denote respectively the 2ϵ-neighborhood of K and $L(\omega)$.

For $\varphi \in C[0, 1]$, let $\widetilde{\varphi}^T$ be the polygonal function defined by $\widetilde{\varphi}^T(t) = \varphi(t_i)$ for $t = t_i \in T \cup \{0, 1\}$ and $=$ linear for $t \in [t_i, t_{i+1}]$ and, for $A \subset C[0, 1]$, let $\widetilde{A}^T = \{\widetilde{\varphi}^T \mid \varphi \in A\}$. If $\omega \in \Omega_0$, then, by Ascoli – Arzela's theorem, for any $\epsilon > 0$, there is a number $m_0 = m_0(\epsilon)$ such that $L(\omega) \subset \widetilde{L}_\epsilon^T(\omega)$ and $\widetilde{L}^T(\omega) \subset L_\epsilon(\omega)$ for all $T = T_m$, $m \geq m_0$. Similarly we have, for any $\epsilon > 0$, $K \subset \widetilde{K}_\epsilon^T$ and $\widetilde{K}^T \subset K_\epsilon$ for $T = T_m$ if m is sufficiently large.

Now let $\omega \in \Omega^*$ and let $\epsilon > 0$ be given. Choose $T = T_m$ such that $L(\omega) \subset \widetilde{L}_\epsilon^T(\omega)$ and $\widetilde{K}^T \subset K_\epsilon$. It is easy to see that the set of limit points of $\{f_n^T(\omega)\}$ is $L^T(\omega)$. Since $\omega \in \Omega_m$, $L^T(\omega) = K^T$ and so $\widetilde{L}^T(\omega) = \widetilde{K}_\epsilon^T$. Hence $L(\omega) \subset \widetilde{L}_\epsilon^T(\omega) = \widetilde{K}_\epsilon^T \subset K_{2\epsilon}$. Similarly we have $K \subset \widetilde{K}_\epsilon^T = \widetilde{L}_\epsilon^T(\omega) \subset L_{2\epsilon}(\omega)$. The proof is complete.

Let $\Gamma(s, t)$ $(0 \leq s, t \leq 1)$ be a strictly positive definite continuous kernel. We denote by $H(\Gamma)$ the RKHS with reproducing kernel (r.k.) Γ

and by $\|\cdot\|_H$ its norm. Let Γ^T denote the restriction of Γ to $T \times T$, and let $H(\Gamma^T)$ be the RKHS with r.k. Γ^T, whose norm is denoted by $\|\cdot\|_T$. The unit ball of $H(\Gamma)$ is compact in $C[0, 1]$ (see, e.g., [9]) and we have the following simple lemma.

Lemma 1. *For any* $T = \{t_1, \ldots, t_m\}$, *the restriction of the unit ball of* $H(\Gamma)$ *to* T *is the unit ball of* $H(\Gamma^T)$.

Proof. Let $h^T \in$ the restriction of the unit ball of $H(\Gamma)$ to T. Then $\|h^T\|_T = \min\{\|\varphi\|_H \mid \varphi \in H(\Gamma)$ such that $\varphi^T = h^T\} \leqslant \|h\|_H \leqslant 1$ (see [1]).

Now let $h^* = (h_1, \ldots, h_m) \in$ the unit ball of $H(\Gamma^T)$. Let $a_1, \ldots, a_m$ be the numbers uniquely determined by $\sum_{j=1}^{m} a_j \Gamma(t_j, t_k) = h_k$, $k = 1, \ldots, m$, and set $h(t) = \sum_{j=1}^{m} a_j \Gamma(t_j, t)$, $0 \leqslant t \leqslant 1$. Then $h \in H(\Gamma)$ and $h^T = h^*$. Furthermore, $\|h\|_H^2 = \sum_{i,j=1}^{m} a_i a_j \Gamma(t_i, t_j) =$ $= \sum_{p,q=1}^{m} h_p \Gamma^{-1}(t_p, t_q) h_q = \|h^*\|_T^2 \leqslant 1$, where $\Gamma^{-1}(t_p, t_q)$ is the (p, q)-element of the matrix $(\Gamma^T)^{-1}$. The lemma is proved.

Thus, if K is the unit ball of $H(\Gamma)$, we have the following

Proposition 2. *Suppose that*

(A) $\{f_n(t)\}$ *is relatively compact a.s., and*

(B) *for any* $T \in \{T_m\}$, *the set of limit points of* $\{f_n^T\}$ *is the unit ball* K^T *of* $H(\Gamma^T)$ *a.s.*

Then the set of limit points of $\{f_n(t)\}$ *coincides with the unit ball* K *of* $H(\Gamma)$ *a.s.*

For the proof of an extension of Theorem C we shall use Finkelstein's method. The following proposition is a modification of her argument, and its proof is immediate.

Let $\{f_n(t)\}$ be a sequence of random functions in $E[0, 1]$ with

$f_n(0) = f_n(1) = 0$, and let $T_m = \left\{\frac{1}{m}, \frac{2}{m}, \ldots, \frac{m-1}{m}\right\}$ $(m = 2, 3, \ldots)$. Let $\tilde{f}_n^T(t)$ be the polygonal function whose vertices are $(t, f_n(t))$ $(t \in T \cup \{0, 1\})$ and, as before, let f_n^T and Γ^T denote the restrictions of $f_n(t)$ to T and of a kernel Γ to $T \times T$, respectively.

Proposition 3. *Suppose that*

(α) *for any* $\epsilon > 0$, *there is a number* $m_0 = m_0(\epsilon)$ *such that, for all* $T = T_m$, $m > m_0$, $\|f_n - \tilde{f}_n^T\|_\infty < \epsilon$ *for all sufficiently large* n *a.s., and*

(β) *for any* $T \in \{T_m\}$, $\limsup_n d(f_n^T, K^T) = 0$ *a.s., and* $\liminf_n \|f_n^T - h^T\|_\infty = 0$ *for all* $h^T \in K^T$ *a.s., where* K^T *is the unit ball of* $H(\Gamma^T)$ *and* $d(f_n^T, K^T) = \inf\{\|f_n^T - h^T\|_\infty \mid h^T \in K^T\}$.

Then $\{f_n(t)\}$ *is relatively compact and the set of its limit points is the unit ball* K *of* $H(\Gamma)$ *a.s.*

3. GAUSSIAN PROCESSES

Let $X = \{X(t, \omega), 0 \leqslant t < \infty\}$ be a real sample continuous Gaussian process with stationary increments, $X(0) = 0$, mean zero and covariance function $R(s, t)$, defined on a probability space $(\Omega, \mathscr{F}, \mathsf{P})$. Define

$$f_n(t, \omega) = \frac{X(nt, \omega)}{\sigma(n)\sqrt{2 \log \log n}} \qquad (0 \leqslant t \leqslant 1,\ n = 3, 4, \ldots)$$

where $\sigma^2(n) = R(n, n)$.

We first assume the following condition:

(C-1) $\sigma^2(n) = n^\rho L(n)$, $\rho > 0$, where $L(n)$ is a slowly varying function.

Proposition 4. *If Condition* (C-1) *is satisfied, then* $\{f_n(t)\}$ *is relatively compact a.s.*

Proof. The proof proceeds in the same manner as that of Theorem 1, [10], and, by virtue of the stationarity of increments of X, it reduces to obtaining an upper exponential bound of $\mathsf{P}(D(k))$, where

$$D(k) = \{ \sup_{0 \leqslant t \leqslant 2^{k-q+2}} |X(t)| \geqslant \frac{\epsilon}{2} \sigma(2^k)\sqrt{2 \log \log 2^k} \}$$

and q is an integer to be specified later (see [10]).

Set $Y(s; k) = X(s \cdot 2^{k-q+2})$ $(0 \leqslant s \leqslant 1)$. Then

$$\mathsf{P}(D(k)) = \mathsf{P}\Big(\sup_{0 \leqslant s \leqslant 1} \Big| \frac{Y(s; k)}{\sigma(2^k)} \Big| \geqslant \frac{\epsilon}{2}\sqrt{2 \log \log 2^k} \Big)$$

and

$$\mathsf{E}\Big| \frac{Y(s, k)}{\sigma(2^k)} \Big|^2 = \frac{\sigma^2(s \cdot 2^{k-q+2})}{\sigma^2(2^k)} =$$

$$= \frac{2^{\rho(k-q+2)} L(s \cdot 2^{k-q+2})}{2^{\rho k} L(2^k)} \sim 2^{-\rho(q-2)} \quad \text{as} \quad k \to \infty .$$

Choose q sufficiently large so that $2^{\rho(q-2)-1} > \dfrac{2(1+\epsilon')}{\epsilon^2}$ for some $\epsilon' > 0$. Then, by Fernique – Marcus – Shepp's theorem ([5], [8]), we have

$$\mathsf{P}(D(k)) < C \exp\{-(1+\epsilon') \log \log 2^k\} \leqslant C' k^{-(1+\epsilon')} ,$$

and, by the first Borel – Cantelli lemma, the proof is completed.

We now assume the following condition:

(C-2) there are a nonnegative function $\nu(r)$ and a strictly positive definite continuous kernel $\Gamma(s, t)$ $(0 \leqslant s,\ t \leqslant 1)$ such that $\Gamma(1, 1) = 1$ and

$$\frac{R(rs, rt)}{\nu(r)} \to \Gamma(s, t) \qquad (0 \leqslant s,\ t \leqslant 1) \qquad \text{as} \qquad r \to \infty .$$

Remark 2. (C-2) implies $\sigma^2(r) \sim \nu(r)$, and so $\nu(r)$ may be replaced by $\sigma^2(r)$. However, the introduction of $\nu(r)$ makes it easy to find the limit kernel Γ. If Condition (C-1) is also assumed, then we have $\Gamma(t, t) = t^\rho$ for $0 \leqslant t \leqslant 1$.

Proposition 5. *If Conditions* (C-1) *and* (C-2) *are satisfied, then, for any finite set* $T = \{t_1, \ldots, t_m\}$ $(t_i \in (0, 1])$, *the set of limit points of*

$\{f_n^T\}$ *is contained in the unit ball* K^T *of* $H(\Gamma^T)$ *a.s.*

Proof. It suffices to show that, for any $\epsilon > 0$, $\{f_n^T\}$ lies ultimately in $K_{3\epsilon}^T$ a.s. Proposition 4 allows us to work only with a subsequence $\{f_{n_k}^T\}$, where $n_k = [c^k]$ with $c = c(\epsilon) > 1$ sufficiently close to 1, and it is sufficient to show that $\{f_{n_k}^T\}$ lies ultimately in $K_{2\epsilon}^T$ a.s. (see [10]). Now we need only show that $\| f_{n_k}^T \|_T \leqslant 1 + 2\epsilon$ ultimately a.s., for, then, $\dfrac{f_{n_k}^T}{1+2\epsilon} \in K^T$ and

$$\left\| f_{n_k}^T - \frac{f_{n_k}^T}{1+2\epsilon} \right\|_\infty = 2\epsilon \left\| \frac{f_{n_k}^T}{1+2\epsilon} \right\|_T \cdot \sup_{1 \leqslant i \leqslant m} \sqrt{\Gamma(t_i, t_i)} \leqslant 2\epsilon .$$

Let $Y_n^T = \left(\dfrac{X(nt_1)}{\sigma(n)}, \ldots, \dfrac{X(nt_m)}{\sigma(n)} \right)$. Then $f_n^T = \dfrac{Y_n^T}{\sqrt{2 \log \log n}}$. Let S_n^T denote the covariance matrix of Y_n^T. Then, by Condition (C-2) and Remark 2, $S_n^T \to \Gamma^T$ elementwise as $n \to \infty$, and so $(S_n^T)^{-1} \to (\Gamma^T)^{-1}$ as $n \to \infty$. Hence, for any vector $\varphi^T \in R^m$, $\| \varphi^T \|_{S(n)} \to \| \varphi^T \|_T$ as $n \to \infty$, where $\| \cdot \|_{S(n)}$ is the norm of $H(S_n^T)$, and the convergence is uniform on a bounded set in R^m. Applying Fernique – Marcus – Shepp's theorem and the first Borel – Cantelli lemma, it is easily seen that $\{f_{n_k}^T\}$ is uniformly bounded ultimately a.s. Hence it is enough to show that $\| f_{n_k}^T \|_{S(n_k)} \leqslant 1 + \epsilon$ ultimately a.s.

Lemma 2. *Let* Z *be a Gaussian random vector in* R^m *with mean vector zero and strictly positive definite covariance matrix* Q. *Then, for any* $\alpha, \beta > 0$,

$$\mathrm{P}\left(\left\| \frac{Z}{\lambda} \right\|_Q > \beta \right) \leqslant e^{-\frac{\lambda^2}{2}(\beta^2 - \alpha)}$$

for all sufficiently large λ, *where* $\| \cdot \|_Q$ *is the norm of RKHS* $H(Q)$.

Proof of Lemma 2. Let $e_1, \ldots, e_m$ be an orthonormal basis in $H(Q)$. Then Z can be represented as $Z = \sum_{i=1}^{m} \xi_i e_i$ where ξ_i are independent standard Gaussian random variables. Hence

$$\mathsf{P}\Big(\Big\|\frac{Z}{\lambda}\Big\|_Q > \beta\Big) = \mathsf{P}(\|Z\|_Q^2 > (\lambda\beta)^2) = \mathsf{P}\Big(\sum_{i=1}^{m} \xi_i^2 > (\lambda\beta)^2\Big) \leqslant$$

$$\leqslant C(\lambda\beta)^2 e^{-\frac{\lambda^2\beta^2}{2}} \leqslant e^{-\frac{\lambda^2}{2}(\beta^2-\alpha)}$$

for any $\alpha > 0$, if λ is sufficiently large. The lemma is proved.

Applying Lemma 2, we have

$$\mathsf{P}(\| f_{n_k}^T \|_{S(n_k)} > 1 + \epsilon) = \mathsf{P}\Big(\Big\|\frac{Y_{n_k}^T}{\sqrt{2 \log\log n_k}}\Big\|_{S(n_k)} > 1 + \epsilon\Big) \leqslant$$

$$\leqslant e^{(-(1+\epsilon)^2+\alpha)\log\log n_k}$$

for any $\alpha > 0$, if k is sufficiently large. Choose $\alpha > 0$ small enough so that $(1+\epsilon)^2 - \alpha = \epsilon' > 1$. Then, for all sufficiently large k, $\mathsf{P}(\| f_{n_k}^T \|_{S(n_k)} > 1 + \epsilon) \leqslant Ck^{-\epsilon'}$, and, by the first Borel – Cantelli lemma, $\mathsf{P}(\| f_{n_k}^T \|_{S(n_k)} > 1 + \epsilon$ i.o.$) = 0$. This completes the proof of Proposition 5.

To prove the reverse inclusion we further assume the following condition (C-3). Let $L(X, t_0)$ denote the closed subspace spanned by $\{X(t),\ 0 \leqslant t \leqslant t_0\}$ in $L^2(\Omega, \mathscr{F}, \mathsf{P})$, and let

$$L^*(X, r\delta) = \bigcap_{h>0} L(X, r\delta + h) \qquad \text{for} \qquad 0 < \delta < 1\,.$$

Denote by $X^*(t, r\delta)$ the projection of $X(t)$ $(0 \leqslant t \leqslant r)$ on $L^*(X, r\delta)$, and, let $R^*(s, t; r\delta)$ $(0 \leqslant s, t \leqslant r)$ denote the covariance function of $\{X^*(t, r\delta),\ 0 \leqslant t \leqslant r\}$.

(C-3) The limits $\Gamma_\delta^*(s, t) = \lim\limits_{r\to\infty} \dfrac{R^*(rs, rt; r\delta)}{v(r)}$ exist for $0 \leqslant s, t \leqslant \leqslant 1$, $0 < \delta < 1$, and $\lim\limits_{\delta\to 0} \Gamma_\delta^*(t, t) = 0$ $(0 \leqslant t \leqslant 1)$.

Proposition 6. *If Conditions* (C-2) *and* (C-3) *are satisfied, then, for any finite set* $T = \{t_1, \ldots, t_m\}$ $(t_i \in (0, 1])$, *the set of limit points of* $\{f_n^T\}$ *contains the unit ball* K^T *of* $H(\Gamma^T)$ *a.s.*

Proof. It suffices to show, because of the compactness of K^T, that, for any $h^T \in K^T$ with $\| h^T \|_T < 1$ and for any $\epsilon > 0$, there are infinitely many n such that $\| f_n^T - h^T \|_\infty < 2\epsilon$ a.s. For $\delta < t_1 = \min t_i$, define the random vectors in R^m

$$Y^{*T}(n, \delta) = \Big(\frac{X^*(nt_1, n\delta)}{\sigma(n)}, \ldots, \frac{X^*(nt_m, n\delta)}{\sigma(n)} \Big),$$

$$Z^T(n, \delta) = Y_n^T - Y^{*T}(n, \delta),$$

and let $Q^T(n, \delta)$ be the covariance matrix of $Z^T(n, \delta)$.

By Conditions (C-2) and (C-3), $Q^T(n, \delta)$ can be made arbitrarily close to Γ^T elementwise for all sufficiently large n, if δ is sufficiently small. Hence, for any vector $\varphi^T \in R^m$, $\| \varphi^T \|_{Q(n,\delta)}$ can be made arbitrarily close to $\| \varphi^T \|_T$, choosing δ sufficiently small. We have also the following

Lemma 3. *Let* $n_k = [c^k]$ *with any* $c > 1$. *Then, for any* $\epsilon > 0$, *there is a* $\delta > 0$ *such that*

$$\Big\| \frac{Y^{*T}(n_k, \delta)}{\sqrt{2 \log \log n_k}} \Big\|_\infty < \epsilon$$

for all sufficiently large k, *a.s.*

Proof of the lemma. Let

$$A(k, \delta) = \{ \| Y^{*T}(n_k, \delta) \|_\infty \geqslant \epsilon \sqrt{2 \log \log n_k} \},$$

and

$$u^2(k, \delta) = \max_{1 \leqslant i \leqslant m} \mathsf{E} \Big[\frac{X^*(n_k t_i, n_k \delta)}{\sigma(n_k)} \Big]^2 .$$

Then $\mathsf{P}(A(k, \delta)) \leqslant C \exp\{-2\alpha\epsilon^2 \log \log n_k\}$ for all $\alpha < \dfrac{1}{2u^2(k, \delta)}$. By Condition (C-3), we can choose a $\delta > 0$ such that $u^2(k, \delta) < \dfrac{\epsilon^2}{2}$ for all sufficiently large k. Let α be a number such that $\dfrac{1}{2\epsilon^2} < \alpha < \dfrac{1}{2u^2(k, \delta)}$.

Then $\mathsf{P}(A(k, \delta)) \leqslant C' k^{-2\alpha\epsilon^2}$, and, by the first Borel – Cantelli lemma,

$\mathsf{P}(\limsup_k A(k, \delta)) = 0$. The lemma is proved.

Thus we can choose $\delta\left(< \frac{t_1}{2}\right)$ sufficiently small so that, for all sufficiently large k, $\| h^T \|_{Q(n_k, \delta)} < 1$ and

$$\left\| f_{n_k}^T - \frac{Z^T(n_k, \delta)}{\sqrt{2 \log \log n_k}} \right\|_\infty < \epsilon \qquad \text{a.s.},$$

where $n_k = [c^k]$, $c > 1$. Then it suffices to show that

$$\mathsf{P}\left(\left\| \frac{Z^T(n_k, \delta)}{\sqrt{2 \log \log n_k}} - h^T \right\|_\infty < \epsilon \text{ i.o.}\right) = 1 .$$

Lemma 4. *Let Z be a Gaussian random vector in R^m with zero mean vector and strictly positive definite covariance matrix Q, and let $\psi \in R^m$. Then, for any $\epsilon, \alpha > 0$,*

$$\mathsf{P}\left(\left\| \frac{Z}{\lambda} - \psi \right\|_\infty < \epsilon\right) \geqslant \exp\left\{- \frac{\lambda^2}{2} (\| \psi \|_Q^2 + \alpha)\right\}$$

for all sufficiently large λ, where $\| \cdot \|_Q$ is the norm of $H(Q)$.

Proof of the lemma. Let μ and ν be the distributions of Z and $Z - \lambda\psi$, respectively. The Radon – Nikodym derivative $\frac{d\nu}{d\mu}$ is given by $\frac{d\nu}{d\mu} = \exp\left\{\Psi(x) - \frac{1}{2} \| \lambda\psi \|_Q^2\right\}$ $(x \in R^m)$, where $\Psi(x)$ satisfies the relation $\lambda^2 \| \psi \|_Q^2 = \int_{R^m} \Psi^2(x)\mu(dx)$. Then

$$\mathsf{P}\left(\left\| \frac{Z}{\lambda} - \psi \right\|_\infty < \epsilon\right) = \mu(\| x - \lambda\psi \|_\infty < \lambda\epsilon) = \nu(\| x \|_\infty < \lambda\epsilon) =$$

$$= \int_{\| x \|_\infty < \lambda\epsilon} \exp\left\{\Psi(x) - \frac{1}{2} \| \lambda\psi \|_Q^2\right\}\mu(dx) \geqslant$$

$$\geqslant \exp\left\{- \frac{\lambda^2}{2} \| \psi \|_Q^2 - \lambda C\right\} \cdot \mu(\{\| x \|_\infty < \lambda\epsilon\} \cap \{\Psi(x) > - \lambda C\}),$$

where $C \geqslant 2 \| \psi \|_Q$. The second factor is $\geqslant \frac{1}{2}$, if λ and C are sufficiently large. Hence

$$\mathsf{P}\Big(\Big\|\frac{Z}{\lambda} - \psi\Big\|_\infty < \epsilon\Big) \geqslant \frac{1}{2}\exp\Big\{-\frac{\lambda^2}{2}\,\|\psi\|_Q^2 - \lambda C\Big\} \geqslant$$

$$\geqslant \exp\Big\{-\frac{\lambda^2}{2}\,(\|\psi\|_Q^2 + \alpha)\Big\}$$

for any $\alpha > 0$, if λ is sufficiently large. The lemma is proved.

Choose $\alpha > 0$ small enough so that $\| h^T \|^2_{Q(n_k, \delta)} + \alpha = \beta < 1$. Then, applying Lemma 4, we have

$$\mathsf{P}\Big(\Big\|\frac{Z^T(n_k, \delta)}{\sqrt{2\log\log n_k}} - h^T\Big\|_\infty < \epsilon\Big) \geqslant Ck^{-\beta}.$$

Let $c = \frac{1}{\delta}$. Then $Z^T(n_k, \delta)$ are independent, and so, by the second Borel – Cantelli lemma, we have

$$\mathsf{P}\Big(\Big\|\frac{Z^T(n_k, \delta)}{\sqrt{2\log\log n_k}} - h^T\Big\|_\infty < \epsilon \text{ i.o.}\Big) = 1 .$$

This completes the proof.

Summing up, we obtain

Theorem 1. *If Conditions* (C - 1) - (C - 3) *are satisfied, then* $\{f_n(t)\}$ *is relatively compact and the set of its limit points is the unit ball of the RKHS* $H(\Gamma)$ *a.s.*

Remark 3. The stationarity of increments of X is used only in the proof of Proposition 4. With some additional conditions on R we may obtain a similar result for some Gaussian processes with nonstationary increments (see [10]).

Remark 4. Lemmas 2 and 4 can be extended to the case of Gaussian measures on $C[0, 1]$, and the extensions have some applications to the high level occupation times for continuous Gaussian processes.

4. DEPENDENT RANDOM SEQUENCES

Let $\{\xi_j\}$ be a strictly stationary sequence with $\mathsf{E}\xi_j = 0$, $\mathsf{E}\xi_j^2 < \infty$, satisfying one of the following mixing conditions:

(I) (φ-mixing)

$$\sup_{A \in \mathcal{M}_{-\infty}^{k},\, B \in \mathcal{M}_{k+n}^{\infty}} \frac{|\mathsf{P}(A \cap B) - \mathsf{P}(A)\mathsf{P}(B)|}{\mathsf{P}(A)} = \varphi(n) \downarrow 0$$

as $n \to \infty$,

(II) (strong mixing)

$$\sup_{A \in \mathcal{M}_{-\infty}^{k},\, B \in \mathcal{M}_{k+n}^{\infty}} |\mathsf{P}(A \cap B) - \mathsf{P}(A)\mathsf{P}(B)| = \alpha(n) \downarrow 0$$

as $n \to \infty$,

where $\mathcal{M}_a^b$ denote the σ-algebra generated by $\{\xi_j,\ a \leqslant j \leqslant b\}$. Set $S_0 = 0$, $S_k = \sum_{j=1}^{k} \xi_j$, $\sigma_n^2 = \mathsf{E}S_n^2$ and $\sigma^2 = \mathsf{E}\xi_1^2 + 2 \sum_{j=2}^{\infty} \mathsf{E}\xi_1 \xi_j$. Assume $0 < \sigma^2 < \infty$ and $\sigma_n^2 = n\sigma^2(1 + o(1))$. Define

$$f_n(t) = \begin{cases} \dfrac{S_k}{\sigma\sqrt{2n \log\log n}} & \text{for } t = \dfrac{k}{n} \quad (k = 0, 1, \ldots, n) \\ \text{linear} & \text{for } t \in \left[\dfrac{k}{n}, \dfrac{k+1}{n}\right] \end{cases}$$

$$(k = 0, \ldots, n-1).$$

The following proposition is a part of the results obtained in [12].

Proposition 7 ([12]). *Suppose that either*

(i) $\{\xi_j\}$ *is* φ-*mixing with* $\sum_n \varphi^{\frac{1}{2}}(n) < \infty$, *and* $\int_{|x|>N} x^2 dF(x) = O((\log N)^{-5})$ $(N \to \infty)$, *where* F *is the distribution of* ξ_j, *or*

(ii) $\{\xi_j\}$ *is strong mixing with* $\alpha(n) = O(n^{-1-\epsilon})$, $\epsilon > 0$, *and uniformly bounded a.s.*

Then $\{f_n(t)\}$ *is relatively compact and the set of its limit points is* K_B *a.s.*

Remark 5. The proof in [12] uses the method of Chover [3]. In a recent paper [7] Heyde and Scott generalized the part (i) (φ-mixing case) of the proposition by a different method, showing that the moment condition is unnecessary.

The functional central limit theorem (Donsker-type invariance principle) for the above mixing sequence $\{\xi_j\}$ states that the sequence $\{f_n(t)\sqrt{2 \log \log n}\}$ converges weakly to a Brownian motion B, and so it is natural that the set of limit points of $\{f_n(t)\}$ is K_B. Observe that if the kernel Γ in Proposition 2 is the covariance function of the Brownian motion, i.e., $\Gamma(s, t) = \min(s, t) = \frac{1}{2}(s + t - |s - t|)$, as in this case, and if $T = \left\{\frac{1}{m}, \frac{2}{m}, \ldots, 1\right\}$, then, for $\psi = (\psi_1, \ldots, \psi_m) \in R^m$, $\|\psi\|_T^2 = m \cdot \{\psi_1^2 + (\psi_2 - \psi_1)^2 + \ldots + (\psi_m - \psi_{m-1})^2\}$. Thus, in this case, $\|f_n^T\|_T^2$ is a simple quadratic form of the above type, and, using the asymptotic independence of ξ_j and a standard technique, the proof is essentially reduced to the case of i.i.d. ξ_j.

However, if the dependence of increments of a random sequence over distant intervals persists, then we should expect that the kernel Γ is the covariance function of a Gaussian process other than Brownian motion. The following proposition is a result in this direction (see [11]).

Let ξ_j be i.i.d., uniformly bounded, with mean zero and variance one, and let

$$X_k = \xi_{k-1} + \frac{\xi_{k-2}}{2^\alpha} + \frac{\xi_{k-3}}{3^\alpha} + \ldots$$

$$\left(k = 1, 2, \ldots, \frac{1}{2} < \alpha < 1\right).$$

Set $S_0 = 0$, $S_n = \sum_{k=1}^{n} X_k$. Define

$$f_n(t) = \begin{cases} \dfrac{S_k}{\sqrt{2\mathrm{E}S_n^2 \log\log n}} & \text{for} \quad t = \dfrac{k}{n} \quad (k = 0, \ldots, n)\,, \\ \text{linear} & \text{for} \quad t \in \left[\dfrac{k}{n}, \dfrac{k+1}{n}\right] \\ & \qquad (k = 0, \ldots, n-1)\,. \end{cases}$$

Then we have

Proposition 8 ([11]). *$\{f_n(t)\}$ is relatively compact and the set of its limit points is contained in the unit ball of RKHS $H(\Gamma_\gamma)$ with r.k.*

$$\Gamma_\gamma(s, t) = \frac{1}{2}\{s^\gamma + t^\gamma - |s - t|^\gamma\} \qquad (\gamma = 3 - 2\alpha)$$

a.s.

Remark 6. Davydov [4] has shown that $\{f_n(t)\sqrt{2 \log\log n}\}$ converges weakly to the Gaussian process with covariance function Γ_γ. The author conjectures that the set of limit points of $\{f_n(t)\}$ does coincide with the unit ball of $H(\Gamma_\gamma)$.

5. EMPIRICAL DISTRIBUTION FUNCTIONS

Let $\{\xi_j\}$ be strictly stationary and either φ-mixing or strong mixing, and suppose that ξ_1 is uniformly distributed over $[0, 1]$. Let $F_n(t)$ be the empirical distribution function at stage n, and define

$$f_n(t) = \sqrt{\frac{n}{2 \log\log n}}\,(F_n(t) - t) \qquad (0 \leqslant t \leqslant 1)\,.$$

Let $Z_j(t) = I_{[0,t]}(\xi_j) - t$, where $I_{[0,t]}(\cdot)$ is the indicator function of $[0, t]$.

Billingsley [2] proved that if $\{\xi_j\}$ is φ-mixing with $\sum n^2 \varphi^{\frac{1}{2}}(n) < \infty$, then $\{f_n(t)\sqrt{2 \log\log n}\}$ converges to X in distribution, where $X = \{X(t),\ 0 \leqslant t \leqslant 1\}$ is the Gaussian process with mean zero and covariance function

$$(*) \qquad \Gamma(s, t) = \mathrm{E}Z_1(s)Z_1(t) + \sum_{j=2}^{\infty} \mathrm{E}Z_1(s)Z_j(t) + \sum_{j=2}^{\infty} \mathrm{E}Z_j(s)Z_1(t)\,.$$

Hence it may be natural to expect that, for some classes of mixing random variables, the set of limit points of $\{f_n(t)\}$ is the unit ball of the RKHS $H(\Gamma)$ with r.k. $(*)$.

We first examine the finite dimensional case. We have

Proposition 9. *Let* $\{\xi_j\}$ *be either* φ*-mixing with* $\sum \varphi^{\frac{1}{2}}(n)$ *or strong mixing with* $\alpha(n) = O(n^{-1-\epsilon})$ $(\epsilon > 0)$ *and assume that the kernel* Γ *defined by* $(*)$ *is strictly positive definite. Then the condition* (β) *of Proposition 3 is satisfied, and so, for any* $T = \{t_1, \ldots, t_m\}$ $(t_i \in (0,1))$, $\{f_n^T\}$ *is relatively compact and the set of its limit points is the unit ball of* $H(\Gamma^T)$ *a.s.*

Proof. We use Finkelstein's argument (see Lemma 2, [6]), which is a reminiscent of the Cramér – Wold device for multi-dimensional characteristic functions, and the "finite dimensional" case will be reduced to the "one dimensional" case.

Let Z_j be the m-dimensional random column vector whose i-th component is $Z_j(t_i)$. Then

$$\Gamma^T = \mathsf{E} Z_1 Z_1' + \sum_{j=2}^{\infty} \mathsf{E} Z_1 Z_j' + \sum_{j=2}^{\infty} \mathsf{E} Z_j Z_1' ,$$

where the prime stands for the transposition. Let $h \in H(\Gamma^T)$ and let $(\cdot, \cdot)_T$ denote the inner product of $H(\Gamma^T)$. Then $(h, Z_j)_T$ are bounded one-dimensional random variables with mean zero, satisfying the same mixing condition as ξ_j, and we have

$$\mathsf{E}(h, Z_1)_T^2 + 2 \sum_{j=2}^{\infty} \mathsf{E}(h, Z_1)_T (h, Z_j)_T = \| h \|_T^2 .$$

Hence, by the "one-dimensional" form of Proposition 7, i.e., the ordinary form of the log log law, we obtain

$$(**) \qquad \limsup_n \left| \left(\frac{h}{\| h \|_T}, \sum_{j=1}^{n} \frac{Z_j}{\sqrt{2n \log \log n}} \right)_T \right| = 1 \qquad \text{a.s.}$$

We note also that

$$\limsup_n \left\| \sum_{j=1}^{n} \frac{Z_j}{\sqrt{2n \log\log n}} \right\|_T < \text{constant} \qquad \text{a.s.},$$

since Proposition 7 applies to each component sequence $\{Z_j(t_i)\}$. Using the separability of $H(\Gamma^T)$ and the compactness of the set $\{h \in H(\Gamma^T) \mid \|h\|_T = 1\}$, we can deduce from (**) that

$$\limsup_n \left\| \sum_{j=1}^{n} \frac{Z_j}{\sqrt{2n \log\log n}} \right\|_T = \limsup_n \| f_n^T \| = 1 \qquad \text{a.s.}$$

The rest of the proof is also quite similar to that of Lemma 2, [6]. We need only observe the following simple fact (see Lemma 1). Let $T_m = \{t_1, \ldots, t_m\}$ and $T_{m+1} = T_m \cup \{t_{m+1}\}$, where $t_{m+1} \notin T_m$, and let Γ_m and Γ_{m+1} be the restrictions of Γ to T_m and T_{m+1}, respectively. Then

(i) if h^* is in the unit ball of $H(\Gamma_{m+1})$, the restriction h of h^* to T_m is in the unit ball of $H(\Gamma_m)$, and

(ii) if h is in the unit ball of $H(\Gamma_m)$, there is at least one $h^* \in H(\Gamma_{m+1})$ such that h is the restriction of h^* to T_m and $\|h^*\|_{m+1} = 1$, where $\|\cdot\|_{m+1}$ is the norm of $H(\Gamma_{m+1})$. Using Finkelstein's argument (just replacing R^m by $H(\Gamma^T)$), we may conclude that the set of limit points of $\{f_n^T\}$ contains the unit ball of $H(\Gamma^T)$ a.s. This completes the proof.

Suppose now that ξ_j are $(p-1)$-dependent (we use $p-1$ instead of the usual m, to avoid notational confusion). Then the condition (α) of Proposition 3 is satisfied, as will be shown below.

Set $k = \left[\frac{n}{p}\right]$, and define, for $\alpha = 1, 2, \ldots, p$,

$$f_{\alpha,k}(t) = \sum_{\beta=0}^{k-1} \frac{Z_{\alpha+\beta p}}{\sqrt{2k \log\log k}} = \sqrt{\frac{k}{2 \log\log k}}\,(F_{\alpha,k}(t) - t),$$

$(k = 3, 4, \ldots)$

where $F_{\alpha,k}(t)$ is the empirical distribution function at stage k for $\xi_\alpha, \xi_{\alpha+p}, \xi_{\alpha+2p}, \ldots$. Then

$$f_n(t) = \sqrt{\frac{k \log\log k}{n \log\log n}} \sum_{\alpha=1}^{p} f_{\alpha,k}(t) + \sum_{j=kp+1}^{n} \frac{Z_j(t)}{\sqrt{2n \log\log n}} .$$

Let $T = \left\{\frac{i}{m}, i = 1, \ldots, m-1\right\}$, and let $\widetilde{f}_n^T(t)$ and $\widetilde{f}_{\alpha,k}^T(t)$ be respectively the polygonal approximations to $f_n(t)$ and $f_{\alpha,k}(t)$ determined by T. Then, for $t \in I_i = \left[\frac{i-1}{m}, \frac{i}{m}\right]$, $(i = 1, \ldots, m)$

$$f_n(t) - \widetilde{f}_n^T(t) = \sqrt{\frac{k \log\log k}{n \log\log n}} \sum_{\alpha=1}^{p} \{f_{\alpha,k}(t) - \widetilde{f}_{\alpha,k}^T(t)\} +$$

$$+ \frac{1}{\sqrt{2n \log\log n}} \sum_{j=kp+1}^{n} \left\{Z_j(t) - Z_j\left(\frac{i-1}{m}\right) - \right.$$

$$\left. - m\left(t - \frac{i-1}{m}\right)\left[Z_j\left(\frac{i}{m}\right) - Z_j\left(\frac{i-1}{m}\right)\right]\right\} .$$

and hence

$$\sup_{t \in I_i} |f_n(t) - \widetilde{f}_n^T(t)| \leqslant \sqrt{\frac{k \log\log k}{n \log\log n}} \times$$

$$\times \sum_{\alpha=1}^{p} \sup_{t \in I_i} |f_{\alpha,k}(t) - \widetilde{f}_{\alpha,k}^T(t)| + \frac{2p}{\sqrt{2n \log\log n}} .$$

Since $\xi_\alpha, \xi_{\alpha+p}, \xi_{\alpha+2p}, \ldots$ are independent, we have, by Lemma 5, [6],

$$\sup_{t \in I_i} |f_{\alpha,k}(t) - \widetilde{f}_{\alpha,k}^T(t)| < \frac{1}{\sqrt{m}} \qquad (\alpha = 1, \ldots, p) ,$$

for all sufficiently large k, a.s. Therefore, for any $\epsilon' > 0$,

$$\| f_n - \widetilde{f}_n^T \|_\infty < \sqrt{\frac{p}{m}} + \epsilon'$$

for all sufficiently large n, a.s. This shows that the condition (α) is satisfied for $(p-1)$-dependent ξ_j.

Combining this with Proposition 9, we have the following

Theorem 2. *Suppose that $\{\xi_j\}$ is m-dependent. Then $\{f_n(t)\}$ is relatively compact and the set of its limit points is the unit ball of $H(\Gamma)$ with r.k.*

$$\Gamma(s, t) = \mathsf{E}Z_1(s)Z_1(t) + \sum_{j=2}^{m+1} \mathsf{E}Z_1(s)Z_j(t) + \sum_{j=2}^{m+1} \mathsf{E}Z_j(s)Z_1(t), \quad a.s.$$

In view of Proposition 9, it appears reasonable to expect that a similar result holds for more general classes of mixing $\{\xi_j\}$.

REFERENCES

[1] N. Aronszajn, The theory of reproducing kernels, *Trans. Amer. Math. Soc.*, 68 (1950), 337-404.

[2] P. Billingsley, *Convergence of probability measures,* Wiley, New York, 1968.

[3] J. Chover, On Strassen's version of the log log law, *Z. Wahrscheinlichkeitstheorie verw. Geb.*, 8 (1967), 83-90.

[4] Yu.A. Davydov, The invariance principle for stationary processes, *Theory of Prob. its Appl,* 15 (1970), 487-498.

[5] X. Fernique, Regularité de processus gaussiens, *Inventiones Math.*, 12 (1971), 304-320.

[6] H. Finkelstein, The law of the iterated logarithm for empirical distributions, *Ann. Math. Statist.*, 42 (1971), 607-615.

[7] C.C. Heyde – D.J. Scott, Invariance principles for the iterated logarithm for martingales and processes with stationary increments, *Ann. Prob.*, 1 (1973), 428-436.

[8] M.B. Marcus – L.A. Shepp, Sample behavior of Gaussian processes, *Proc. Sixth Berkeley Symp. Math. Statist. Prob.* 2, Univ. of California Press (1972), 423-441.

[9] H. Oodaira, On Strassen's version of the law of the iterated logarithm for Gaussian processes, *Z. Wahrscheinlichkeitstheorie verw. Geb.*, 21 (1972), 289-299.

[10] H. Oodaira, The law of the iterated logarithm for Gaussian processes, *Ann. Prob.*, 1 (1973), 954-967.

[11] H. Oodaira, The log log law for certain dependent random sequences, *Proc. Second Japan – USSR Symp. Prob. Theory,* Lecture Notes in Math. 330, Springer-Verlag (1973), 355-369.

[12] H. Oodaira – K. Yoshihara, Note on the law of the iterated logarithm for stationary processes satisfying mixing conditions, *Kodai Math. Sem. Rep.*, 23 (1971), 335-342.

[13] V. Strássen, An invariance principle for the law of the iterated logarithm, *Z. Wahrscheinlichkeitstheorie verw. Geb.*, 3 (1964), 211-226.

COLLOQUIA MATHEMATICA SOCIETATIS JÁNOS BOLYAI
11. LIMIT THEOREMS OF PROBABILITY THEORY, KESZTHELY (HUNGARY), 1974.

ASYMPTOTIC FLUCTUATION BEHAVIOR OF SUMS OF WEAKLY DEPENDENT RANDOM VARIABLES*

W. PHILIPP — W.F. STOUT

1. INTRODUCTION

The purpose of our research is to investigate the asymptotic fluctuation behavior of sums of weakly dependent random variables, such as lacunary trigonometric, mixing, and Gaussian. We present here a brief exposition of the results obtained and a detailed sketch of the method leading to these results. A complete presentation is given in Philipp and Stout [26].

In essence, $\{x_n\}$ are weakly dependent if

$$\mathsf{E}\,|\,\mathsf{E}(x_{n+k}\,|\,x_1,\ldots,x_n)\,|\to 0$$

as $k\to\infty$ for each $n\geqslant 1$. By asymptotic fluctuation behavior, we mean

*Research was partially supported by the national Science Foundation. Help in preparation was provided by the University of North Carolina Dept. of Statistics and by Office of Naval Research Grant N 00014-67-A-0321-002; TSK-NR-042-214.

results such as the law of the iterated logarithm, Strassen's functional law of the iterated logarithm, the upper and lower class refinement of the law of the iterated logarithm, and Chung's upper and lower class result for the maxima of partial sums.

We obtain these results by first establishing almost sure invariance principles. The idea of an almost sure invariance principle is due to Strassen [30], [31]. Strassen proves, among other things, that a martingale with finite variances is with probability one close to Brownian motion on $[0, \infty)$ in a sense made precise in Section 3. The asymptotic fluctuation behavior of Brownian motion has, of course, been thoroughly investigated. In particular, the upper and lower class refinement of the law of the iterated logarithm is known, as well as the functional form of the law of the iterated logarithm (Strassen [30]) and the upper and lower class refinement for the maximum of Brownian motion up to time t (Jain and Taylor [21]). Thus, if the approximation of the martingale by Brownian motion given by the almost sure invariance principle is sufficiently close, then all the above fluctuation results for Brownian motion also hold for the martingale.

If we are able to approximate sufficiently closely sums of weakly dependent random variables by a martingale, we can then conclude, in view of the above remarks, that these sums are close to Brownian motion with probability 1. Consequently, the fluctuation results for Brownian motion will continue to hold for the weakly dependent random variables under consideration.

Let us be more specific about this last point. Let $\{x_n\}$ be a sequence of random variables, centered at expectations with finite $(2 + \delta)$ moments. Put

$$(1.1) \qquad S_t = S(t) = \sum_{n \leq t} x_n .$$

Suppose

$$\lim_{n \to \infty} \mathrm{D}^2\left(\frac{S_n}{\sqrt{n}}\right) = \sigma^2 > 0$$

exists and is positive so that without loss of generality we can and do assume $\sigma^2 = 1$. Our goal is to prove for a large class of weakly dependent random variables the basic almost sure invariance principle

$$(1.2) \qquad S(t) - X(t) \ll t^{\frac{1}{2} - \eta} \qquad \text{a.s.}$$

for some $\eta > 0$. (We use the Vinogradov symbol $\ll$ instead of big O.) Here $X(t)$ is standard Brownian motion on $[0, \infty)$ and $\eta > 0$ depends on the sequence $\{x_n\}$ considered. Such a result immediately translates almost sure fluctuation results from $\{X(t)\}$ to $\{S(t)\}$ and hence to $\{S_n\}$. Indeed, suppose we have an arbitrary sequence $\{x_n\}$ such that its "bookkeeping function" $\{S(t)\}$ satisfies (1.2). Then the following four theorems are straightforward consequences of known results for Brownian motion.

Theorem A. *Let* $\{x_n\}_{n=1}^{\infty}$ *be any sequence of random variables satisfying* (1.2). *Let* $\varphi(t)$ *be a positive, nondecreasing real-valued function. Then*

$$\mathsf{P}\{S_n > \sqrt{n}\,\varphi(n) \ \ i.o.\} = 0 \quad or \quad 1$$

according as

$$\int_1^{\infty} \frac{\varphi(t)}{t}\, e^{-\frac{\varphi^2(t)}{2}}\, dt$$

converges or diverges.

This result follows from Kolmogorov's test for Brownian motion. For the details of the proof see for example Jain, Jogdeo and Stout [20].

Using a recent result on the maximum of Brownian motion due to Jain and Taylor [21] we get (again, for the details see Jain, Jogdeo and Stout [20])

Theorem B. *Let* $\{x_n\}$ *and* $\varphi(t)$ *be as in Theorem* A. *Put*

$$M_n = \max_{1 \leqslant i \leqslant n} |S_i| .$$

Then

$$\mathrm{P}\{M_n < \sqrt{n}\,\varphi^{-1}(n) \ \ i.o.\} = 0 \quad or \quad 1$$

according as

$$\int_1^\infty \frac{\varphi^2(u)}{u} e^{-\frac{8\varphi^2(u)}{\pi^2}} du$$

converges or diverges.

Next, let $C[0, 1]$ be the space of all real-valued continuous functions $h(t)$, $t \in [0, 1]$, with the supremum norm $\| h \| = \sup_{0 \leq t \leq 1} | h(t) |$. Let $K \subset C[0, 1]$ be the set of absolutely continuous functions with $h(0) = 0$, $\int_0^1 (h'(t))^2 dt \leq 1$. Let

$$(1.3) \qquad S_n(t) = S(nt) = \sum_{k \leq nt} x_k \qquad (0 \leq t \leq 1)\,.$$

Define another type of bookkeeping functions $f_n(t) = f_n(t, \omega)$ by

$$(1.4) \qquad f_n(t) = \frac{S(nt)}{\sqrt{2n \log \log n}} \qquad (0 \leq t \leq 1)\,.$$

Theorem C. *Let* $\{x_n\}_{n=1}^\infty$ *be a sequence of random variables satisfying* (1.2). *Then with probability* 1 *the sequence of functions* $\{f_n(t)\}$ *defined by* (1.4) *is relatively compact in the topology of uniform convergence and has* K *as its derived set.*

Indeed, by (1.2) and (1.3),

$$S_n(t) - X(nt) \ll (nt)^{\frac{1}{2}-\eta} \ll n^{\frac{1}{2}-\eta} \qquad \text{a.s.}$$

uniformly in $0 \leq t \leq 1$. Write $\zeta_n(t) = X(nt)$. Then, of course,

$$(1.5) \qquad \| S_n - \zeta_n \| \ll n^{\frac{1}{2}-\eta} \qquad \text{a.s.,} \quad n > 0\,.$$

Consequently,

$$\frac{\| S_n - \zeta_n \|}{\sqrt{n \log\log n}} \ll n^{-\eta} .$$

Theorem C follows now from Strassen's [30] Theorem 1 which states that the conclusion of Theorem C holds for the sequence $\left\{\frac{\zeta_n(t)}{\sqrt{2n \log\log n}},\ n \geq 3\right\}$.

Similarly, (1.2) implies distribution type invariance principles:

Theorem D. *Let* $\{x_n\}_{n=1}^{\infty}$ *be a sequence of random variables satisfying* (1.2). *Then*

$$\frac{S_n(\cdot)}{\sqrt{n}} \to W(\cdot)$$

in distribution where $W(t)$ *is standard Brownian motion on* $[0, 1]$ *and* $S_n(t)$ *is defined by* (1.4).

Indeed, (1.5) implies that

$$\frac{S_n - \zeta_n}{\sqrt{n}} \to 0$$

in probability. But $\frac{\zeta_n}{\sqrt{n}}$ has the same distribution as $\{W(t),\ 0 \leq t \leq 1\}$ for $n \geq 1$ and the result follows (see e.g. Billingsley [4], p. 25).

Both Theorems C and D have a large number of corollaries spelled out in detail in Strassen's paper [30] and Billingsley's book [4].

In addition to the stationary case, several applications are made to the nonstationary case where

$$\lim_n \frac{\mathrm{E}S_n^2}{n} \to 0$$

fails. Then our goal is still to prove the basic relation (1.2), where the definition of $\{S(t)\}$ is modified appropriately. Suppose $s_n^2 = \mathrm{E}S_n^2 \to \infty$. Moreover, to simplify the exposition, we make the easily removable assumption that s_n^2 is monotone. Put

$$S(t) = \sum_{k=1}^{n} x_k \qquad \text{for} \qquad s_n^2 = \mathsf{E}S_n^2 \leqslant t < s_{n+1}^2 .$$

Theorems A, B and D continue to hold, provided the statements are also modified appropriately.

In Theorem A replace

$$\mathsf{P}\{S_n > \sqrt{n}\,\varphi(n) \text{ i.o.}\} = 0 \quad \text{or} \quad 1$$

by

$$\mathsf{P}\{S_n > s_n \varphi(s_n^2) \text{ i.o.}\} = 0 \quad \text{or} \quad 1 .$$

Similarly, in Theorem B, replace

$$\mathsf{P}\{M_n < \sqrt{n}\,\varphi^{-1}(n) \text{ i.o.}\} = 0 \quad \text{or} \quad 1$$

by

$$\mathsf{P}\{M_n < s_n \varphi^{-1}(s_n^2) \text{ i.o.}\} = 0 \quad \text{or} \quad 1 .$$

In Theorem D redefine

$$S_n(t) = S(s_n^2 t) \qquad (0 \leqslant t \leqslant 1)$$

and replace $\dfrac{S_n(t)}{\sqrt{n}}$ by $\dfrac{S_n(t)}{s_n}$.

For all cases of weakly dependent random variables that we consider the conlusions of Theorems A and B are new. The conlusions of Theorem C and D, however, are new only in special cases.

It will be clear that the present method is rather general and is thus applicable to many situations other than those considered in this paper. We will give an outline of our method in Section 3.

2. STATEMENT OF RESULTS

Let $\{n_k,\ k \geqslant 1\}$ be a lacunary sequence of real numbers, i.e. $\dfrac{n_{k+1}}{n_k} \geqslant q > 1$ and let $\{a_k\}$ be another sequence of real numbers. Put

$$A_N^2 = \frac{1}{2} \sum_{k \leqslant N} a_k^2 .$$

Suppose that $A_N \to \infty$ and that there exists a constant δ with $0 < \delta \leqslant 1$ such that

$$(2.1) \qquad a_k \ll A_k^{1-\delta} .$$

We consider trigonometric series

$$\sum_k a_k \cos 2\pi n_k \omega$$

where $0 \leqslant \omega \leqslant 1$. For $t \geqslant 0$ put

$$S(t) = \sum_{k \leqslant N} a_k \cos 2\pi n_k \cdot \qquad \text{if} \qquad A_N^2 \leqslant t < A_{N+1}^2 \cdot$$

Then we have the following theorem.

Theorem 1. *Without changing the distribution of the process* $\{S(t), t \geqslant 0\}$ *we can redefine the process* $\{S(t), t \geqslant 0\}$ *on a richer probability space together with standard Brownian motion* $\{X(t), t \geqslant 0\}$ *such that*

$$S(t) - X(t) \ll t^{\frac{1}{2} - c\delta} \qquad a.s.$$

for each $c < \frac{1}{32}$.

Condition (2.1) can quite likely be replaced by a weaker one, say $a_k \ll \frac{A_k}{\log A_k}$. It is also quite likely that the gap condition could be relaxed to $\frac{n_{k+1}}{n_k} \geqslant 1 + \frac{c_k}{\sqrt{k}}$ with $c_k \uparrow \infty$. Perhaps, one could also combine these two possible generalizations.

Theorem 1 can be considered as a refinement of M. Weiss's [35] law of the iterated logarithm under the restriction (2.1). Also Billingsley's functional central limit theorem for lacunary trigonometric series should be mentioned in this context (Billingsley [3]).

Finally, it should be remarked that Theorem 1 includes the unweighted case $a_k = 1$. In this special case, a much simpler proof can be given. Recently and independently from the authors Berkes [2] obtained a similar result in the unweighted case, making more stringent assumptions on the sequence $\{n_k\}$.

Given a stochastic sequence $\{x_n, n \geqslant 1\}$, let $\mathscr{F}_a^b$ denote the σ-field generated by $x_a, x_{a+1}, \dots, x_b$ $(1 \leqslant a \leqslant b < \infty)$ and $\mathscr{F}_m^\infty$ the σ-field generated by $x_m, x_{m+1}, \dots$. Then the sequence is said to be φ-mixing if there exists a sequence $\{\varphi(n)\}$ of real numbers with $\varphi(n) \downarrow 0$ such that for each $t \geqslant 1$, $n \geqslant 0$, $A \in \mathscr{F}_1^t$, $B \in \mathscr{F}_{t+n}^\infty$ we have

$$(2.2) \qquad |\mathsf{P}(AB) - \mathsf{P}(A)\,\mathsf{P}(B)| \leqslant \varphi(n)\,\mathsf{P}(A).$$

We assume that

$$(2.3) \qquad \sum_{n=1}^{\infty} \varphi^{\frac{1}{2}}(n) < \infty.$$

Suppose $\{x_n\}$ is stationary with $\mathsf{E}x_1 = 0$ and $\mathsf{E}x_1^2 < \infty$. Then (2.3) is easily seen to imply the existence of the limit

$$\sigma^2 = \lim_{n\to\infty} \frac{1}{n}\,\mathsf{E}\Big(\sum_{k\leqslant n} x_k\Big)^2.$$

We assume throughout that $\sigma^2 > 0$, the case $\sigma^2 = 0$ being a degenerate one. Hence we assume without loss of generality that

$$(2.4) \qquad \sigma^2 = 1.$$

Let

$$S(t) = \sum_{k\leqslant t} x_k \qquad (t \geqslant 0).$$

Then we obtain the following almost sure invariance principle.

Theorem 2. *Let* $\{x_n, n \geqslant 1\}$ *be a stationary sequence, centered at expectations and satisfying* (2.2), (2.3), *and* (2.4). *Suppose that for some* $\delta > 0$

$$\mathsf{E}|x_1|^{2+\delta} < \infty.$$

Then, without changing the distribution of $\{S(t), t \geqslant 0\}$, *we can redefine the process* $\{S(t),\ t \geqslant 0\}$ *on a richer probability space together with standard Brownian motion* $\{X(t),\ t \geqslant 0\}$ *such that*

$$S(t) - X(t) \ll t^{\frac{1}{2} - c\delta}$$

a.s. for each $c < (24 + 12\delta)^{-1}$.

Remark. If $\| x_1 \|_\infty < \infty$ then the exponent reduces to $\frac{5}{12} + \epsilon$.

Theorem 2 contains one of Reznik's [27] theorems as a special case. Independently from the authors, Berkes [1] establishes a similar result under stronger hypotheses.

It might be interesting to remark that if, instead of $\mathsf{E}\,|x_1|^{2+\delta} < \infty$, only the finiteness of the second moments is assumed then the conclusion of Theorem 2 has to be weakened to

$$S(t) - X(t) = o(\sqrt{t \log \log t}) \qquad \text{a.s.}$$

This result is due to Heyde and Scott [17].

At the relatively minor cost of strengthening the assumption (2.3) and a more complicated proof, Theorem 2 can be considerably generalized. This is done in the next four theorems. Before stating these four theorems, we make some preparatory remarks.

Let $\{\xi_n\}$ be a sequence of random variables. Let f be a measurable mapping from the space of infinite sequences $(\alpha_1, \alpha_2, \ldots)$ of real numbers into the reals. Put

$$\eta_n = f(\xi_n, \xi_{n+1}, \ldots) \qquad (n \geqslant 1)\,. \tag{2.5}$$

Instead of φ-mixing we shall assume that the ξ_n's satisfy what we call a retarded strong mixing condition. Denote, as usual, by $\mathscr{F}_a^b$ the σ-field generated by the ξ_n's $(a \leqslant n \leqslant b)$. We shall assume that

$$|\,\mathsf{P}(AB) - \mathsf{P}(A)\,\mathsf{P}(B)\,| \leqslant \alpha(nt^{-\kappa}) \tag{2.6}$$

for all $A \in \mathscr{F}_1^t$ and all $B \in \mathscr{F}_{t+n}^\infty$. Here κ is a nonnegative constant, depending only on the exponent of the moments of the η_n's and $\alpha(s)$

converges monotonically to zero at a certain rate. The case $\kappa = 0$ gives the so-called strong mixing condition introduced by M. Rosenblatt [28]. Conditions of the form (2.6) occur in the metric theory of Diophantine approximation (see for example Szüsz [32] or Philipp [25], p. 48). Finally, we shall make no stationarity assumptions. As is customary, we shall assume that η_n can be closely approximated by

$$\eta_{ln} = \mathsf{E}(\eta_n \mid \mathscr{F}_n^{n+l}) .$$

With this notation we have the following theorem:

Theorem 3. *Let* $\{\xi_n\}$ *be a sequence of random variables and let* η_n *be defined by* (2.5). *We shall assume of the function* f *and the sequence* $\{\xi_n\}$ *that*

$$\mathsf{E}\eta_n = 0 .$$

Suppose that there exists constants $0 < \delta \leqslant 2$ *and* $C > 0$ *such that*

$$\mathsf{E}|\eta_n|^{2+\delta} \leqslant C$$

and

$$\|\eta_n - \eta_{ln}\|_{2+\delta} \leqslant Cl^{-2-\frac{7}{\delta}} \tag{2.7}$$

for all $n, l = 1, 2, 3, \ldots$. *Moreover, suppose that*

$$\mathsf{E}\Big(\sum_{n\leqslant N} \eta_n\Big)^2 = N + O\Big(N^{1-\frac{\delta}{30}}\Big)$$

as $N \to \infty$. *Finally, assume that* $\{\xi_n\}$ *satisfies a retarded strong mixing condition of the form* (2.6) *with*

$$\kappa = \frac{\delta}{11 + 4\delta}$$

and

$$\alpha(s) \ll s^{-168\left(1+\frac{2}{\delta}\right)} . \tag{2.8}$$

Define a continuous parameter process $\{S(t),\ t \geqslant 0\}$ *by setting*

$$S(t) = \sum_{n \leqslant t} \eta_n .$$

Then, without changing the distribution of $\{S(t),\ t \geqslant 0\}$ *we can redefine the process* $\{S(t),\ t \geqslant 0\}$ *on a richer probability space together with standard Brownian motion* $\{X(t),\ t \geqslant 0\}$ *such that*

$$S(t) - X(t) \ll t^{\frac{1}{2} - c\delta} \qquad \text{a.s. as} \qquad t \to \infty$$

for each $c < \frac{1}{588}$.

Except for the rates of decay in (2.7) and (2.8), Theorem 3 contains in the stationary case almost all previous results in this direction. For example, it contains Reznik's [27] and Iosifescu's [19] theorems on the law of the iterated logarithm for stationary φ-mixing random variables except for the convergence rates in (2.7) and (2.8). The same comment holds for Reznik's law of the iterated logarithm for strong mixing sequences. Notice that in this latter case we only assume a uniform bound on the $(2 + \delta)$ moments of η_n. Reznik either assumes uniform bounds on the η_n's themselves or on the $(4 + \delta)$ moments.

Theorem 3 also contains recent upper and lower class results of Jain, Jogdeo and Stout [20] on functionals of a Markov process satisfying Doeblin's condition. Independently of the authors, Berkes [1] establishes a result which is essentially the same as Theorem 3 for the speciel case that $\kappa = 0$.

Again, except for the rates of convergence in (2.7) and (2.8), Theorem 3 also implies a result of Davydov [10].

Although strict stationarity was not assumed in Theorem 3, restrictions consistent with stationarity on the growth of the variance of the partial sums of the random variables were imposed. In the same vein we assumed that the $(2 + \delta)$ moments of the random variables were uniformly bounded. In the next two theorems we relax these restrictions. However, for the sake of simplicity we shall restrict ourselves to sequences of random variables satisfying a strong mixing condition without introducing the retardation of Theorem 3.

For the next two theorems let $\{x_n\}$ be a sequence of random variables centered at expectations and with finite $(2+\delta)$ moments where

$$(2.9) \qquad 0 < \delta \leqslant 2\,.$$

Suppose that

$$(2.10) \qquad s_N^2 = \mathsf{E}\Big(\sum_{n \leqslant N} x_n\Big)^2 \to \infty$$

as $N \to \infty$ and that

$$(2.11) \qquad \max_{k \leqslant n} \mathsf{E}|x_k|^{2+\delta} \leqslant s_n^{\rho\delta}$$

for some $0 \leqslant \rho \leqslant 1$. Moreover, suppose that $\{x_n\}$ satisfies a strong mixing condition with

$$(2.12) \qquad \alpha(k) \leqslant k^{-300\left(1+\frac{2}{\delta}\right)}.$$

That is

$$|\mathsf{P}(AB) - \mathsf{P}(A)\,\mathsf{P}(B)| \leqslant \alpha(n)$$

for all $A \in \mathscr{F}_1^t$ and all $B \in \mathscr{F}_{t+n}^{\infty}$. Here, as usual, $\mathscr{F}_a^b$, denotes the σ-field generated by $\{x_n,\ a \leqslant n \leqslant b\}$.

With this notation we have the following two theorems.

Theorem 4. *Let* $\{x_n\}$ *be a sequence of random variables satisfying* (2.9), (2.10), *and* (2.12). *Suppose that there is a constant* C *such that*

$$\mathsf{E}|x_n|^{2+\delta} \leqslant C \qquad (n = 1, 2, \ldots)\,.$$

Let F *be an arbitrary monotonically increasing function. Suppose that*

$$(2.13) \qquad \sum_{n=M+1}^{M+N} \|x_n\|_{2+\delta} \leqslant F(A)$$

whenever

$$(2.14) \qquad \mathsf{E}\Big(\sum_{n=M+1}^{M+N} x_n\Big)^2 \leqslant A$$

for some A. *In other words suppose that the left-hand side of* (2.13) *does not exceed* F *evaluated at the left-hand side of* (2.14).

Define, recalling s_n^2 *assumed strictly increasing,*

$$S(t) = \sum_{k \leqslant N} x_n \quad \textit{for} \quad s_N^2 \leqslant t < s_{N+1}^2 .$$

Then, without changing the distribution of $\{S(t),\ t \geqslant 0\}$ *we can redefine* $\{S(t),\ t \geqslant 0\}$ *on a richer probability space together with standard Brownian motion* $\{X(t),\ t \geqslant 0\}$ *such that*

$$S(t) - X(t) \ll t^{\frac{1}{2} - c\delta} \qquad \textit{a.s.}$$

for each $c < \frac{1}{588}$.

Theorem 5. *Let* $\{x_n\}$ *be a sequence of random variables satisfying* (2.9)-(2.12) *with* $\rho \leqslant \frac{1}{4}$. *Let* σ *be a constant with*

$$\rho\sigma \leqslant \frac{1}{10} .$$

Suppose that uniformly in $(M = 1, 2, \ldots)$,

$$\sum_{n=M+1}^{M+N} \| x_n \|_{2+\delta} \ll \Big(\mathsf{E} \Big(\sum_{n=M+1}^{M+N} x_n \Big)^2 \Big)^\sigma \tag{2.15}$$

as $N \to \infty$. *Then the conclusion of Theorem* 4 *remains valid for each* $c < \frac{1}{1232}$.

Remarks. Conditions (2.13)-(2.14) and (2.15) are of a similar structure as the Ljapounov condition for the central limit theorem for sequences of independent random variables.

Except for the rate of decay of $\alpha(k)$, Theorem 5 contains a result of Philipp [24] as a special case. This result of Philipp's is, to the best of our knowledge, so far the only law of the iterated logarithm for sequences of random variables satisfying a mixing condition where the variance of the n-th partial sum is not necessarily asymptotically equal to a constant multiple of n.

We can considerably relax the retarded mixing condition in the special case where $\eta_n = \xi_n$ in (2.5). In other words let $\{\xi_n\}_{n=1}^{\infty}$ be a sequence of random variables, centered at expectations and with uniformly bounded fifth moments. Suppose that

$$(2.16)\qquad \mathsf{E}\Big(\sum_{n\leqslant N} \xi_n\Big)^2 = N + o\big(N^{\frac{14}{15}}\big)\,.$$

Let κ be a positive constant. We shall assume that

$$(2.17)\qquad |\,\mathsf{P}(AB) - \mathsf{P}(A)\,\mathsf{P}(B)| \leqslant \alpha(nt^{-\kappa})$$

for all $A \in \mathscr{F}_1^t$ and all $B \in \mathscr{F}_{t+n}^{t+n}$. Here $\alpha(s)$ converges monotonically to zero. We call sequences $\{\xi_n\}$ satisfying (2.17) retarded weakly mixing. This condition is less restrictive than the concept of (*)-mixing, introduced by Blum, Hanson and Koopmans [5] because of the retardation factor $t^{-\kappa}$ and because we do not require that the right-hand side of (2.17) contains the factor $\mathsf{P}(A)\,\mathsf{P}(B)$. Of course, (2.17) is also less restrictive than what we called in (2.6) a retarded strong mixing condition since we require less concerning the future of the process $\{\xi_n\}$.

Moreover, we assume that for all $i \leqslant j < m \leqslant n$

$$(2.18)\qquad |\,\mathsf{E}(\xi_i\xi_j\xi_m\,\xi_n) - \mathsf{E}(\xi_i\xi_j)\,\mathsf{E}(\xi_m\,\xi_n)| \leqslant \{\alpha((m-j)j^{-\kappa})\}^{\frac{1}{5}}\,.$$

Of course, if we would assume (2.6), instead of (2.17), this estimate would immediately follow from a well-known lemma of Ibragimov [18].

Theorem 6. *Let* $\{\xi_n\}$ *be a sequence of random variables, centered at expectations, with uniformly bounded fifth moments, and satisfying* (2.16), (2.17). *and* (2.18) *with*

$$\kappa = \frac{2}{19}$$

and

$$\alpha(s) \ll s^{-336}\,.$$

Then, without changing the distribution of $\{S(t),\ t \geqslant 0\}$, *we can redefine the process* $\{S(t),\ t \geqslant 0\}$ *on a richer probability space together with standard Brownian motion* $\{X(t),\ t \geqslant 0\}$ *such that*

$$S(t) - X(t) \ll t^{\frac{1}{2} - \eta} \qquad a.s.$$

for each $\eta < \frac{1}{294}$.

Let $\{x_n\}$ denote a Gaussian sequence centered at expectations. Theorems A-D are well-known for the case of stationary uncorrelated (that is, independent identically distributed) x_n. As a matter of fact, for this special case relation (1.2) is rather trivial to prove.

Here we consider Gaussian sequences whose n-th partial sums have variances close to n and that have covariances converging to zero as the distance between indices approaches infinity. In this more general setting the proof of (1.2) is far from being trivial.

We assume that uniformly in m

$$(2.19) \qquad \mathsf{E}\Big(\sum_{k=m+1}^{m+n} x_k\Big)^2 = \sigma^2 n + O(n^{1-\epsilon})$$

for some $\epsilon > 0$ and some constant $\sigma^2 > 0$, excluding the degenerate case $\sigma = 0$. Hence without loss of generality we assume

$$(2.20) \qquad \sigma^2 = 1 .$$

Moreover, we assume that uniformly in m

$$(2.21) \qquad \mathsf{E}(x_m x_{m+n}) \ll n^{-2} .$$

Since by (2.19) the variances $\mathsf{E}x_k^2$ are uniformly bounded, condition (2.21) is less restrictive than the requirement that the correlations converge to zero at the given rate.

Theorem 7. *Without changing the distribution of* $\{S(t),\ t \geqslant 0\}$, *we can redefine the process* $\{S(t),\ t \geqslant 0\}$ *on a richer probability space together with standard Brownian motion* $\{X(t),\ t \geqslant 0\}$ *such that*

$$S(t) - X(t) \ll t^{\frac{1}{2} - \eta} \qquad a.s.$$

for each $\eta < \min\left(\frac{1}{60}, \frac{4\epsilon}{15}\right)$.

Corollary. *Let* $\{x_n\}$ *be a stationary Gaussian sequence, centered at expectations and with covariances*

$$\mathsf{E}(x_1 x_n) \ll \frac{1}{n^2}\,.$$

The conclusion of Theorem 7 holds with

$$S(t) - X(t) \ll t^{\frac{1}{2} - \eta} \qquad \textit{for each} \quad \eta < \frac{1}{60} \qquad a.s.$$

Similar results are obtained for functionals of certain Markov processes and for the Shannon – McMillan – Breiman theorem in information theory.

3. DESCRIPTION OF THE METHOD

Let $\{x_n\}_{n=1}^{\infty}$ be a weakly dependent sequence with $\mathsf{E}x_n = 0$ and $\mathsf{E}|x_n|^{2+\delta}$ uniformly bounded. Here $\delta > 0$ is fixed. For ease of explanation suppose that

$$\text{(3.1)} \qquad \lim_{n \to \infty} \mathsf{D}^2\left(\frac{S_n}{\sqrt{n}}\right) = \sigma^2 > 0\,.$$

Recall that S_n was defined in (1.1) as the n-th partial sum. Without loss of generality we assume that $\sigma^2 = 1$. As already explained in Section 1 our goal is to establish the fundamental relation (1.2) for various weakly dependent sequences of random variables. The proof of (1.2) is accomplished in two main steps. In Section 3.1 we describe the first step and in Section 3.2 the second step.

3.1. The first step consists of approximating $\{S_n\}$ by a martingale. The following simple lemma concerning such approximations of sums of arbitrary random variables by martingales is useful.

Lemma 1. *Let* $\{y_j\}_{j=1}^{\infty}$ *be an arbitrary sequence of random variables and let* $\{\mathscr{L}_j\}_{j=0}^{\infty}$ *be a nondecreasing sequence of* σ*-fields such that* y_j

is $\mathscr{L}_j$*-measurable. (Here* $\mathscr{L}_0$ *denotes the trivial* σ*-field.) Suppose that the series*

$$(3.2) \qquad \sum_{k=0}^{\infty} \mathsf{E}\,|\,\mathsf{E}(y_{j+k}\,|\,\mathscr{L}_j)\,| < \infty \qquad a.s.$$

for each $j \geqslant 1$. *Then for each* $j \geqslant 1$

$$y_j = Y_j + u_j - u_{j+1}$$

where $\{Y_j, \mathscr{L}_j\}_{j=1}^{\infty}$ *is a martingale difference sequence and*

$$u_j = \sum_{k=0}^{\infty} \mathsf{E}(y_{j+k}\,|\,\mathscr{L}_{j-1})\,.$$

Indeed, the desired martingale difference sequence is given by

$$Y_j = \sum_{k=0}^{\infty} (\mathsf{E}(y_{j+k}\,|\,\mathscr{L}_j) - \mathsf{E}(y_{j+k}\,|\,\mathscr{L}_{j-1})) \qquad (j \geqslant 1)\,,$$

thus proving the lemma.

The idea for this lemma can be traced back at least to Statuljevičius (1969) and Gordin [16]. Both authors gave a martingale representation of certain strict sense stationary sequences, Gordin in terms of unitary operators on Hilbert space.

The significance of the lemma obviously lies in the fact that the partial sums of any sequence of random variables satisfying (3.2) equal a martingale plus a telescoping sum which under certain restrictions can be discarded. However, in most cases Lemma 1 turns out to be a rather weak tool when applied directly to the given sequence of random variables. It only then gains in strength when combined with another essential ingredient of the method which we describe now.

We define new random variables y_j which are sums of progressively larger blocks of the given x_n. Further, we sometimes have to construct sums z_j of blocks of the given x_n smaller than the corresponding blocks defining the y_j. As a typical example, consider the construction of the blocks required for the analysis of the Gaussian random variables of Theorem 6. There we define the y_j and the z_j inductively by adding $[j^{7/8}]$ and $[j^{6/8}]$ consecutive x_n respectively, leaving no gaps between the blocks. For example $y_1 = x_1$, $z_1 = x_2$, $y_2 = x_3$, $z_2 = x_4$, $y_3 = x_5 + x_6$, $z_3 = x_7 + x_8$, $y_4 = x_9 + x_{10} + x_{11}, \ldots$. The z_j are defined in such a way that they provide enough separation between consecutive y_j's so that (3.2) holds for each $j \geqslant 1$. For then, by Lemma 1,

$$y_j = Y_j + u_j - u_{j+1}$$

where $\{Y_j, \mathcal{L}_j\}$ is a martingale difference sequence and $\mathcal{L}_j$ is the σ-field generated by $Y_1, \ldots, Y_j$. Moreover, and essential to the subsequent analysis, the separation that the z_j are providing between consecutive y_j's is so large that even

$$u_j = \sum_{k=0}^{\infty} \mathsf{E}(y_{j+k} \mid \mathcal{L}_{j-1}) \tag{3.3}$$

is small compared to y_j for large j. For then

$$y_j \doteq Y_j \tag{3.4}$$

for large j. Lastly, since the blocks defining the z_j are much smaller than the blocks defining y_j, we have

$$\sum_{j=1}^{M} y_j \doteq \sum_{j=1}^{M} (y_j + z_j) \qquad \text{a.s.} \tag{3.5}$$

for large M. In other words the z_j can be discarded without affecting the almost sure behaviour of the partial sums S_N. Of course, we are deliberately vague when saying that u_j is small compared with y_j, etc.

In the construction of the y_j and z_j there is a trade-off involved: If the blocks defining the z_j are too small, (3.2) and (3.4) will fail to hold. However, if these blocks are too large, then (3.5) will fail to hold. That is, the z_j's could not be neglected in the subsequent analysis.

Assuming that the blocks have been chosen so that (3.2), (3.4), and (3.5) are satisfied, we then concentrate on the sums

$$\sum_{j \leqslant M} y_j$$

in the remainder of the discussion. However, consideration of these sums will produce fluctuation results only for a certain subsequence of the sequence $\{S_N\}$ of partial sums. Fortunately, it is relatively easy to break into the blocks defining the y_j's and thus recover the desired fluctuation results for $\{S_N\}$, provided that the blocks defining the y_j's are not chosen too large.

By the above arguments, noting (3.4), the proof of the fundamental relation (1.2) is reduced by the first step of the method to proving a corresponding almost sure invariance principle for the martingale

$$\sum_{j \leqslant M} Y_j . \tag{3.6}$$

3.2. The second step of the method is the approximation of the martingale (3.6) in an appropriate manner by Brownian motion. This is accomplished by means of a martingale version of the Skorokhod representation theorem (see Strassen [31], Theorem 4.3): *Let $\{X(t),\ t \geqslant 0\}$ be standard Brownian motion. Then there exist non-negative random variables T_j such that*

$$\sum_{j \leqslant M} Y_j = X\Big(\sum_{j \leqslant M} T_j\Big) \quad \textit{a.s.}, \tag{3.7}$$

$$\mathsf{E}(T_j \mid \mathscr{L}_{j-1}) = \mathsf{E}(Y_j^2 \mid \mathscr{L}_{j-1}) \quad \textit{a.s.}, \tag{3.8}$$

and

$$\mathsf{E}T_j^p \ll \mathsf{E}\,|\,Y_j\,|^{2p} \tag{3.9}$$

for each $p > 1$.

Let M_N denote the index of the y_j or z_j which contains x_N and let $[t]$ denote, as usual, the greatest integer not exceeding t. In order to exploit (3.7) we establish a strong law of large numbers for the T_j in the form

$$\sum_{j=1}^{M_N} T_j = N + O(N^{1-\eta_1}) \quad \text{a.s.} \tag{3.10}$$

where $\eta_1 > 0$. For then we obtain for each $\eta_2 < \frac{1}{2}\eta_1$, omitting some calculations and using (3.10),

$$X\Big(\sum_{j=1}^{M_N} T_j\Big) \doteq X(N + O(N^{1-\eta_1})) =$$

$$(3.11) \qquad = X(N) + O\big(N^{\frac{1}{2}-\eta_2}\big) = X(t) + O\big(t^{\frac{1}{2}-\eta_2}\big) \quad \text{a.s.}$$

for $N \leqslant t < N + 1$. Thus if we set

$$S^*(t) = \sum_{j=1}^{M_{[t]}} Y_j$$

we obtain, using (3.7) and (3.11),

$$(3.12) \qquad S^*(t) - X(t) \ll t^{\frac{1}{2}-\eta_2} \quad \text{a.s.}$$

as $t \to \infty$.

Now we are almost done since, in view of (3.4), the reduction to the martingale case described in Section 3.1 results in the estimate

$$(3.13) \qquad S(t) - S^*(t) = \sum_{n \leqslant t} x_n - S^*(t) = \sum_{j=1}^{M_{[t]}} (y_j - Y_j) \ll t^{\frac{1}{2}-\eta_3} \quad \text{a.s.}$$

for some $\eta_3 > 0$. We combine (3.12) and (3.13) and get

$$S(t) - X(t) \ll t^{\frac{1}{2}-\eta} \quad \text{a.s.}$$

for some $\eta > 0$, which is the desired fundamental relation (1.2). This completes the second step of the method.

How can we get (3.10) which is, as we just have seen, the key to establishing the fundamental relation (1.2)? Consider the decomposition

$$\sum_{j=1}^{M_N} T_j - N = \sum_{j=1}^{M_N} (T_j - \mathsf{E}(T_j \mid \mathscr{L}_{j-1})) +$$

$$(3.14) \qquad + \sum_{j=1}^{M_N} (\mathsf{E}(Y_j^2 \mid \mathscr{L}_{j-1}) - Y_j^2) + \sum_{j=1}^{M_N} Y_j^2 - N .$$

Here we have used (3.8). We first establish a strong law of large numbers for the Y_j^2 in the form

$$(3.15)\qquad \sum_{j=1}^{M_N} Y_j^2 = N + O(N^{1-\eta_4}) \qquad \text{a.s.}$$

for some $\eta_4 > 0$. This takes care of the third sum on the right-hand side of (3.14). As a by-product of the proof of (3.15) we obtain a bound on $\mathsf{E}|Y_j|^{2+\delta}$ which, in view of (3.9), yields a bound on $\mathsf{E}T_j^{1+\frac{1}{2}\delta}$. Using these two bounds and a standard martingale convergence theorem it is not difficult to show that the first two sums on the right-hand side of (3.14) are $\ll N^{1-\eta_5}$ almost surely, proving (3.10). (In general, T_j is not measurable with respect to $\mathscr{L}_j$. But this is only a technicality which we shall not worry about at this point.)

For general martingales, even with nice moment properties, (3.15) may not hold. But using (3.4) it follows that it is enough to prove

$$(3.16)\qquad \sum_{j=1}^{M_N} y_j^2 = N + O(N^{1-\eta_6}) \qquad \text{a.s.}$$

for some $\eta_6 > 0$. In view of the weak dependence of the y_i's, relation (3.16) might appear to be straight-forward. But typically, proving (3.16) provides the most difficulty.

REFERENCES

[1] I. Berkes, Almost sure invariance principles for mixing processes, *Ann. of Prob.*, (to appear).

[2] I. Berkes, An almost sure invariance principle for lacunary trigonometric series, *Acta Math. Sci. Hungar.*, (to appear).

[3] P. Billingsley, Unpublished manuscript, 1967.

[4] P. Billingsley, *Convergence of Probability Measures,* Wiley, New York, 1968.

[5] J.R. Blum – D.L. Hanson – L.H. Koopmans, On the strong law of large numbers for a class of stochastic processes, *Z. Wahrscheinlichkeitstheorie,* 2 (1963), 1-11.

[6] Y.S. Chow, Local convergence of martingales and the law of large numbers, *Ann. Math. Statist.*, 36 (1965), 552-558.

[7] K.L. Chung, *Markov Chains with Stationary Transition Probabilities,* 2nd ed. Springer-Verlag, Berlin and New York, 1967.

[8] K.L. Chung, *A Course in Probability Theory,* Harcourt, Brace and World, New York, 1968.

[9] H. Cohn, On a class of dependent random variables, *Rev. Roum. Math. Pures et Appl.*, 10 (1965), 1593-1606.

[10] Ju.A. Davydov, The invariance principle for stationary processes, *Theor. Probability Appl.*, 15 (1970), 487-498.

[11] Ch.M. Deo, A note on empirical processes of strong-mixing sequences, *Ann. of Prob.*, 1 (1973), 870-875.

[12] P. Erdős – I.S. Gál, On the law of the iterated logarithm, *Proc. Koningl. Nederl. Akad. Wetensch. Ser. A,* 58 (1955), 65-84.

[13] S. Gaal – L. Gaal, The discrepancy of the sequence $\{(2n_x)\}$, *Proc. Koningl. Nederl. Akad. Wetensch. Ser. A,* 67 (1964), 129-143.

[14] I.S. Gál – J.F. Koksma, Sur l'ordre de grandeur des fonctions sommables, *Proc. Koningl. Nederl. Akad. Wetensch. Ser. A,* 53 (1950) 638-653.

[15] V.F. Gapoškin, Lacunary series and independent functions, *Russian Math. Surveys,* 21 (1966), 3-82.

[16] M.I. Gordin, The central limit theorem for stationary processes, *Soviet Math. Doklady,* 10 (1969), 1174-1176.

[17] C.C. Heyde – D.J. Scott, Invariance principles for the law of the iterated logarithm for martingales and processes with stationary increments, *Ann. of Prob.*, 1 (1973), 428-437.

[18] I.A. Ibragimov, Some limit theorems for stationary processes, *Theor. Probability Appl.*, 7 (1962), 349-382.

[19] M. Iosifescu, La lai du logarithme itéré pour une classe de variables aletoires dependent, *Teorija Verojatn.*, 13 (1968), 315-325.

[20] N.C. Jain – K. Jogdeo – W.F. Stout, Upper and lower functions for martingales and mixing processes, *Ann. of Prob.*, 3 (1975), 119-145.

[21] N.C. Jain – S.J. Taylor, Local asymptotic laws for Brownian motion, *Ann. of Prob.*, 1 (1973), 527-549.

[22] D.F. Morrison, *Multivariate Statistical Methods,* McGraw-Hill, New York, 1967.

[23] H. Oodaira, The law of the iterated logarithm for Gaussian processes, *Ann. of Prob.*, 1 (1973), 954-967.

[24] W. Philipp, The law of the iterated logarithm for mixing stochastic processes, *Ann. Math. Statist.*, 40 (1969), 1985-1991.

[25] W. Philipp, *Mixing Sequences of Random Variables and Probabilistic Number Theory,* Amer. Math. Soc. Mem. No. 114, Amer. Math. Soc., Providence, Rhode Island, 1971.

[26] W. Philipp – W.F. Stout, *Almost Sure Invariance Principles for Sums of Dependent Random Variables,* Amer. Math. Soc. Mem. No. 161, Amer. Math. Soc., Providence, Rhode Island, 1975.

[27] M.Kh. Reznik, The law of the iterated logarithm for some classes of stationary processes, *Theor. Probability Appl.*, 8 (1968), 606-621.

[28] M. Rosenblatt, A central limit theorem and a maxing condition, *Proc. Nat. Acad. USA,* 42 (1956), 412-413.

[29] W.F. Stout, *Almost Sure Convergence,* Academic Press, New York, 1974.

[30] V. Strassen, An invariance principle for the law of the iterated logarithm, *Z. Wahrscheinlichkeitstheorie,* 3 (1964), 211-226.

[31] V. Strassen, Almost sure behavior of sums of independent random variables and martingales, *Proc. Fifth Berkeley Symp. Math. Statist. Prob.*, 2 (1965), 315-343.

[32] P. Szüsz, Über die metrische Theorie der Diophanlischen Approximation, *Acta Arith.*, 8 (1963), 225-241.

[33] S. Takahashi, On the law of the iterated logarithm for lacunary trigonometric series, *Tohoku Math. J.*, 24 (1972), 319-329.

[34] W. Vervaat, *Success epochs in Bernoulli trials,* Mathematisch centrum, Amsterdam, 1972.

[35] M. Weiss, The law of the iterated logarithm for lacunary trigonometric series, *Trans. Amer. Math. Soc.*, 91 (1959), 444-469.

COLLOQUIA MATHEMATICA SOCIETATIS JÁNOS BOLYAI
11. LIMIT THEOREMS OF PROBABILITY THEORY, KESZTHELY (HUNGARY), 1974.

THE ASYMPTOTIC NORMALITY AND ASYMPTOTIC EXPANSIONS FOR THE JOINT DISTRIBUTION OF SEVERAL ORDER STATISTICS

R.-D. REISS

1. INTRODUCTION

The asymptotic normality of order statistics is well-known for a number of special cases. The case of a single order statistic $Z_{r_n:n}$ has been studied extensively in the literature. The first results were given by Smirnov [14]. Smirnov [16] and [17] also found conditions on the "underlying" distribution function which are necessary and sufficient for the asymptotic normality of the central order statistics ($r_n \to \infty$ and $\frac{r_n}{n} \to \lambda^* \in [0, 1)$ or $n - r_n \to \infty$ and $\frac{r_n}{n} \to 1$ for $n \to \infty$).

The accuracy of the normal approximation may be very bad. If the "underlying" distribution function has a bounded second derivative the author (Reiss [9]) proved that the error of the normal approximation is of order $\frac{1}{\sqrt{n}}$. Asymptotic expansions for sample quantiles were derived in Reiss [10]. The expansions given there reveal that the approximation by the normal distribution is of order $\frac{1}{n}$ for the distributions induced by sample medians and symmetric distributions. For Borel sets which are symmetric about the underlying quantile this order of approximation always holds true.

Given k order statistics $Z_{r_{1,n}:n} \leqslant Z_{r_{2,n}:n} \leqslant \ldots \leqslant Z_{r_{k,n}:n}$ with $\sqrt{n}\left(\frac{r_{i,n}}{n} - \lambda_i^*\right) \to 0$ for $n \to \infty$ (where $0 < \lambda_1^* < \ldots < \lambda_k^* < 1$; λ_i^* fixed) the joint asymptotic normal distribution was derived by Smirnov [15] (for the case $k = 2$) and by Mosteller [8]. In the present paper λ_1^* and λ_k^* are permitted to be equal to zero or one, respectively, and some of the λ_i^*'s may be identical.

Weiss [22] and [23] proved that the joint distribution of $k(n)$ "equi-distant" order statistics (that is: $r_{i+1,n} - r_{i,n} = r_{2,n} - r_{1,n}$ for $i \in \{1, \ldots, k(n) - 1\}$) can be approximated by $k(n)$-variate normal distributions if, roughly speaking, $r_{2,n} - r_{1,n} \to \infty$ and $k(n) \to \infty$ for $n \to \infty$, and $k(n) = o(n^{1/3})$. He showed (by counterexamples) that this result does not hold if $k(n) \sim n^{\frac{1}{2} + \delta}$ for some $\delta > 0$. The question whether normal approximation is possible for sequences $k(n)$ with $n^{1/3} \leqslant k(n) < n^{1/2}$ can now be answered positively: In the Theorem we only assume that, roughly speaking, $\sum_{i=0}^{k(n)} \frac{1}{r_{i+1,n} - r_{i,n}}$ converges to zero (where $r_{0,n} = 0$ and $r_{k(n)+1,n} = n$).

Whereas the papers of Weiss [22] and [23] and Reiss [10] and the paper in hand are concerned with a uniform approximation over the class of all Borel sets the other papers mentioned above deal with weak convergence, only.

The notations are collected in Section 2. In Section 3 the Theorem is formulated and some polynomials related to the expansions are given explicitely. Section 4 contains some remarks and a short discussion of the method of the proof and of the assumptions. In Section 5 the Theorem is applied to obtain a limit theorem for the distribution of the maximal deviation of the histogram estimator (based on order statistics) from the "underlying" probability density function. Sections 6 and 7 contain the proof of the Theorem and auxiliary results. Some of the lemmas are of interest in connection with applications of the main results.

2. NOTATIONS

Denote by $R(N)$ the set of all real numbers (positive integers). Let $\mathscr{B}$ denote the Borel-algebra on R. $\lambda|\mathscr{B}$ denotes the Lebesgue-measure, and $\mathsf{Q}|\mathscr{B}$ denotes the uniform distribution on (0, 1). Let $(R^m, \mathscr{B}^m)$ be the Cartesian product of m identical components $(R, \mathscr{B})$ and $\nu^m|\mathscr{B}^m$ the independent product of m identical measures $\nu|\mathscr{B}$. For any signed measure $\nu|\mathscr{B}^m$, measurable space $(\Omega, \mathscr{A})$ and $\mathscr{B}^m$, $\mathscr{A}$-measurable function $\psi: R^m \to \Omega$ let $\nu * \psi|\mathscr{A}$ denote the induced measure defined by $\nu * \psi(A) = \nu(\psi^{-1}(A))$ for $A \in \mathscr{A}$. $\bar{A}$ denotes the complement of $A \subset \Omega$.

Throughout this paper n denotes the sample size and $k(n)$ denotes the number of order statistics under consideration. Suppressing the dependence on $k(n)$ and n, respectively, we denote the elements of $R^{k(n)}$ (R^n) by $\boldsymbol{x}$ and $\boldsymbol{y}$ $(\boldsymbol{z})$ and the components of $\boldsymbol{x} \in R^{k(n)}$ $(\boldsymbol{z} \in R^n)$ by x_i, $i = 1, \ldots, k(n)$ $(z_i$, $i = 1, \ldots, n)$. Let always $x_0 = x_{k(n)+1} = 0$.

The i-th order statistic $Z_{i:n}: R^n \to R$, for the sample size n, is defined by $Z_{i:n}(\boldsymbol{z}) = z_{i:n}$ for $\boldsymbol{z} \in R^n$ where $z_{1:n} \leqslant \ldots \leqslant z_{n:n}$ are the components of $\boldsymbol{z} \in R^n$ arranged in the increasing order.

Given a probability measure $\mathsf{P}|\mathscr{B}$ with distribution function F, $k(n) \in \{1, \ldots, n\}$ and a vector

$$r(n) = (r_{0,n}, r_{1,n}, \ldots, r_{k(n),n}, r_{k(n)+1,n}) \tag{2.1}$$

with

$$0 = r_{0,n} < r_{1,n} < \ldots < r_{k(n),n} < r_{k(n)+1,n} = n,$$

it will be convenient to use the following notation:

For $i \in \{0, \ldots, k(n)+1\}$ let $\lambda_{i,n} = \dfrac{r_{i,n}}{n}$ and $\sigma_{i,n}^2 = \lambda_{i,n}(1 - \lambda_{i,n})$.

Let

$$\gamma_{r(n)} = \sum_{i=0}^{k(n)} \frac{1}{r_{i+1,n} - r_{i,n}} . \tag{2.2}$$

Denote by $p(x)$ the derivative of F at the point x whenever it exists.

Under the Assumptions (i) the following expressions are well defined for $i \in \{1, \ldots, k(n)\}$ and $j \in \{1, \ldots, l+1\}$: $\mu_{i,n}$ denotes a solution of the equation

$$F(y) = \lambda_{i,n} .$$

For the derivatives of p at $\mu_{i,n}$ we use the abbreviations

$$p_{i,n} = p(\mu_{i,n})$$

and

$$p_{i,n}^{(j)} = p^{(j)}(\mu_{i,n}) .$$

In the following a_s denotes some "sufficiently large" fixed real number depending on s, only.

Let

$$\Gamma_{r(n),i}^{(s)} = \{x \in R\colon |x| < a_s \sigma_{i,n} \sqrt{\log n}\}$$

and

$$\Lambda_{r(n),i}^{(s)} = \{(x, y) \in R^2\colon |x - y| < a_s \sqrt{(\lambda_{i+1,n} - \lambda_{i,n}) \log n}\} .$$

Let

$$\theta_{r(n),j,i}^{(s)}(\mathsf{P}) = \sup \left\{ \frac{\left| p^{(j)}\left(\mu_{i,n} + \frac{x}{\sqrt{n}\, p_{i,n}} \right) \right|}{p_{i,n}^{j+1}} : x \in \Gamma_{r(n),i}^{(s)} \right\},$$

and for $i \in \{1, \ldots, k(n) - 1\}$

$$\rho^{(s)}_{r(n),j,i}(\mathsf{P}) = \sup\left\{\left|\frac{p^{(j)}\left(\mu_{i+1,n} + \dfrac{y}{\sqrt{n}p_{i+1,n}}\right)}{p^{j+1}_{i+1,n}} - \right.\right.$$

$$\left. - \frac{p^{(j)}\left(\mu_{i,n} + \dfrac{x}{\sqrt{n}p_{i,n}}\right)}{p^{j+1}_{i,n}}\right| :$$

$$\left.(x, y) \in (\Gamma^{(s)}_{r(n),i} \times \Gamma^{(s)}_{r(n),i+1}) \cap \Lambda^{(s)}_{r(n),i}\right\}.$$

The error bound in the Theorem heavily depends on the number

$$\begin{aligned}(2.3)\qquad \delta^{(s)}_{r(n),j}(\mathsf{P}) = &\sum_{i=1}^{k(n)} \theta^{(s)}_{r(n),j,i}(\mathsf{P})(\sigma_{i,n} + \sigma_{i+1,n})^j + \\ &+ \sum_{i=1}^{k(n)-1} \rho^{(s)}_{r(n),j,i}(\mathsf{P}) \frac{(\sigma_{i,n} + \sigma_{i+1,n})^{j+1}}{\sqrt{\lambda_{i+1,n} - \lambda_{i,n}}} + \\ &+ \Big[\sum_{i=1}^{k(n)} \theta^{(s)}_{r(n),1,i}(\mathsf{P})(\sigma_{i,n} + \sigma_{i+1,n}) + \\ &+ \sum_{i=1}^{k(n)-1} \rho^{(s)}_{r(n),1,i}(\mathsf{P}) \frac{(\sigma_{i,n} + \sigma_{i+1,n})^2}{\sqrt{\lambda_{i+1,n} - \lambda_{i.n}}}\Big]^j .\end{aligned}$$

The approximating normal distributions $\mathsf{N}_{r(n)}$ have Lebesgue-density $h_{r(n)}$ given by

$$(2.4)\qquad h_{r(n)}(\boldsymbol{x}) = \frac{1}{C_{r(n)}} \exp\left(-\frac{1}{2}\sum_{i=0}^{k(n)} \frac{(x_{i+1} - x_i)^2}{\lambda_{i+1,n} - \lambda_{i,n}}\right) \quad \text{for } \boldsymbol{x} \in R^{k(n)}$$

where $C_{r(n)}$ denotes the normalizing constant (see Remark (3.15)).

Furthermore, the univariate normal distribution with expectation zero and variance σ^2 is denoted by N_{σ^2}.

For $i \in \{0, \ldots, k(n)\}$ and $j \in N$ let

$$t_{i,j,n}(x) = \frac{\frac{p^{(j)}_{i+1,n}}{p^{j+1}_{i+1,n}} x^{j+1}_{i+1} - \frac{p^{(j)}_{i,n}}{p^{j+1}_{i,n}} x^{j+1}_i}{\sqrt{\lambda_{i+1,n} - \lambda_{i,n}}}.$$

(with $\frac{p^{(j)}_{0,n}}{p^{j+1}_{0,n}} = \frac{p^{(j)}_{k(n)+1,n}}{p^{j+1}_{k(n)+1,n}} = 0$).

The exponent $-\frac{1}{2}\sum_{i=0}^{k(n)} \frac{(x_{i+1}-x_i)^2}{\lambda_{i+1,n}-\lambda_{i,n}} \left(= -\frac{1}{2}\sum_{i=0}^{k(n)} t^2_{i,0,n}(x)\right)$ is denoted by $R_{r(n),0}$. Furthermore, for $j \in N$ let

$$\begin{aligned} R_{r(n),j}(x) &= \frac{(-1)^{j-1}}{j+2} \sum_{i=0}^{k(n)} (r_{i+1,n} - r_{i,n})^{-\frac{j}{2}} t^{j+2}_{i,0,n}(x) + \\ &+ \frac{(-1)^j}{j} \sum_{i=0}^{k(n)-1} (r_{i+1,n} - r_{i,n})^{-\frac{j}{2}} t^{j}_{i,0,n}(x). \end{aligned} \tag{2.5}$$

3. THE MAIN RESULTS

The order of the expansion is determined by $l, m, s \in \{0, 1, 2, \ldots\}$. Hereafter, let l, m and s be fixed (with $l, m < s$). Remember that the numbers $\delta^{(s)}_{r(n),j}(\mathsf{P})$ (see (2.3)) depend on some "sufficiently large" $a_s > 0$.

Concerning the polynomials given in the Theorem we have especially

$$G_{r(n),0} \equiv 0 \quad \text{and} \quad H_{r(n),0,m}(\mathsf{P}) \equiv 0 \quad \text{for all} \quad m \in \{0, 1, 2, \ldots\}. \tag{3.1}$$

Hence, after a suitable standardization of the order statistic (depending on the "underlying" probability measure P) the approximating signed measures have the Lebesgue-densities $h_{r(n)}(1 + G_{r(n),m})$, $n \in N$, if $l = 0$. Note that the polynomials $G_{r(n),m}$ are not dependent on P. If, additionally, $m = 0$ then these measures are the normal distributions $\mathsf{N}_{r(n)}$ (see (2.4)).

Theorem. *There exist numbers $a_s > 0$ and $c_s > 0$ (only depending on s) such that for all probability measures $\mathsf{P} \mid \mathscr{B}$, $n \in N$, $k(n) \in \in \{1, \ldots, n\}$ and vectors $r(n)$ (see (2.1)) which fulfill the Assumptions* (i)-(iii) *the following holds true:*

There exist polynomials $G_{r(n),m}$ *and* $H_{r(n),l,m}(\mathsf{P})$ *[where the coefficients of* $H_{r(n),l,m}(\mathsf{P})$ *only depend on* P *through* $\frac{p_{i,n}^{(j)}}{p_{i,n}^{j+1}}$ *for* $i = 1, \ldots, k(n)$ *and* $j = 1, \ldots, l$*; see also* (3.1) *and* (3.9)-(3.12)] *such that for all* $B \in \mathscr{B}^{k(n)}$

$$
\begin{aligned}
&|\mathsf{P}^n * (\sqrt{n}p_{i,n}(Z_{r_{i,n}:n} - \mu_{i,n}))_{i=1}^{k(n)}(B) - \\
&- \int_B (1 + G_{r(n),m} + H_{r(n),l,m}(\mathsf{P}))d\mathsf{N}_{r(n)}| \leqslant \\
&\leqslant c_s\Big(\Big[\Big(\log^5 n \sum_{i=0}^{k(n)} \frac{1}{r_{i+1,n} - r_{i,n}}\Big)^{\frac{m+1}{2}} + \\
&+ \Big(\frac{\log^3 n}{n}\Big)^{\frac{l+1}{2}} \delta_{r(n),l+1}^{(s)}(\mathsf{P})\Big] \mathsf{N}_{r(n)}(B) + \frac{1}{n^s}\Big) .
\end{aligned}
\tag{3.2}
$$

Assumptions of the Theorem.

(i) $\mu_{i,n}$ denotes a solution of $F(y) = \lambda_{i,n}$. The first derivative $p_{i,n}$ $(= p(\mu_{i,n}))$ of F at $\mu_{i,n}$ exists for each $i \in \{1, \ldots, k(n)\}$ and $p_{i,n} > 0$. (Hence, $\mu_{i,n}$ is uniquely determined.) F has $l + 2$ derivatives on the set

$$\bigcup_{i=1}^{k(n)} \{\mu_{i,n} + \frac{x}{p_{i,n}\sqrt{n}} : |x| \leqslant a_s \sqrt{\log n}\,\sigma_{i,n}\} .$$

(ii) $\gamma_{r(n)} \log^5 n + \big(\frac{\log^3 n}{n}\big)^{\frac{l+1}{2}} \delta_{r(n),l+1}^{(s)}(\mathsf{P}) \leqslant 1.$

(iii) $\sigma_{i,n}\theta_{r(n),1,i}^{(s)}(\mathsf{P}) \leqslant \big(\frac{n(r_{i+1,n} - r_{i,n})}{\log^2 n}\big)^{\frac{1}{4}}$

for all $i \in \{1, \ldots, k(n) - 1\}$.

To make the inequality (3.2) more transparent we state the following corollaries (the proofs are simple and therefore omitted):

(3.3) **Corollary**. *We introduce numbers*

$\xi_n \geqslant \max_{i=1,\dots,k(n)-1} \left(\frac{n(r_{i+1,n} - r_{i,n})}{\log^2 n}\right)^{-\frac{1}{8}}$, $n \in N$, and intervals $\Xi^{(s)}_{r(n)} = \left[\mu_{1,n} - \frac{a_s\sqrt{\log n}\,\sigma_{1,n}}{\xi_n\sqrt{n}},\ \mu_{k(n),n} + \frac{a_s\sqrt{\log n}\,\sigma_{k(n),n}}{\xi_n\sqrt{n}}\right]$ where a_s denotes some sufficiently large number. Assume that F has a second derivative $p^{(1)}$ on $\Xi^{(s)}_{r(n)}$ such that for some $\epsilon, \eta > 0$: $|p^{(1)}(x)| \leqslant \eta$ for all $x \in \Xi^{(s)}_{r(n)}$ and $|p^{(1)}(x) - p^{(1)}(y)| \leqslant \epsilon |x - y|$ for all $x, y \in \Xi^{(s)}_{r(n)}$. Assume, furthermore, that $p(x) \geqslant \xi_n$ for all $x \in \Xi^{(s)}_{r(n)}$. Then for all $B \in \mathscr{B}^{k(n)}$

$$
\begin{aligned}
&|\mathsf{P}^n * (n^{\frac{1}{2}} p_{i,n}(Z_{r_{i,n}:n} - \mu_{i,n}))_{i=1}^{k(n)}(B) - \mathsf{N}_{r(n)}(B)| \leqslant \\
&\leqslant c(s, \epsilon, \eta)(\zeta_{r(n)}(\mathsf{P})\mathsf{N}_{r(n)}(B) + n^{-s})
\end{aligned} \tag{3.4}
$$

if

$$
\begin{aligned}
\zeta_{r(n)}(\mathsf{P}) &= (\log n)^{\frac{5}{2}} \gamma_{r(n)}^{\frac{1}{2}} + \\
&+ \left(\frac{\log^3 n}{n}\right)^{\frac{1}{2}} \left(\frac{k(n)}{\xi_n^2} + \frac{1}{\xi_n^4} \sum_{i=1}^{k(n)-1} \sqrt{\lambda_{i+1,n} - \lambda_{i,n}}\right) \leqslant 1\,.
\end{aligned}
$$

Without the Lipschitz condition we have $c(s, \eta)$ and

$$
(\log n)^{\frac{5}{2}} \gamma_{r(n)}^{\frac{1}{2}} + (\log n)^{\frac{3}{2}} \frac{1}{\xi_n^2} \sum_{i=1}^{k(n)-1} \frac{1}{\sqrt{r_{i+1,n} - r_{i,n}}} \tag{3.5}
$$

in place of $c(s, \epsilon, \eta)$ and $\zeta_{r(n)}(\mathsf{P})$.

If ξ_n, $n \in N$, is bounded away from zero then (3.4) together with (7.3) implies that we get normal approximation for the joint distribution of "equi-distant" order statistics if $k(n) = o\left(n^{\frac{1}{2}} (\log n)^{-\frac{5}{2}}\right)$. (3.5) yields the restriction $k(n) = o\left(n^{\frac{1}{3}} (\log n)^{-\frac{3}{2}}\right)$.

For special families of probability measures it is possible to improve the error bound given in (3.4) by a more accurate computation of $\delta^{(s)}_{r(n),1}(\mathsf{P})$.

The following corollary can be proved with the help of the polynomials $G_{r(n),1}$ and $H_{r(n),1,1}(\mathsf{P})$ which are explicitely given in (3.9) and (3.10) (see also Remark (3.14)).

(3.6) **Corollary**. *Assume that* $\gamma_{r(n)} = o((\log n)^{-5})$ *and* $n\alpha_1 \leqslant r_{1,n} < < r_{k(n),n} \leqslant n\alpha_2$, $n \in N$, *for some* α_1, α_2 *with* $0 < \alpha_1 < \alpha_2 < 1$. *Let* μ_i^* *denote* α_i*-quantiles of the probability measure* P. *Assume that the distribution function of* P *has a bounded third derivative on an open neighborhood of* $[\mu_1^*, \mu_2^*]$ *and the first derivative is positive on* $[\mu_1^*, \mu_2^*]$. *Then*

$$\sup_{B \in \mathscr{B}^{k(n)}} |\mathsf{P}^n * (\sqrt{n} p_{i,n}(Z_{r_{i,n}:n} - \mu_{i,n}))_{i=1}^{k(n)}(B) - \mathsf{N}_{r(n)}(B)| =$$

$$= O(\sqrt{\gamma_{r(n)}}) .$$

(3.7) **Corollary**. *Let* $k = k(n) \geqslant 1$ *be fixed and* $\lim_{n \in N} \frac{r_{i,n}}{n} - \lambda_i^* = 0$ *(where* $0 < \lambda_1^* < \lambda_2^* < \ldots < \lambda_k^* < 1$; λ_i^* *fixed),* $p(\mu_i^*) > 0$ *(where* $F(\mu_i^*) = \lambda_i^*$*) for* $i = 1, \ldots, k$. *Assume that* F *has* $l + 2$ *continuous derivatives on some neighborhood of* μ_i^* *for each* $i \in \{1, \ldots, k\}$. *Then the expansion given in* (3.2) *can be written in a more conventional form: There exist polynomials* $L_{r(n),j}(\mathsf{P})$, $j = 1, \ldots, l$ *(the coefficients of* $L_{r(n),j}(\mathsf{P})$ *only depend on* P *by means of* $\frac{p_{i,n}^{(\nu)}}{p_{i,n}^{\nu+1}}$ *for* $i = 1, \ldots, k$ *and* $\nu = 1, \ldots, j$*) such that for all* $B \in \mathscr{B}^k$

$$|\mathsf{P}^n * (\sqrt{n}\, p_{i,n}(Z_{r_{i,n}:n} - \mu_{i,n}))_{i=1}^{k}(B) -$$

$$- \int_B 1 + \sum_{j=1}^{l} n^{-\frac{j}{2}} L_{r(n),j}(\mathsf{P}) d\mathsf{N}_{r(n)} | = \tag{3.8}$$

$$= O\Big(\Big(\frac{\log^5 n}{n}\Big)^{\frac{l+1}{2}} \mathsf{N}_{r(n)}(B) + \frac{1}{n^s}\Big) .$$

For $L_{r(n),1}$ and $L_{r(n),2}$ see (3.13).

Expansions for the joint distribution of the sample λ_i^*-quantiles are of special interest with μ_i^*, $p(\mu_i^*)$, $\frac{p^{(j)}(\mu_i^*)}{p^{j+1}(\mu_i^*)}$, $r^* = (0, n\lambda_1^*, \ldots, n\lambda_k^*, n)$

and N_{r*} in place of $\mu_{i,n}$, $p_{i,n}$, $\frac{p_{i,n}^{(j)}}{p_{i,n}^{j+1}}$, $r(n)$, and $\mathsf{N}_{r(n)}$, respectively. For $k = 1$ such an expansion can be found in Reiss [10]. Note that N_{r*} does not depend on n, whereas the polynomials of the expansion still depend on n.

The polynomials $G_{r(n),m}$ and $H_{r(n),l,m}(\mathsf{P})$ used in the Theorem are not uniquely determined. In some problems we may find polynomials with a minimal number of terms such that (3.2) holds (e.g. in Corollary (3.7)).

For $m = 1, 2$ we may take in (3.2)

$$G_{r(n),1} = R_{r(n),1} ,$$

$$G_{r(n),2} = R_{r(n),1} + \frac{1}{2} R_{r(n),1}^2 + R_{r(n),2} - \int\left(\frac{1}{2} R_{r(n),1}^2 + R_{r(n),2}\right) d\mathsf{N}_{r(n)} . \tag{3.9}$$

The integrals $\int R_{r(n),1}^2 d\mathsf{N}_{r(n)}$ and $\int R_{r(n),2} d\mathsf{N}_{r(n)}$ are explicitely given in (7.27) and (7.28). For $m > 2$ the polynomials $G_{r(n),m}$ also depend on the polynomials $R_{r(n),j}$ only; see (6.5).

$$H_{r(n),1,1}(\mathsf{P}) = \frac{1}{\sqrt{n}} \sum_{i=1}^{3} T_{r(n),i} \tag{3.10}$$

where

$$T_{r(n),1}(x) = \sum_{i=1}^{k(n)} \frac{p_{i,n}^{(1)}}{p_{i,n}^2} x_i$$

$$T_{r(n),2} = -\frac{1}{2} \sum_{i=0}^{k(n)} t_{i,0,n} t_{i,1,n}$$

$$T_{r(n),3} = \frac{1}{2}\left(\sum_{i=0}^{k(n)} \frac{t_{i,0,n}^2 t_{i,1,n}}{\sqrt{r_{i+1,n} - r_{i,n}}} - \sum_{i=0}^{k(n)-1} \frac{t_{i,1,n}}{\sqrt{r_{i+1,n} - r_{i,n}}} \right)$$

$$H_{r(n),1,2}(\mathrm{P}) = H_{r(n),1,1}(\mathrm{P}) + \tag{3.11}$$
$$+ n^{-\frac{1}{2}} R_{r(n),1}(T_{r(n),1} + T_{r(n),2} + T_{r(n),3}) .$$

To reduce the number of terms of the polynomial $H_{r(n),2,2}(\mathrm{P})$ we assume additionally that $\delta^{(s)}_{r(n),2}(\mathrm{P}) \leqslant 2(\delta^{(s)}_{r(n),1}(\mathrm{P}))^2$.

Let

$$T_{r(n),4}(x) = \frac{1}{2} \sum_{i=1}^{k(n)} \frac{p^{(2)}_{i,n}}{p^3_{i,n}} - \frac{(p^{(1)}_{i,n})^2}{p^4_{i,n}} x_i^2 -$$
$$- \sum_{i=0}^{k(n)} \left(\frac{1}{6} t_{i,0,n}(x) t_{i,2,n}(x) + \frac{1}{8} t^2_{i,1,n}(x) \right) .$$

Then

$$H_{r(n),2,2}(\mathrm{P}) = H_{r(n),1,2}(\mathrm{P}) +$$
$$+ \frac{1}{n}\Bigg[\frac{1}{2} T^2_{r(n),1} + \frac{1}{2} T^2_{r(n),2} + \frac{1}{2} T^2_{r(n),3} +$$
$$+ \sum_{\substack{i,j \in \{1,2,3\} \\ i<j}} T_{r(n),i} T_{r(n),j} + T_{r(n),4} + \tag{3.12}$$
$$+ \sum_{i=0}^{k(n)} \frac{\frac{1}{6} t^2_{i,0,n} t_{i,2,n} + \frac{1}{4} t_{i,0,n} t^2_{i,1,n}}{\sqrt{r_{i+1,n} - r_{i,n}}} -$$
$$- \frac{1}{6} \sum_{i=0}^{k(n)-1} \frac{t_{i,2,n}}{\sqrt{r_{i+1,n} - r_{i,n}}} \Bigg] .$$

Collecting the terms of order $n^{-\frac{j}{2}}$ ($j = 1, 2; \ldots$) we obtain

$$L_{r(n),1}(\mathrm{P}) = n^{\frac{1}{2}} R_{r(n),1} + T_{r(n),1} + T_{r(n),2} \tag{3.13}$$
$$L_{r(n),2}(\mathrm{P}) = n\Big[\frac{1}{2} R^2_{r(n),1} + R_{r(n),2} -$$

$$- \int\left(\frac{1}{2} R^2_{r(n),1} + R_{r(n),2}\right) d\mathsf{N}_{r(n)}\Big] + n^{\frac{1}{2}} T_{r(n),3} +$$

$$+ \frac{1}{2}\left[T^2_{r(n),1} + T^2_{r(n),2} + T_{r(n),1} T_{r(n),2} + T_{r(n),4} +\right.$$

$$\left. + n^{\frac{1}{2}} R_{r(n),1}[T_{r(n),1} + T_{r(n),2}\right] .$$

(3.14) **Remark.** By some direct estimates of the integral of the absolute values of the polynomials given in (3.9)-(3.13) with respect to $\mathsf{N}_{r(n)}$ we may compute a more accurate error bound in (3.2), (3.4) and (3.8) (without the factor $\mathsf{N}_{r(n)}(B)$). Especially: Since $\int | G_{r(n),1} | d\mathsf{N}_r \leqslant$ $\leqslant \left(\int G^2_{r(n),1} d\mathsf{N}_{r(n)}\right)^{\frac{1}{2}}$ we have by (7.27)

$$\sup_{B \in \mathscr{B}^{k(n)}} \left| \int_B G_{r(n),1} d\mathsf{N}_{r(n)} \right| \leqslant \left(\frac{1}{6} \gamma_{r(n)} + \frac{1}{4(n - r_{k(n),n})}\right)^{\frac{1}{2}} .$$

Furthermore, by (7.27) and a formula corresponding to (7.28)

$$\sup_{B \in \mathscr{B}^{k(n)}} \left| \int_B (G_{r(n),2} - G_{r(n),1}) d\mathsf{N}_{r(n)} \right| \leqslant \frac{25}{12} \gamma_{r(n)} .$$

(3.15) **Remark.** The matrix of the coefficients of the quadratic expression in the exponent of $h_{r(n)}$ (see (2.4)) has determinant $\prod_{i=0}^{k(n)} \frac{1}{\lambda_{i+1,n} - \lambda_{i,n}}$. The covariance matrix $(\sigma_n^{(i,j)})_{i,j}$ of $\mathsf{N}_{r(n)}$ is given by $\sigma_n^{(i,j)} = \lambda_{i,n}(1 - \lambda_{j,n})$ for $1 \leqslant i \leqslant j \leqslant k(n)$ (see Mosteller [8], p. 385). Hence, especially $\sigma^2_{i,n} = \sigma_n^{(i,i)}$.

4. FURTHER COMMENTS

A. The Theorem can be applied to functions of order statistics in the following way: Consider the sequences of

(a) probability measures $\mathsf{P}_n \mid \mathscr{B}$, $n \in N$,

(b) measurable spaces $(\Omega_n, \mathscr{A}_n)$, $n \in N$, and

(c) $\mathscr{B}^{k(n)}$, $\mathscr{A}_n$-measurable maps $\psi_n : R^{k(n)} \to \Omega_n$, $n \in N$.

Let $\nu_{r(n),l,m}(\mathsf{P}_n)$ denote the signed measure with Lebesgue-density $h_{r(n)}(1 + G_{r(n),m} + H_{r(n),l,m}(\mathsf{P}_n))$. (3.2) immediately yields an error bound for

$$\sup_{A \in \mathscr{A}_n} |\mathsf{P}_n^n * (\psi_n \circ (\sqrt{n} p_{i,n}(Z_{r_{i,n}:n} - \mu_{i,n}))_{i=1}^{k(n)})(A) - \nu_{r(n),l,m}(\mathsf{P}_n) * \psi_n(A)| .$$

If $\Omega_n = R^{i(n)}$, $i(n) \leq k(n)$, the Lebesgue-density (if it exists) of $\nu_{r(n),l,m}(\mathsf{P}_n) * \psi_n$ can often be computed by the transformation theorem for densities (see Lemma (7.7)) and by computing the density of the marginal distribution. If $(\Omega_n, \mathscr{A}_n) = (R, \mathscr{B})$ and $B_n \in \mathscr{B}$ are such that $\mathsf{N}_{r(n)} * \psi_n(B_n) \geq n^{-(s-1)}$ (probabilities of moderate deviations) then we get a non-trivial estimate for

$$\left| \frac{\mathsf{P}_n^n * (\psi_n \circ (\sqrt{n} p_{i,n}(Z_{r_{i,n}:n} - \mu_{i,n}))_{i=1}^{k(n)})(B_n)}{\mathsf{N}_{r(n)} * \psi_n(B_n)} - 1 \right| .$$

In nonparametric applications the quantities $p_{i,n}$ are not known (besides others) and should be estimated by

$$\hat{p}_{i,n}(Z_{r'_{i,n}:n}, Z_{r''_{i,n}:n}) = \frac{r''_{i,n} - r'_{i,n}}{n(Z_{r''_{i,n}:n} - Z_{r'_{i,n}:n})}$$

where $r'_{i,n} \leq r_{i,n} \leq r''_{i,n}$, $r''_{i,n} - r'_{i,n} \to \infty$ and $\dfrac{r''_{i,n} - r'_{i,n}}{n} \to 0$ for $n \to \infty$ (see Section 5).

Then for suitable chosen $r'_{i,n}$ and $r''_{i,n}$ the Theorem is still applicable to the function

$$(\sqrt{n} \hat{p}_{i,n}(Z_{r'_{i,n}:n}, Z_{r''_{i,n}:n})(Z_{r_{i,n}:n} - \mu_{i,n}))_{i=1}^{k(n)} .$$

The author intends to do some research work concerning the asymptotic behavior of functions of that kind.

B. In the simple case of a single sample quantile a practically useful estimate of the constant, corresponding to the constant c_1 in the Theorem, was given in Reiss [9]. We expect that the actual error terms in

(3.2) are samll enough to get approximations of practical relevance. This opinion is affirmed by Remark (3.14). There is not much hope to find reasonable estimates for the constants a_s and c_s in the Theorem for small sample sizes but this might be possible under more restrictive conditions on P and $r(n)$.

C. Our proof starts with expansions of the known density function $g_{r(n)}$ of the standardized distribution of the order statistics (as it was done in the classical proofs of Smirnov [14] and Mosteller [8]). Mosteller's proof is not rigorous and not all assumptions are stated explicitely (assume additionally $\lim\limits_{n \in N} \sqrt{n}\left(\frac{n_i}{n} - \lambda_i^*\right) = 0$ in Condition 1 given there). Rigorous proofs can be found in many text-books. Similar as in the papers of Weiss [22], [23] and Reiss [10] we prove that $|g_{r(n)}(x) - h_{r(n)}(x)| = o(h_{r(n)}(x))$ with probability approaching one (see (6.4), (6.19) and (6.22)). The conditions (in the "equi-distant" case of Weiss) $k(n) = o(n^{1/4})$ (see Weiss [22]), $k(n) = o(n^{1/3})$ (see Weiss [23]), and $k(n) = o(n^{1/2})$ (given here) correspond, roughly speaking, to the fact that the relation given above is derived on the sets $\Gamma_{r(n)}$, $\Gamma_{r(n)} \cap \Delta_{r(n)}$ and $\theta_{r(n)}$ (see (6.2)), respectively.

In the Mosteller case (k and λ_i^*, $i = 1, \ldots, k$, fixed and $0 < \lambda_1^* < \ldots < \lambda_k^* < 1$) another proof was given by Walker [21] using characteristic functions. For single order statistics a particularly simple proof has been given by van der Vaart [18] who reduced the problem to an application of the De Moivre – Laplace theorem (for independent, binomial random variables). A refinement of this idea together with an application of the Berry – Esseen theorem was used in Reiss [9] to obtain the error bound of order $\frac{1}{\sqrt{n}}$. This method can be extended to the finite dimensional case of Mosteller. In this connection we should mention the Bahadur representation for sample quantiles (see Bahadur [1]) which has recently attained much attention in the literature. Bahadur considered the convergence, with probability one, of the difference of a sample quantile and binomial random variables. The reduction of the "continuously" distributed order statistics to binomial random variables (having a discrete distribution) does no longer lead to asymptotic expansions.

D. The Assumptions of the Theorem guarantee that the expression on the right side of (3.2) is (a) defined and is (b) smaller than one. If the assertion is weakened by omitting the term $N_{r(n)}(B)$ on the right side of (3.2) then the condition (b) obviously means no restriction at all. Remember that in this case the error bound can be improved slightly (see Remark (3.14)). Then the corresponding Assumption (ii) still restricts the possible sets of order statistics under consideration.

We only assume that the "underlying" distribution function F is absolutely continuous on some neighborhoods of the points $\mu_{i,n}$ (and not necessarily on the real line). It might be possible to weaken the differentiability conditions slightly, but then the representation of the error bound in (3.2) would be more complicated.

Let $\lim_{n \in N} \sqrt{n}\left(\frac{r_n}{n} - \lambda^*\right) = 0$ where $\lambda^* \in (0, 1)$. The necessary and sufficient conditions (stated by Smirnov [16]) for the weak convergence of the distribution of $Z_{r_n:n}$ to the normal distribution are very complicated. The following condition is sufficient: F has the derivative $p(\mu^*) > 0$ where $F(\mu^*) = \lambda^*$ (see Smirnov [16], p. 116). To obtain convergence for all Borel sets one has to assume in addition that the derivative p of F exists on a neighborhood of μ^* and p is continuous at μ^* (see Reiss [10]).

The sufficient conditions used by Mosteller [8] and by Walker [21], respectively, are too strong (although Walker regarded his conditions to be minimal). It should be possible to find conditions which correspond to Smirnov's conditions in the case of a single order statistic. Weiss [23] assumed that $p^{(1)}$ exists on some interval containing the quantities $\mu_{i,n}$. Remember that the number of order statistics under consideration has to be less than $n^{1/3}$ if $p^{(1)}$ fulfills no further smoothness conditions (see (3.5)).

Extreme order statistics (r_n or $n - r_n$ fixed for all n) cannot be asymptotically normally distributed (see Smirnov [16]). As far as central order statistics are concerned the differentiability conditions imposed on F are always used to reduce the general problem to the case of the uniform distribution. For this special case we discuss further restrictions on the vector $r(n)$ (which describes the respective set of order statistics). For fixed k Assumption (ii) is not much stronger than the condition $\lim_{n\in N} (r_{i+1,n} - r_{i,n}) = \infty$ for all $i \in \{0, \ldots, k\}$. If $r_{i+1,n} - r_{i,n}$ is fixed for some $i \in \{0, \ldots, k\}$ and all $n \in N$ then the joint distribution of the k order statistics cannot be asymptotically normal. Otherwise, $Z_{r_{i+1,n}:n} - Z_{r_{i,n}:n}$ would be asymptotically normally distributed in contradiction to the fact that $Z_{r_{i+1,n}:n} - Z_{r_{i,n}:n}$ is distributed as $Z_{(r_{i+1,n}-r_{i,n}):n}$ (see David [3], (2.3.4)).

As stated by Weiss [23], page 109, we cannot get asymptotic normality (uniformly for all Borel sets) for the joint distribution of $k(n) \sim n^{\frac{1}{2}+\delta}$, $\delta > 0$, order statistics in general. In one counterexample concerning the uniform distribution (communicated to the author by Prof. Weiss) Corollary (3.3) implies asymptotic normality if $k(n) = o\left(n^{\frac{1}{2}} (\log n)^{\frac{5}{2}}\right)$.

5. AN APPLICATION

Using the univariate form of the density estimator proposed by Loftsgaarden and Quesenberry [7] the following histogram type estimator was constructed by van Ryzin [19]: Given $m_n \in N$ let $j_n = \{i \in N: im_n + 1 \leq n - m_n\}$. Define

$$f_n(y) = \begin{cases} \dfrac{m_n}{n(Z_{(i+1)m_n+1:n} - Z_{im_n+1:n})} & \text{if } Z_{im_n+1:n} \leq y < Z_{(i+1)m_n+1:n} \\ & \text{for } i \in \{0, \ldots, j_n - 1\}, \\ \dfrac{n - j_n m_n - 1}{n(Z_{n:n} - Z_{j_n m_n+1:n})} & \text{if } Z_{j_n m_n+1:n} \leq y \leq Z_{n:n}, \\ 0 & \text{if } y < Z_{1:n} \text{ or } y > Z_{n:n}. \end{cases}$$

Van Ryzin [19] proved that this estimator is asymptotically normally distributed for each $y \in R$. For $\frac{1}{f_n(y)}$ the corresponding result was already derived by Siddiqui [13].

In this section we consider the maximal deviation of $f_n(y)$ from the "underlying" density function p. The results apply for confidence procedures for p. The Application Theorem is proved by Corollary (3.3) combined with a well-known limit theorem for the largest order statistic.

Application Theorem. *Assume that* P *has a Lebesgue-density* p.

Let $r_{1,n} = i_n m_n + 1$ *and* $r_{k(n),n} = (i_n + k(n) - 1)m_n + 1$ *for some* $i_n, i_n + k(n) - 1 \in \{1, \ldots, j_n\}$. *Let* $p(x) \geq \xi_n$ *for all* $x \in U_n = \left[\mu_{1,n} - \frac{(\log n)\sigma_{1,n}}{\xi_n \sqrt{n}},\ \mu_{k(n),n} + \frac{(\log n)\sigma_{k(n),n}}{\xi_n \sqrt{n}}\right]$ *for some sequence* $\xi_n > 0$, $n \in N$.

Assume that $p^{(1)}(x)$ *exists for all* $x \in \bigcup_{n \in N} U_n$ *and* $|p^{(1)}(x) - p^{(1)}(y)| \leq \epsilon |x - y|$ *for all* $x, y \in \bigcup_{n \in N} U_n$ *for some* $\epsilon > 0$. *Let* $\frac{(r_{k(n),n} - r_{1,n})}{n}$, $n \in N$, *be bounded away from zero.*

Assume that m_n *and* ξ_n *fulfill the conditions*

(a) $$\lim_{n \in N} \frac{\sqrt{n \log^5 n}}{m_n \xi_n^3} = 0$$

and

(b) $$\lim_{n \in N} \frac{\sqrt{m_n^3 \log n}}{n \xi_n^2} = 0.$$

Then

$$\lim_{n \in N} \mathsf{P}^n \Big\{ z \in R^n :\ p(y) \leq f_n^z(y) + \frac{f_n^z(y)}{\sqrt{m_n}} \Big(d(k(n)) + \frac{t}{\sqrt{2 \log k(n)}}\Big) \quad (5.1)$$
$$\text{for all } y \in [z_{r_{1,n}:n}, z_{r_{k(n),n}:n})\Big\} = e^{-e^{-t}}$$

where

$$d(x) = \sqrt{2 \log x} - \frac{\log \log x + \log 4\pi}{2\sqrt{2 \log x}} .$$

Furthermore

$$\lim_{n \in N} \mathrm{P}^n \Big\{ z \in R^n : |p(y) - f_n^z(y)| \leqslant$$

$$\text{(5.2)} \qquad \leqslant \frac{f_n^z(y)}{\sqrt{m_n}} \Big(\hat{d}(k(n)) + \frac{t}{\sqrt{2 \log k(n)}} \Big)$$

$$\textit{for all} \quad y \in [z_{r_{1,n}:n}, z_{r_{k(n),n}:n}) \Big\} = e^{-e^{-t}}$$

where

$$\hat{d}(x) = \sqrt{2 \log x} - \frac{\log \log x + \log \pi}{2\sqrt{2 \log x}} .$$

A short examination of the proof given below reveals that the convergence in (5.1) and (5.2) takes place uniformly for all probability measures P fulfilling the assumptions (given $r_{1,n}, r_{k(n),n}, \xi_n, \eta, \epsilon, m_n$).

If the maximal deviation of f_n from p between the $\alpha_{1,n}$- and the $\alpha_{2,n}$-quantile of P is investigated these two quantiles should be estimated by the corresponding sample quantiles. If $r_{1,n} \leqslant [n\alpha_{1,n}] \leqslant r_{2,n}$ and $r_{k(n)-1,n} \leqslant [n\alpha_{2,n}] < r_{k(n),n}$ then (5.1) and (5.2) still hold true with $[z_{[n\alpha_{1,n}]:n}, z_{[n\alpha_{2,n}]:n}]$ in place of $[z_{r_{1,n}:n}, z_{r_{k(n),n}:n})$. Therefore, we easily derive for fixed quantiles:

(5.3) **Corollary.** *Let* μ_i^* *denote the* α_i*-quantiles of* P *for* $i = 1, 2$ *(with* $0 < \alpha_1 < \alpha_2 < 1$*) and denote by* U *an open neighborhood of* $[\mu_1^*, \mu_2^*]$. *Assume that* P *has a Lebesgue-density* p *with* $p \,|\, U > 0$. *Assume, furthermore, that* $p^{(1)}$ *exists on* U *and* $|p^{(1)}(x) - p^{(1)}(y)| \leqslant \leqslant \epsilon |x - y|$ *for all* $x, y \in U$ *for some* $\epsilon > 0$. *Then*

$$\lim_{n\in N} \mathsf{P}^n\Big\{z\in R^n:\ |p(y)-f_n^z(y)|\leqslant$$

$$\leqslant n^{-\frac{\beta}{2}} f_n^z(y)\Big(\hat{d}((\alpha_2-\alpha_1)n^{1-\beta})+\frac{t}{\sqrt{2\log((\alpha_2-\alpha_1)n^{1-\beta})}}\Big)$$

$$\text{for all}\quad y\in[z_{[n\alpha_1]:n}, z_{[n\alpha_2]:n}]\Big\}=e^{-e^{-t}}$$

if the estimator f_n *is defined with* $m_n=[n^\beta]$ *for some* $\beta\in\left(\frac{1}{2},\frac{2}{3}\right)$.

Bickel and Rosenblatt [2] and Révész [11] proved a corresponding result for the kernel type estimator and the related histogram estimator, respectively. There the maximal deviation between the estimator and the density function was considered on predetermined bounded intervals.

Proof. As always in the proofs the index n will be suppressed. We shall prove (5.1) with the help of

$$\lim_{k\in N} \mathsf{N}_1^k\{x\in R^k:\ \sqrt{2\log k}\max_{i=1,\dots,k}(x_i-d(k))<t\}=e^{-e^{-t}}. \tag{5.4}$$

To prove (5.2) use the following formula instead of (5.4):

$$\lim_{n\in N} \mathsf{N}_1^k\{x\in R^k:\ \sqrt{2\log k}\max_{i=1,\dots,k}(|x_i|-\hat{d}(k))<t\}=e^{-e^{-t}}. \tag{5.5}$$

(5.4) and (5.5) can be easily derived from a well-known limit theorem for the largest order statistic (see von Mises [20]).

Condition (a) implies that the right side of (3.4) tends to zero. Therefore, Corollary (3.3) combined with Lemma (7.22) and (5.4) yields (with $\psi_{r,i}$ defined as in Lemma (7.22))

$$\begin{aligned}&\lim_{n\in N} \mathsf{P}^n\{z\in R^n:\ \sqrt{2\log k}\ \times\\ &\times\max_{i=2,\dots,k}\psi_{r,i}((\sqrt{n}p_j(z_{r_j:n}-\mu_j))_{j=1}^k)-d(k)<t\}=e^{-e^{-t}}.\end{aligned} \tag{5.6}$$

We easily derive that for each $i\in\{2,\dots,k\}$

$$\Big| \psi_{r,i}((\sqrt{n}\, p_j(Z_{r_j:n} - \mu_j))_{j=1}^k) -$$

$$- \sqrt{m_n} \max_{Z_{r_{i-1}:n} \leqslant y < Z_{r_i:n}} \Big(\frac{p(y)}{f_n(y)} - 1\Big) \Big| \leqslant$$

$$\text{(5.7)} \qquad \leqslant \sqrt{m}\, \frac{\eta}{\xi^2}\, p_{i-1} \,|\, Z_{r_{i-1}:n} - \mu_{i-1} \,| +$$

$$+ 2\, \frac{\sqrt{m_n}\, p_k}{\lambda_k \sigma_k} \,|\, Z_{r_k:n} - \mu_k \,| + \frac{m^{\frac{3}{2}}}{n}\, \frac{\eta}{\xi^2} +$$

$$+ \frac{n}{\sqrt{m}} \max_{Z_{r_{i-1}:n} \leqslant y < Z_{r_i:n}} |\, p(y) - p_i \,|\,|\, Z_{r_i:n} - Z_{r_{i-1}:n} \,| = \chi_{r,i}\,,$$

say.

Under the conditions (a) and (b) it follows from (6.22) that for all $\epsilon > 0$

$$\lim_{n\in N} \mathsf{P}^n \bigcup_{i=2}^{k} \{z \in R^n : \sqrt{2 \log k}\, \chi_{r,i}(z) \geqslant \epsilon\} = 0\,.$$

This together with (5.6) implies the assertion.

6. PROOF OF THE THEOREM

Hereafter a_s and c_s denote some "sufficiently large" constants depending on s (with $s > l, m$) only. We write $\hat{a}_s$ etc. if two different a_s's occur in one formula. In this way we obtain the constants a_s and c_s of the Theorem after finitely many steps.

Whenever a two-sided inequality is asserted we shall only prove one part of it as the other part always follows similarly. In the proofs of the Theorem and of the lemmas the index n will be suppressed.

I. For the uniform distribution Q on the interval (0, 1) we easily derive that $\mathsf{Q}^n * (n^{1/2}(Z_{r_i:n} - \lambda_i))_{i=1}^k$ has Lebesgue-density g_r^* given by

$$\text{(6.1)} \qquad g_r^*(x) = \frac{u_r(x)}{\alpha_r}$$

where

$$u_r(x) = \left(\prod_{i=0}^{k-1} \left(1 + \frac{x_{i+1} - x_i}{\sqrt{n}(\lambda_{i+1} - \lambda_i)}\right)^{r_{i+1} - r_i - 1} \right) \times$$
$$\times \left(1 - \frac{x_k}{\sqrt{n}(1 - \lambda_k)}\right)^{n - r_k}$$

for $x \in \left\{ y \in R^k : 0 < \lambda_1 + \frac{y_1}{\sqrt{n}} < \lambda_2 + \frac{y_2}{\sqrt{n}} < \ldots < \lambda_k + \frac{y_k}{\sqrt{n}} < 1 \right\}$ ($u_r(x) = 0$ otherwise). α_r denotes the standardizing constant. To prove (6.1) use Lemma (7.7) and formula (2.2.3) in David [3], page 9.

We introduce numbers ϵ_r with $a_s (\log n)^{5/2} \gamma_r + \epsilon_r \leqslant 1$. The meaning of ϵ_r will become apparent in the second part of this proof.

Let

$$\Gamma_r^{(s)} = \bigcap_{i=1}^{k} \{x \in R^k : x_i \in \Gamma_{r,i}^{(s)}\},$$

(6.2)
$$\Lambda_r^{(s)} = \bigcap_{i=1}^{k-1} \{x \in R^k : (x_{i+1}, x_i) \in \Lambda_{r,i}^{(s)}\},$$

$$\Delta_{r,j}^{(s)} = \left\{ x \in R^k : \left| \sum_{i=0}^{k} \frac{t_{i,0}^j}{\sqrt{r_{i+1} - r_i}} \right| \leqslant \right.$$
$$\left. \leqslant a_s (\log n)^{\frac{5}{2}} \gamma_r^{\frac{1}{2}} + \epsilon_r \right\} \qquad \text{for} \qquad j \in \{1, 3\}$$

and

$$\Theta_r^{(s)} = \Gamma_r^{(s)} \cap \Lambda_r^{(s)} \cap \Delta_{r,1}^{(s)} \cap \Delta_{r,3}^{(s)}.$$

The basic formulas (6.3) and (6.4) are an immediate consequence of the Lemmas (7.9), (7.10), (7.12) and (7.20), (7.21), (7.23), respectively.

We have

(6.3) $$Q^n * (\sqrt{n}\,(Z_{r_{i,n}:n} - \lambda_i))_{i=1}^k (\overline{\Theta_r^{(s)}}) \leqslant c_s n^{-s}$$

and

(6.4) $\quad \mathsf{N}_{r(n)}(\overline{\Theta_r^{(s)}}) \leqslant c_s n^{-s}$.

For all $x \in \Theta_r^{(s)}$ we derive

$$|g_r^*(x) - h_r(x)\big(1 + \sum_{i=1}^{m} S_{r,i}(x)\big)(1 + V_{r,1,m})| \leqslant \tag{6.5}$$
$$\leqslant c_s h_r(x)\Big((\gamma_r \log^5 n)^{\frac{m+1}{2}} + \epsilon_r^{\frac{m+1}{2}}\Big)$$

where the polynomials $S_{r,i}$ are given by

$$S_{r,i} = \sum_{\substack{1 \leqslant j_1 \leqslant j_2 \leqslant \ldots \leqslant j_q \leqslant i \\ j_1 + \ldots + j_q = i}} \alpha(j_1, \ldots, j_q) R_{r,j_1} \ldots R_{r,j_q}$$

where $\alpha(j_1, \ldots, j_q)$ are some fixed constants. Furthermore,

$$V_{r,1,m} = \sum_{j=1}^{m} (-1)^j \Big(\sum_{i=2}^{m} \int S_{r,i} d\mathsf{N}_r\Big)^j .$$

Especially,

$$S_{r,1} = R_{r,1} \tag{6.6}$$

and

$$S_{r,2} = R_{r,2} + \frac{1}{2} R_{r,1}^2 .$$

(6.5) will be proved with the help of (6.7). For all $x \in \Theta_r^{(s)}$

$$\Big|\frac{u_r(x)}{C_r} - h_r(x)\big(1 + \sum_{i=1}^{m} S_{r,i}(x)\big)\Big| \leqslant \tag{6.7}$$
$$\leqslant c_s h_r(x)\Big((\gamma_r \log^5 n)^{\frac{m+1}{2}} + \epsilon_r^{\frac{m+1}{2}}\Big).$$

Assumption (ii) implies that $\dfrac{\log^5 n}{r_{i+1} - r_i} \leqslant 1$ for $i \in \{0, \ldots, k\}$.
Therefore, $u_r(x) > 0$ for all $x \in \Gamma_r^{(s)} \cap \Lambda_r^{(s)}$. (7.1) implies

$$u_r(x) \geqslant \exp\Big(\sum_{i=0}^{k-1} (r_{i+1} - r_i - 1) \times$$

$$\times \Big[\sum_{j=1}^{m+2} \frac{(-1)^{j-1}}{j} \Big(\frac{x_{i+1} - x_i}{\sqrt{n}(\lambda_{i+1} - \lambda_i)}\Big)^j -$$

$$- c_s \Big(\frac{|x_{i+1} - x_i|}{\sqrt{n}(\lambda_{i+1} - \lambda_i)}\Big)^{m+3}\Big] +$$

$$+ (n - r_k)\Big[\sum_{j=1}^{m+2} \frac{(-1)^{j-1}}{j} \Big(- \frac{x_k}{\sqrt{n}(1 - \lambda_k)}\Big)^j -$$

$$- c_s \Big(\frac{|x_k|}{\sqrt{n}(1 - \lambda_k)}\Big)^{m+3}\Big]\Big) =$$

$$= \exp\Big(\sum_{j=0}^{m} R_{r,j}(x) - c_s \hat{R}_{r,m+1}(x)\Big)$$

where $\hat{R}_{r,m+1}$ is defined by the last equation.

For $x \in \Theta_r^{(s)}$:

$$|R_{r,1}(x)| \leqslant a_s \sqrt{\gamma_r \log^5 n} + \epsilon_r$$

and for $j > 1$

$$\left.\begin{array}{l} |R_{r,j}(x)| \\ |\hat{R}_{r,j}(x)| \end{array}\right\} \leqslant a_s (\log n)^{\frac{j+2}{2}} \sum_{i=0}^{k} (r_{i+1} - r_i)^{-\frac{j}{2}} . \tag{6.8}$$

(7.4) implies that $\sum_{i=0}^{k} (r_{i+1} - r_i)^{-\frac{j}{2}} \leqslant \gamma_r^{\frac{j}{2}}$ for $j > 1$. This together with Assumption (ii) yields that $R_{r,j}$, $j = 1, \ldots, m$ and $\hat{R}_{r,m+1}$ are uniformly bounded on $\Theta_r^{(s)}$ by some fixed constant.

Therefore, by (7.2) we obtain for each $x \in \Theta_r^{(s)}$ (with $\alpha = R_{r,0}(x)$)

$$u_r(x) \geqslant \exp(R_{r,0}(x))\Big[1 + \Big(\sum_{j=1}^{m} \frac{1}{j!}\Big(\sum_{i=1}^{m} R_{r,i}(x) -$$

$$- c_s \hat{R}_{r,m+1}(x)\Big)^j\Big) - c_s\Big(\Big|\sum_{i=1}^{m} R_{r,i}(x)\Big| + R_{r,m+1}(x)\Big)^{m+1}\Big] .$$

This together with (6.8) implies (6.7).

Because of $\int g_r^* \, d\lambda^k = 1$ we have $\alpha_r = \int u_r \, d\lambda^k$.

We prove

$$(6.9) \qquad \left| \frac{\alpha_r}{C_r} - \int \left(1 + \sum_{i=1}^{m} S_{r,i}\right) d\mathrm{N}_r \right| \leq c_s (\gamma_r \log^5 n)^{\frac{m+1}{2}} .$$

By (6.3) and (6.7) (with $\epsilon_r = 0$)

$$\frac{\alpha_r}{C_r} = \int_{\Theta_r^{(s)}} \frac{u_r}{C_r} \, d\lambda^k + \frac{\alpha_r}{C_r} \int_{\overline{\Theta_r^{(s)}}} g_r^* \, d\lambda^k \leq$$

$$\leq \int_{\Theta_r^{(s)}} \left(1 + \sum_{i=1}^{m} S_{r,i}\right) d\mathrm{N}_r + c_s \mathrm{N}_r(\Theta_r^{(s)}) (\gamma_r \log^5 n)^{\frac{m+1}{2}} + \frac{\alpha_r c_s}{C_r n^s} .$$

This together with a straightforward application of Lemma (7.26) implies (6.9).

Combining (6.1), (6.7), (6.9) and using the simple formula

$$(6.10) \qquad \int S_{r,1} \, d\mathrm{N}_r = 0$$

we obtain for $x \in \Theta_r^{(s)}$

$$g_r^*(x) \leq \frac{h_r(x)\left(1 + \left(\sum_{i=1}^{m} S_{r,i}(x)\right) + c_s (\gamma_r \log^5 n)^{\frac{m+1}{2}} + \epsilon_r^{\frac{m+1}{2}}\right)}{1 + \left(\sum_{i=2}^{m} \int S_{r,i} \, d\mathrm{N}_r\right) - c_s (\gamma_r \log^5 n)^{\frac{m+1}{2}}}$$

A Taylor expansion of $\frac{1}{x}$ at one completes the proof of (6.5).

II. Assumption (ii) implies that $\theta_{r,1,i}^{(s)}(\mathrm{P})\sigma_i \leq n^{1/2} (\log n)^{-3/2}$ for all $i = 1, \ldots, k$. Therefore, for all sufficiently large n (only depending on a_s)

$$(6.11) \qquad \frac{1}{2} \leq \frac{1}{p_i} \, p\left(\mu_i + \frac{1}{p_i \sqrt{n}}\right) \leq \frac{3}{2} \qquad \text{for all} \quad x \in \Gamma_{r,i}^{(s)}, \; i = 1, \ldots, k .$$

Let $\tau_r: R^k \to R^k$ be defined by

$$\tau_r(x) = (\tau_{r,i}(x))_{i=1}^k = \sqrt{n}\left(F\left(\mu_i + \frac{x_i}{p_i\sqrt{n}}\right) - \lambda_i\right)_{i=1}^k .$$

The Assumptions (i) together with (6.11) imply that the restricted map $\tau_r | \Gamma_r^{(s)}: \Gamma_r^{(s)} \to R^k$ is injective and differentiable. From the explicit form of the distribution function of $\mathsf{P}^n * (Z_{r_i:n})_{i=1}^k$ (see e.g. David [3], (2.2.4), page 10) together with (6.1) and Lemma (7.7) we derive: $\mathsf{P}^n * (\sqrt{n}\, p_i(Z_{r_i:n} - \mu_i))_{i=1}^k | (\mathscr{B}^k \cap \Gamma_r^{(s)})$ has $\lambda^k | (\mathscr{B}^k \cap \Gamma_r^{(s)})$-density $g_r: \Gamma_r^{(s)} \to [0, \infty)$ given by

$$(6.12) \qquad g_r(x) = e_r(x) g_r^*(\tau_r(x)) \qquad \text{for} \qquad x \in \Gamma_r^{(s)}$$

where $e_r(x) = \prod_{i=1}^k e_{r,i}(x)$ and $e_{r,i}(x) = \frac{1}{p_i} p\left(\mu_i + \frac{x_i}{p_i\sqrt{n}}\right)$.

For $i \in \{1, \ldots, k\}$ let

$$\nu_{r,l,i}(x) = \sum_{j=1}^{l} \frac{1}{j!} n^{-\frac{j}{2}} \frac{p_i^{(j)}}{p_i^{j+1}} x_i^j .$$

For $i \in \{0, \ldots, k\}$ let

$$\omega_{r,l,i}(x) = \sum_{j=1}^{l} \frac{1}{(j+1)!} n^{-\frac{j}{2}} t_{i,j}(x) .$$

Using Taylor's theorem we obtain for each $x \in \Gamma_r^{(s)}$ and $i \in \{1, \ldots, k\}$

$$(6.13) \qquad |\tau_{r,i}(x) - x_i| \leq c_s \theta_{r,1,i}^{(s)}(\mathsf{P}) \sigma_i^2 \frac{\log n}{\sqrt{n}}$$

and

$$(6.14) \qquad |e_{r,i}(x) - (1 - \nu_{r,l,i}(x))| \leq c_s \left(\frac{\log n}{n}\right)^{\frac{l+1}{2}} \theta_{r,l+1,i}^{(s)} \sigma_i^{l+1} .$$

For $x \in \Gamma_r^{(s)} \cap \Lambda_r^{(s)}$ and $i \in \{0, \ldots, k\}$

$$(6.15) \qquad \left| \frac{\tau_{r,i+1}(x) - \tau_{r,i}(x)}{\sqrt{\lambda_{i+1} - \lambda_i}} - t_{i,0}(x) + \omega_{r,l,i}(x)) \right| \leq$$

$$\leq c_s n^{-\frac{l+1}{2}} (\log n)^{\frac{l+2}{2}} \Bigg(\theta^{(s)}_{r,l+1,i}(\mathrm{P})(\sigma_i + \sigma_{i+1})^{l+1} + $$

$$+ \frac{\rho^{(s)}_{r,l+1,i}(\mathrm{P})\sigma_i^{l+2}}{\sqrt{\lambda_{i+1} - \lambda_i}} \Bigg)$$

with $\tau_{r,i} \equiv 0$ and $\rho_{r,j,i}(\mathrm{P}) = 0$ for $i \in \{0, k+1\}$.

By (6.14) for all $x \in \Gamma_r^{(s)}$ and $i \in \{1, \ldots, k\}$,

$$(6.16) \qquad |\nu_{r,l,i}(x)| \leq c_s \sum_{j \in \{1, l+1\}} \left(\frac{\log n}{n}\right)^{\frac{j}{2}} \theta^{(s)}_{r,j,i} \sigma_i^j .$$

By (6.15) for $x \in \Gamma_r^{(s)} \cap \Lambda_r^{(s)}$ and $i \in \{0, \ldots, k\}$

$$(6.17) \qquad |\omega_{r,l,i}(x)| \leq c_s \sum_{j \in \{1, l+1\}} n^{-\frac{j}{2}} (\log n)^{\frac{j+1}{2}} \Bigg(\theta^{(s)}_{r,j,i}(\sigma_i + \sigma_{i+1})^j + $$

$$+ \frac{\rho^{(s)}_{r,j,i}\sigma_i^{j+1}}{\sqrt{\lambda_{i+1} - \lambda_i}} \Bigg).$$

Let $\hat{\Theta}_r^{(s)}$ and $\hat{\hat{\Theta}}_r^{(s)}$ be defined as $\Theta_r^{(s)}$ with $\hat{a}_s = 2a_s$ and $\hat{\hat{a}}_s = \frac{a_s}{2}$ in place of a_s, respectively. $\hat{\Gamma}_r^{(s)}$ etc. are defined analogously. (6.3) and (6.5) still hold true with $\hat{\hat{\Theta}}_r^{(s)}$ and $\hat{\Theta}_r^{(s)}$, respectively, in place of $\Theta_r^{(s)}$. Let

$$\epsilon_r = \epsilon_r(\mathrm{P}) = \sqrt{\frac{\log^3 n}{n}} \sum_{i=0}^{k} \frac{1}{\sqrt{r_{i+1} - r_i}} \left(\theta^{(s)}_{r,1,i}(\mathrm{P})(\sigma_i + \sigma_{i+1}) + \frac{\rho_{r,1,i}(\mathrm{P})\sigma_i^2}{\sqrt{\lambda_{i+1} - \lambda_i}} \right).$$

(6.11), (6.13) and (6.15) (with $l = 0$) imply that

$$(6.18) \qquad \tau_r(\Theta_r^{(s)}) \subset \hat{\Theta}_r^{(s)} .$$

Therefore, for all $x \in \Theta_r^{(s)}$ (6.5) is applicable to $\tau_r(x)$ in place of x and yields

$$(6.19) \qquad \begin{aligned} &\Big| g_r(x) - e_r(x) h_r(\tau_r(x)) \Big(1 + \sum_{i=1}^{m} S_{r,i}(\tau_r(x))\Big)(1 + V_{r,1,m}) \Big| \leq \\ &\leq c_s e_r(x) h_r(\tau_r(x)) \Big((\gamma_r \log^5 n)^{\frac{m+1}{2}} + \epsilon_r(\mathrm{P})^{\frac{m+1}{2}} \Big). \end{aligned}$$

From (6.11) and (6.13) it follows also that $\hat{\hat{\Gamma}}_r^{(s)} \subset \tau_r(\Gamma_r^{(s)})$ for sufficiently large n (only depending on a_s). Hence the inverse function $\tau_r^{-1} \mid \Gamma_r^{(s)}$ is well defined. Let $x \in \hat{\hat{\Gamma}}_r^{(s)} \cap \hat{\hat{\Lambda}}_r^{(s)}$. Under the Assumptions (ii) and (iii) we obtain by some tedious calculations (for some $\kappa_i \in (0, 1)$) that

$$
\begin{aligned}
& |\tau_{r,i+1}^{-1}(x) - \tau_{r,i}^{-1}(x)| = \\
& = \Big| \frac{p_{i+1}}{p\left(F^{-1}\left(\lambda_{i+1} + \kappa_i \frac{x_{i+1}}{\sqrt{n}}\right)\right)} x_{i+1} - \\
& - \frac{p_i}{p\left(F^{-1}\left(\lambda_i + \kappa_i \frac{x_i}{\sqrt{n}}\right)\right)} x_i \Big| \leq a_s \sqrt{(\lambda_{i+1} - \lambda_i) \log n}\,.
\end{aligned}
\tag{6.20}
$$

This implies that $\hat{\hat{\Gamma}}_r^{(s)} \cap \hat{\hat{\Lambda}}_r^{(s)} \subset \tau_r(\Lambda_r^{(s)})$. The proof of $\hat{\hat{\Theta}}_r^{(s)} \subset \Delta_{r,j}^{(s)}$ for $j \in \{1, 3\}$ can also be reduced to (6.20). Therefore,

$$
\hat{\hat{\Theta}}_r^{(s)} \subset \tau_r(\Theta_r^{(s)})\,. \tag{6.21}
$$

Note that throughout the paper Assumption (iii) is only used in the proof of (6.20).

By the transformation theorem for integrals

$$
\int_{\Theta_r^{(s)}} e_r(x) g_r^*(\tau_r(x))\, dx = \int_{\tau_r(\Theta_r^{(s)})} g_r^*(x)\, dx\,.
$$

Therefore, by (6.3), (6.12) and (6.21)

$$
\mathsf{P}^n * (\sqrt{n}\, p_i (Z_{r_i:n} - \mu_i))_{i=1}^k (\Theta_r^{(s)}) \geq 1 - \frac{c_s}{n^s}\,. \tag{6.22}
$$

Next we give a Taylor expansion for $e_r(x)$, $S_{r,i}(\tau_r(x))$ and $h_r(\tau_r(x))$.

Writing $e_r(x) = \exp\left(\sum_{i=1}^k \log(e_{r,i}(x))\right)$ we conclude with the help of (6.14), (6.16), (7.1) and (7.2) (applied for $\alpha = 0$) that for each $x \in \Theta_r^{(s)}$

$$(6.23)\qquad |e_r(x) - (1 - V_{r,2,l}(x))| \leqslant c_s\left(\frac{\log^3 n}{n}\right)^{\frac{l+1}{2}} \delta^{(s)}_{r,l+1}(\mathrm{P})$$

where $V_{r,2,l}(x) = \sum_{q=1}^{l} \frac{1}{q!}\left[\sum_{i=1}^{l} \frac{(-1)^{i-1}}{i}\left(\sum_{j=1}^{k} \nu^i_{r,l,j}(x)\right)\right]^q$.

Let

$$R^*_{r,j,l}(x) = R_{r,j}(x) + \frac{(-1)^{j-1}}{j+2}\sum_{i=0}^{k}(r_{i+1} - r_i)^{-\frac{j}{2}} \times$$

$$\times\left(\sum_{q=1}^{j+2}\binom{j+2}{q} t_{i,0}^{j-q+2}(x)\omega_{r,l,i}(x)^q\right) +$$

$$+\frac{(-1)^j}{j}\sum_{i=0}^{k-1}(r_{i+1} - r_i)^{-\frac{j}{2}} \times$$

$$\times\left(\sum_{q=1}^{j}\binom{j}{q} t_{i,0}^{j-q}(x)\omega_{r,l,i}(x)^q\right).$$

Then

$$|R_{r,j}(\tau_r(x)) - R^*_{r,j,l}(x)| \leqslant c_s\left(\frac{\log^3 n}{n}\right)^{\frac{l+1}{2}} \delta^{(s)}_{r,l+1}(\mathrm{P}).$$

Therefore, for each $x \in \Theta^{(s)}_r$

$$(6.24)\qquad |S_{r,i}(\tau_r(x)) - V_{r,3,l,i}(x)| \leqslant c_s\left(\frac{\log^3 n}{n}\right)^{\frac{l+1}{2}} \delta^{(s)}_{r,l+1}(\mathrm{P})$$

where $V_{r,3,l,i}(x) = \sum_{\substack{1 \leqslant j_1 \leqslant j_2 \leqslant \ldots \leqslant j_q \leqslant i \\ j_1 + \ldots + j_q = i}} \alpha(j_1, \ldots, j_q) R^*_{r,j_1,l} \ldots R^*_{r,j_q,l}$.

Furthermore,

$$|R_{r,0}(\tau_r(x)) - R^*_{r,0,l}(x)| \leqslant c_s\left(\frac{\log^3 n}{n}\right)^{\frac{l+1}{2}} \delta^{(s)}_{r,l+1}(\mathrm{P})$$

where $R^*_{r,0,l}(x) = R_{r,0}(x) - \frac{1}{2}\sum_{i=0}^{k}\left(\sum_{q=1}^{2}\binom{2}{q} t_{i,0}^{2-q}(x)\omega^q_{r,l,i}(x)\right)$.

The inequality (7.2), applied for $\alpha = R_{r,0}(x)$, yields for each $x \in \Theta_r^{(s)}$

$$|h_r(\tau_r(x)) - h_r(x)(1 + V_{r,4,l}(x))| \leqslant \tag{6.25}$$
$$\leqslant c_s \left(\frac{\log^3 n}{n}\right)^{\frac{l+1}{2}} \delta_{r,l+1}^{(s)}(\mathrm{P})$$

where $V_{r,4,l}(x) = \sum_{j=1}^{l} \frac{1}{j!}\left(-\frac{1}{2}\sum_{i=0}^{k}\sum_{q=1}^{2}\binom{2}{q} t_{i,0}^{2-q}(x)\omega_{r,l,i}(x)^q\right)^j$.

Assume without loss of generality that $m \geqslant l$. (6.19) together with (6.16), (6.17) and (6.23)-(6.25) implies that for all $x \in \Theta_r^{(s)}$

$$|g_r(x) - h_r(x)(1 + V_{r,1,m})(1 + V_{r,2,l}(x)) \times$$
$$\times \left(1 + \sum_{i=1}^{m} V_{r,3,l,i}(x)\right)(1 + V_{r,4,l}(x))| \leqslant \tag{6.26}$$
$$\leqslant c_s h_r(x)\left((\gamma_r \log^5 n)^{\frac{m+1}{2}} + \left(\frac{\log^3 n}{n}\right)^{\frac{l+1}{2}} \delta_{r,l+1}^{(s)}(\mathrm{P})\right).$$

Finally, we have to prove that

$$\left| \int_{\Theta_r^{(s)}} (1 + V_{r,2,l})\left(1 + \sum_{i=1}^{m} V_{r,3,l,i}\right)(1 + V_{r,4,l})\, d\mathrm{N}_r \right| \leqslant \frac{c_s}{n^s}. \tag{6.27}$$

From Assumption (ii) we derive that $\left|\frac{p_i^{(j)}}{p_i^{j+1}}\right| \leqslant c_s n^{q(l)}$ for some $q(l) \in N$ (depending only on l) for $i = 1, \ldots, k$ and $j = 1, \ldots, l$. Hence (6.27) follows from Lemma (7.26) by some straightforward calculations.

The assertion of the Theorem follows from (6.26) and (6.27) by integration.

7. AUXILIARY RESULTS

For the sake of reference we state the following simple inequalities:

(7.1) For all $\eta \in \left(-\frac{1}{2}, 1\right)$

$$\left|\log(1+\eta) - \sum_{i=1}^{l} (-1)^{i-1} \frac{\eta^i}{i}\right| \leqslant c_l |\eta|^{l+1} .$$

(7.2) If $|\eta| \leqslant \beta$ then for all $\alpha \in R$

$$\left|\exp(\alpha+\eta) - \exp(\alpha)\left(1 + \sum_{i=1}^{l} \frac{\eta^i}{i!}\right)\right| \leqslant c_\beta \exp(\alpha) |\eta|^{l+1} .$$

Let $\alpha_i \geqslant 0$ for $i = 1, \ldots, k$. By Jensen's inequality (see e.g. Ferguson [5], Lemma 1, page 76):

(7.3) $\sum_{i=1}^{k} \alpha_i = 1$ implies that $k^2 \leqslant \sum_{i=1}^{k} \frac{1}{\alpha_i}$.

By elementary calculations:

(7.4) $\sum_{i=1}^{k} \alpha_i \geqslant \left(\sum_{i=1}^{k} \alpha_i^q\right)^{\frac{1}{q}}$ for all $q \geqslant 1$.

For all $t > 0$

(7.5) $N_1(t, \infty) \leqslant \frac{1}{\sqrt{2\pi}\, t} e^{-\frac{t^2}{2}}$.

For the proof of (7.5) see Feller [4], Lemma 2, page 166.

The following lemma is a simple extension of the theorem for exponential bounds (see Loève [6], page 254).

(7.6) **Lemma.** *Let* $(\Omega, \mathscr{A}, \mathsf{M})$ *be a probability space. Let* $f_i\colon \Omega \to R$, $i = 1, \ldots, k$ *be* M*-independent bounded functions with* $\mathsf{E}(f_i) = 0$. *Let* $\xi_i^2 = \mathsf{E}(f_i^2)$ *and* $\zeta_k^2 = \sum_{i=1}^{k} \xi_i^2$. *If* $t \leqslant \frac{\zeta_k}{\|f_i\|}$ *for* $i = 1, \ldots, k$ *(where* $\|f_i\| = \sup\{|f_i(\omega)|\colon \omega \in \Omega\}$*) then for each* $\epsilon > 0$

$$\mathsf{M}\{\omega \in \Omega : \frac{1}{\zeta_k} \mid \sum_{i=1}^{k} f_i(\omega) \mid \geqslant \epsilon\} \leqslant$$

$$\leqslant 2 \exp\left(-t\epsilon + \frac{t^2}{2}\left(1 + \frac{t}{2\zeta_k^3} \sum_{i=1}^{k} \|f_i\| \, \xi_i^2\right)\right).$$

The proof of the following lemma is essentially that of the transformation theorem for probability densities (see e.g. Richter [12], page 228).

(7.7) **Lemma.** *Let* $\Xi \in \mathscr{B}^m$. *Let* $\psi : R^m \to R^m$ *be a measurable map such that* $\psi \mid \Xi$ *is injective and* $\Xi^* = \psi(\Xi)$ *is open. Assume that the finite signed measure* $\nu \mid \mathscr{B}^m$ *has Lebesgue-density* h *with* $h \mid \bar{\Xi} \equiv 0$. *If the inverse function* $\psi^{-1} : \Xi^* \to \Xi$ *of* $\psi \mid \Xi$ *is differentiable then* $\nu * \psi$ *has Lebesgue-density* h^* *defined by* $h^*(w) = h(\psi^{-1}(w)) \left| \det\left(\frac{\partial \psi^{-1}}{\partial v}(w)\right)\right|$ *for* $w \in \Xi^*$ *and* $h^*(w) = 0$ *elsewhere. (*$\det\left(\frac{\partial \psi^{-1}}{\partial v}\right)$ *denotes the jacobian of* ψ^{-1} *on* Ξ^*.*)*

Denote by b_{α_1, α_2} the beta-distribution with Lebesgue-density

$$x \to \frac{x^{\alpha_1 - 1}(1-x)^{\alpha_2 - 1}}{B(\alpha_1, \alpha_2)} \qquad \text{for} \quad x \in (0, 1).$$

Remember that Euler's beta function $B(\alpha_1, \alpha_2)$ is defined by

$$B(\alpha_1, \alpha_2) = \int_0^1 t^{\alpha_1 - 1}(1-t)^{\alpha_2 - 1}\, dt.$$

(7.8) **Lemma.** *If* $q \in N \cap [a_s \log n, \; n - a_s \log n]$ *then*

$$b_{q, n-q+1}(\overline{t_*, t^*}) \leqslant \frac{c_s}{n^s}$$

where

$$t^* = \frac{q}{n} + \frac{\hat{a}_s (\log n)^{\frac{1}{2}} \left(\frac{q}{n}\left(1 - \frac{q}{n}\right)\right)^{\frac{1}{2}}}{\sqrt{n}}$$

and

$$t_* = \frac{q}{n} - \frac{\hat{a}_s (\log n)^{\frac{1}{2}} \left(\frac{q}{n}\left(1 - \frac{q}{n}\right)\right)^{\frac{1}{2}}}{\sqrt{n}} .$$

Proof. Concerning the equation used below see e.g. David [3], (2.1.6) and (2.1.3). We have

$$b_{q,n-q+1}[t^*, \infty) =$$

$$= Q^n\left\{z \in (0,1)^n : \sum_{i=1}^{n} 1_{(0,t^*)}(z_i) < q\right\} \leq$$

$$\leq Q^n\left\{z \in (0,1)^n : \frac{1}{\xi\sqrt{n}} \sum_{i=1}^{n} (1_{(0,t^*)}(z_i) - t^*) < -\frac{a_s\sqrt{\log n}}{2}\right\}$$

where $\xi^2 = t^*(1-t^*)$. (Note that $q \geq a_s \log n$ implies $\dfrac{\frac{q}{n}\left(1 - \frac{q}{n}\right)}{\xi^2} \geq \frac{1}{4}$.)

Because of $a_s^2 \log n \leq \xi^2 n$ Lemma (7.6) implies that $b_{q,n-q+1}[t^*, \infty) \leq \frac{c_s}{n^s}$. Similarly, we may prove that $b_{q,n-q+1}(-\infty, t_*] \leq \frac{c_s}{n^s}$.

It is well known that $Q^n * Z_{r:n} = b_{r,n-r+1}$ for $r \in \{1, \ldots, n\}$ and $Q^n * (Z_{r_2:n} - Z_{r_1:n}) = b_{r_2-r_1, n-(r_2-r_1)+1}$ for $r_1, r_2 \in \{1, \ldots, n\}$ with $r_2 > r_1$ (see e.g. David [3], (2.1.6) and (2.3.4)). Therefore, we easily derive from Lemma (7.8) the following inequalities:

(7.9) **Lemma.** *If* $a_s \log n \leq r_{1,n}$ *and* $r_{k(n),n} \leq n - a_s \log n$, *then*

$$Q^n * \left(\sqrt{n}\,(Z_{r_{i,n}:n} - \lambda_{i,n})\right)_{i=1}^{k(n)} \left(\overline{\Gamma_{r(n)}^{(s)}}\right) \leq \frac{c_s}{n^s} .$$

(7.10) **Lemma.** *If* $a_s \log n \leq r_{i+1,n} - r_{i,n} \leq n - a_s \log n$ *for all* $i \in \{0, \ldots, k\}$ *then*

$$Q^n * (\sqrt{n}(Z_{r_{i,n}:n} - \lambda_{i,n}))_{i=1}^{k(n)}(\overline{\Lambda_r^{(s)}}) \leqslant \frac{c_s}{n^s}\,.$$

To obtain the corresponding formula for the sets $\Delta^{(s)}_{r(n),j}$ the measure $Q^n * (\sqrt{n}(Z_{r_{i,n}:n} - \lambda_{i,n}))_{i=1}^{k(n)}$ is transformed to a product measure. Let $Z_{0:n} \equiv 0$.

(7.11) **Lemma.**

$$Q^n * \left(\frac{Z_{r_{i,n}:n} - Z_{r_{i-1,n}:n}}{1 - Z_{r_{i-1,n}:n}}\right)_{i=1}^{k(n)} = \prod_{i=1}^{k(n)} b_{r_{i,n}-r_{i-1,n},\, n-r_{i,n}+1}\,.$$

(The right side denotes the independent product measure with components $b_{r_{i,n}-r_{i-1,n},\, n-r_{i,n}+1}$ $(i = 1, \ldots, k(n))$.)

Proof. Using formula (2.2.3) in David [3], page 9, it is easy to see that $Q^n * (Z_{r_i:n})_{i=1}^k$ has Lebesgue-density f_r given by

$$f_r(x) = \Big(\prod_{i=1}^{k} \frac{1}{B(r_i - r_{i-1}, n - r_i + 1)}\Big) \times$$

$$\times \Big(\prod_{i=0}^{k-1} (x_{i+1} - x_i)^{r_{i+1} - r_i - 1}\Big)(1 - x_k)^{n - r_k}$$

for $0 < x_1 < x_2 < \ldots < x_k < 1$ (and $f_r(x) = 0$ otherwise).

Define $\kappa = (\kappa_i)_{i=1}^k : \{x \in (0,1)^k : x_1 < x_2 < \ldots < x_k\} \to (0,1)^k$ by

$$\kappa_i(x) = \frac{x_i - x_{i-1}}{1 - x_{i-1}} \qquad (i = 1, \ldots, k)\,.$$

κ is a bijective function. The inverse function $\kappa^{-1} = (\kappa_i^{-1})_{i=1}^k : (0,1)^k \to$ $\to \{x \in (0,1)^k : x_1 < x_2 < \ldots < x_k\}$ is defined by

$$\kappa_i^{-1}(x) = 1 - \prod_{j=1}^{i} (1 - x_j) \qquad (i = 1, \ldots, k)\,.$$

Lemma (7.7) implies that $Q^n * \left(\dfrac{Z_{r_i:n} - Z_{r_{i-1}:n}}{1 - Z_{r_{i-1}:n}}\right)_{i=1}^k$ has

Lebesgue-density $x \to \left|\det\left(\frac{\partial \kappa^{-1}}{\partial y}(x)\right)\right| f_r(\kappa^{-1}(x))$ for $x \in (0,1)^k$ (and zero otherwise).

Let $\kappa_0^{-1} \equiv 0$. For $x \in (0,1)^k$

$$\left|\det\left(\frac{\partial \kappa^{-1}}{\partial y}(x)\right)\right| = \prod_{i=1}^{k} (1-x_i)^{k-i}$$

and

$$\Big(\prod_{i=0}^{k-1} (\kappa_{i+1}^{-1}(x) - \kappa_i^{-1}(x))^{r_{i+1}-r_i-1}\Big)(1-\kappa_k^{-1}(x))^{n-r_k} =$$

$$= x_1^{r_1-1}\Big[\prod_{i=1}^{k-1} x_{i+1}\Big(\prod_{j=1}^{i}(1-x_j)\Big)\Big]^{r_{i+1}-r_i-1}\Big(\prod_{i=1}^{k}(1-x_i)\Big)^{n-r_k} =$$

$$= \Big(\prod_{i=0}^{k-1} x_{i+1}^{r_{i+1}-r_i-1}\Big)\prod_{i=1}^{k}(1-x_i)^{n-r_i-(k-i)} =$$

$$= \frac{\prod_{i=1}^{k} x_i^{r_i-r_{i-1}-1}(1-x_i)^{n-r_i}}{\prod_{i=1}^{k}(1-x_i)^{k-i}} .$$

Therefore,

$$\left|\det\left(\frac{\partial \kappa^{-1}}{\partial y}(x)\right)\right| f_r(\kappa^{-1}(x)) = \prod_{i=1}^{k} \frac{x_i^{r_i-r_{i-1}-1}(1-x_i)^{n-r_i}}{B(r_i-r_{i-1}, n-r_i+1)},$$

and the assertion follows immediately.

The following lemma plays a basic role in the proof of the Theorem. In this section the sets $\Delta_{r(n),j}^{(s)}$ are always defined with $\epsilon_{r(n)} = 0$.

(7.12) **Lemma.** *For* $j = 1, 3$

$$Q^n * (\sqrt{n}(Z_{r_i,n:n} - \lambda_{i,n}))_{i=1}^{k(n)}(\overline{\Delta_{r(n),j}^{(s)}}) \leqslant \frac{c_s}{n^s} .$$

Proof. We shall only prove the assertion for $j = 3$ as the proof for $j = 1$ runs analogously. Let $\hat{k} = \max\{j \in \{0, 1, \ldots, k-1\}\colon \lambda_j \leq \frac{1}{2}\}$, $\hat{a}_s = \frac{a_s}{2}$, $\hat{\gamma}_r = \sum_{i=0}^{\hat{k}} \frac{1}{r_{i+1} - r_i}$ and $\hat{\hat{\gamma}}_r = \sum_{i=\hat{k}+1}^{k} \frac{1}{r_{i+1} - r_i}$. We have

$$Q^n * (\sqrt{n}(Z_{r_i:n} - \lambda_i))_{i=1}^k (\overline{\Delta_{r,3}^{(s)}}) \leq Q^n(\overline{\Delta_{r,3,2}^{(s)}}) + Q^n(\overline{\Delta_{r,3,1}^{(s)}})$$

where

$$\Delta_{r,3,1}^{(s)} = \Bigg\{ z \in (0,1)^n \colon \Bigg| \sum_{i=0}^{\hat{k}} \frac{1}{\sqrt{r_{i+1} - r_i}} \times$$

$$\times \left(\frac{\sqrt{n}(z_{r_{i+1}:n} - z_{r_i:n} - (\lambda_{i+1} - \lambda_i))}{\sqrt{\lambda_{i+1} - \lambda_i}} \right)^3 \Bigg| \leq \hat{a}_s \sqrt{\hat{\gamma}_r} \log^5 n \Bigg\}$$

and

$$\Delta_{r,3,2}^{(s)} = \Bigg\{ z \in (0,1)^n \colon \Bigg| \sum_{i=\hat{k}+1}^{k-1} \frac{1}{\sqrt{r_{i+1} - r_i}} \times$$

$$\times \left(\frac{\sqrt{n}(z_{r_{i+1}:n} - z_{r_i:n} - (\lambda_{i+1} - \lambda_i))}{\sqrt{\lambda_{i+1} - \lambda_i}} \right)^3 -$$

$$- \frac{1}{\sqrt{n - r_k}} \left(\frac{\sqrt{n}(z_{r_k:n} - \lambda_k)}{\sqrt{1 - \lambda_k}} \right)^3 \Bigg| \leq \sqrt{\hat{\hat{\gamma}}_r} \log^5 n \Bigg\}.$$

Using the transformation $z \to (1 - z_i)_{i=1}^n$, $z \in (0,1)^n$, we obtain

$$Q^n(\Delta_{r,3,2}^{(s)}) = Q^n \Bigg\{ z \in (0,1)^n \colon \Bigg| \sum_{i=\hat{k}+1}^{k-1} \frac{1}{\sqrt{r_{i+1} - r_i}} \times$$

$$\times \left(\frac{\sqrt{n}(z_{n-r_i+1:n} - z_{n-r_{i+1}+1:n} - (\lambda_{i+1} - \lambda_i))}{\sqrt{\lambda_{i+1} - \lambda_i}} \right)^3 +$$

$$+ \frac{1}{\sqrt{n - r_k}} \left(\frac{\sqrt{n}(z_{n-r_k+1:n} - (1 - \lambda_k))}{\sqrt{1 - \lambda_k}} \right)^3 \Bigg| \leq \hat{a}_s \sqrt{\hat{\hat{\gamma}}_r} \log^5 n \Bigg\}.$$

Notice that $\frac{n - r_{\hat{k}+1} + 1}{n} \leqslant \frac{1}{2}$. Hence $\mathrm{Q}^n(\overline{\Delta^{(s)}_{r,3,2}}) \leqslant \frac{c_s}{n^s}$ can be proved in a similar way as $\mathrm{Q}^n(\overline{\Delta^{(s)}_{r,3,1}}) \leqslant \frac{c_s}{n^s}$. These two inequalities together yield the assertion.

For $i = 0, \ldots, \hat{k}$ let

$$Y_{r,i} = \frac{n - r_i}{\sqrt{r_{i+1} - r_i}} \left(\frac{Z_{r_{i+1}:n} - Z_{r_i:n}}{1 - Z_{r_i:n}} - \frac{r_{i+1} - r_i}{n - r_i} \right)$$

and

$$X_{r,i} = - \frac{n}{\sqrt{r_{i+1} - r_i}} \, \frac{(Z_{r_i:n} - \lambda_i)(Z_{r_{i+1}:n} - Z_{r_i:n})}{1 - Z_{r_i:n}} .$$

Thus for $i = 0, \ldots, \hat{k}$

$$\frac{\sqrt{n}\,(Z_{r_{i+1}:n} - Z_{r_i:n} - (\lambda_{i+1} - \lambda_i))}{\sqrt{\lambda_{i+1} - \lambda_i}} = Y_{r,i} + X_{r,i} . \tag{7.13}$$

Therefore

$$\mathrm{Q}^n(\Delta^{(s)}_{r,3,1}) =$$

$$= \mathrm{Q}^n\Big\{ z \in (0,1)^n : \Big| \sum_{i=0}^{\hat{k}} \frac{1}{\sqrt{r_{i+1} - r_i}} (Y_{r,i}(z) + X_{r,i}(z))^3 \Big| \leqslant$$

$$\leqslant \hat{a}_s \sqrt{\hat{\gamma}_r} \log^5 n \Big\} .$$

Because of $\lambda_{\hat{k}} \leqslant \frac{1}{2}$ we may derive from Lemma (7.9) and Lemma (7.10) that

$$\mathrm{Q}^n \bigcup_{i=0}^{\hat{k}} \{ z \in (0,1)^n : |X_{r,i}(z)| > \hat{a}_s \sqrt{(\lambda_{i+1} - \lambda_i) \log n} \} \leqslant \frac{c_s}{n^s} . \tag{7.14}$$

This together with Lemma (7.10) and (7.13) implies that

$$\mathrm{Q}^n \bigcup_{i=0}^{\hat{k}} \{ z \in (0,1)^n : |Y_{r,i}(z)| \geqslant \hat{a}_s \sqrt{\log n} \} \leqslant \frac{c_s}{n^s} . \tag{7.15}$$

Below we shall prove that

$$(7.16)\qquad Q^n\left\{z \in (0,1)^n : \Big|\sum_{i=1}^{\hat{k}} \frac{Y_{r,i}^3(z)}{\sqrt{r_{i+1}-r_i}}\Big| \geq \hat{a}_s \sqrt{\hat{\gamma}_r \log^5 n}\right\} \leq \frac{c_s}{n^s}.$$

(7.14)-(7.16) together with (7.3) immediately imply $Q^n(\overline{\Delta_{r,3,1}^{(s)}}) \leq$ $\leq \frac{c_s}{n^s}$ and hence the assertion follows.

Lemma (7.11) implies that the functions $Y_{r,i}$, $i = 1, \dots, \hat{k}$ are Q^n-independent. We apply (7.6) to

$$f_i = \frac{1}{\sqrt{r_{i+1}-r_i}}\,[Y_{r,i}^3 1_{(-\hat{a}_s\sqrt{\log n},\ \hat{a}_s\sqrt{\log n})}(Y_{r,i}) -$$

$$- Q^n(Y_{r,i}^3 1_{(-\hat{a}_s\sqrt{\log n},\ \hat{a}_s\sqrt{\log n})}(Y_{r,i}))] \quad \text{for} \quad i = 0, \dots, \hat{k}.$$

According to Lemma (7.11)

$$|Q^n(Y_{r,i}^3 1_{(-\hat{a}_s\sqrt{\log n},\ \hat{a}_s\sqrt{\log n})}(Y_{r,i}))| \leq$$

$$(7.17)\qquad \leq \frac{n^3}{(r_{i+1}-r_i)}\left(\Big|b_{r_{i+1}-r_i,\,n-r_{i+1}+1}\Big(\Big(x-\frac{r_{i+1}-r_i}{n-r_i}\Big)^3\Big)\Big| + \right.$$

$$\left. + \Big|b_{r_{i+1}-r_i,\,n-r_{i+1}+1}\Big(\Big(x-\frac{r_{i+1}-r_i}{n-r_i}\Big)^3 \cdot 1_{I_{r,i}}(x)\Big)\Big|\right)$$

where $I_{r,i} = \left\{y \in R : \Big|y - \frac{r_{i+1}-r_i}{n-r_i}\Big| \geq \hat{a}_s \sqrt{\log n}\,\frac{\sqrt{r_{i+1}-r_i}}{n-r_i}\right\}$.

Since

$$b_{r_{i+1}-r_i,\,n-r_{i+1}+1}(x^j) = \frac{(r_{i+1}-r_i)\dots(r_{i+1}-r_i+j-1)}{(n-r_i+1)\dots(n-r_i+j)}$$

(see e.g. Richter [12], page 346) we obtain by some direct computations (for some $\alpha > 0$)

$$(7.18)\qquad \left| b_{r_{i+1}-r_i,\, n-r_{i+1}+1}\Big(\Big(x-\frac{r_{i+1}-r_i}{n-r_i}\Big)^3\Big)\right| \leqslant \alpha\, \frac{r_{i+1}-r_i}{n^3}\,.$$

Furthermore, in a similar way as in (7.15) we derive for $j = 0, 1, 2, \ldots$

$$b_{r_{i+1}-r_i,\, n-r_{i+1}+1}(x^j 1_{I_{r,i}}) = b_{r_{i+1}-r_i+j,\, n-r_{i+1}+1}(I_{r,i}) \leqslant$$

$$\leqslant b_{r_{i+1}-(r_i-j),\, n-r_{i+1}+1}\Big\{x \in R\colon \Big|x - \frac{r_{i+1}-(r_i-j)}{n-(r_i-j)}\Big| \geqslant$$

$$\geqslant \hat{a}_s \sqrt{\log n}\, \frac{\sqrt{r_{i+1}-(r_i-j)}}{n-(r_i-j)}\Big\} \leqslant \frac{c_s}{n^s}\,.$$

This together with (7.17) and (7.18) implies that (7.16) holds true if

$$(7.19)\qquad \mathrm{Q}^n\Big\{z \in (0,1)^n : \Big|\sum_{i=0}^{\hat{k}} f_i(z)\Big| \geqslant \hat{a}_s \sqrt{\hat{\gamma}_r \log^5 n}\Big\} \leqslant \frac{c_s}{n^s}\,.$$

By arguments similar to those which lead to (7.18) we may prove that $\mathrm{Q}^n(f_i^2) \leqslant \dfrac{\alpha}{r_{i+1}-r_i}$ for some $\alpha > 0$.

Now (7.19) follows immediately from (7.6) with $t = \hat{a}_s \log^{-\frac{3}{2}} n$.

(7.20) **Lemma.** $\mathrm{N}_{r(n)}(\overline{\Gamma^{(s)}_{r(n)}}) \leqslant \dfrac{c_s}{n^s}$.

Proof. Using (3.15) and (7.5) we obtain by some standard calculations

$$\mathrm{N}_{r(n)}(\overline{\Gamma^{(s)}_{r(n)}}) \leqslant \sum_{i=1}^{k(n)} \mathrm{N}_{\sigma^2_{i,n}}(\overline{\Gamma^{(s)}_{r(n),i}}) \leqslant \frac{c_s}{n^s}\,.$$

Similarly, we prove

(7.21) **Lemma.** $\mathrm{N}_{r(n)}(\overline{\Lambda^{(s)}_{r(n)}}) \leqslant \dfrac{c_s}{n^s}$.

Let $\psi_{r(n)} = (\psi_{r(n),i})_{i=1}^{k(n)} : R^{k(n)} \to R^{k(n)}$ *be defined by*

$$\psi_{r(n),i}(x) = \frac{x_i - x_{i-1}}{\sqrt{\lambda_{i,n} - \lambda_{i-1,n}}} - \alpha_{i,n} x_{k(n)}$$

where

$$\alpha_{i,n} = \left(1 + \frac{1}{\sqrt{1 - \lambda_{k(n),n}}}\right) \frac{\sqrt{\lambda_{i,n} - \lambda_{i-1,n}}}{\lambda_{k(n),n}}$$

Lemma (7.7) yields

(7.22) **Lemma.** *Let* $\varphi_{r(n)}(x) = \sum_{j=1}^{k(n)} x_j \sqrt{\lambda_{j,n} - \lambda_{j-1,n}}$. $\psi_{r(n)}$ *is a bijective function and the inverse function* $\psi_{r(n)}^{-1} = (\psi_{r(n),i}^{-1})_{i=1}^{k(n)}$ *of* $\psi_{r(n)}$ *is given by*

(i) $\psi_{r(n),i}^{-1}(x) =$

$$= \left(\sum_{j=1}^{i} x_j \sqrt{\lambda_{j,n} - \lambda_{j-1,n}}\right) - \varphi_{r(n)}(x) \frac{\lambda_{i,n} \sqrt{1 + (1 - \lambda_{k(n),n}}}{\lambda_{k(n),n}} .$$

Furthermore,

(ii) $\mathsf{N}_{r(n)} * \psi_{r(n)} = \mathsf{N}_1^{k(n)}$.

With the help of Lemma (7.22) we prove

(7.23) **Lemma.** $\mathsf{N}_{r(n)}(\Delta_{r(n),j}^{(s)}) \leqslant \frac{c_s}{n^s}$ *for* $j \in \{1, 3\}$

Proof for $j = 3$. Without loss of generality let $\lambda_k \geqslant \frac{1}{2}$. (Otherwise $\lambda_1 \leqslant \frac{1}{2}$, and we use the corresponding transformation with

$$\hat{\psi}_{r,i}^{-1}(x) = \sum_{j=i}^{k} x_j \sqrt{\lambda_{j+1} - \lambda_j} - \frac{(1 - \lambda_i)(1 + \sqrt{\lambda_1})}{1 - \lambda_i} \sum_{j=1}^{k} \sqrt{\lambda_{j+1} - \lambda_j}$$

in place of $\psi_{r,i}^{1}$.) By Lemma (7.22)

$$N_r(\overline{\Delta^{(s)}_{r,3}}) \leqslant N_1^k\Bigg\{x \in R^k :$$

$$\Bigg| \sum_{i=0}^{k-1} \frac{\left[x_{i+1} - \varphi_r(x)\sqrt{\lambda_{i+1} - \lambda_i}\left(1 + \frac{\sqrt{1-\lambda_k}}{\lambda_k}\right)\right]^3}{\sqrt{r_{i+1} - r_i}} +$$

$$+ \frac{\varphi_r^3(x)}{\sqrt{n - r_k}} \Bigg| \geqslant a_s\sqrt{\gamma_r \log^5 n}\Bigg\} .$$

Let

$$\Delta^{(s)}_{r,3,1} = \left\{x \in R^k : \left| \sum_{i=1}^{k} \frac{x_i^3}{\sqrt{r_i - r_{i-1}}} \right| \leqslant a_s\sqrt{\gamma_r \log^5 n}\right\} .$$

If

$$N_1^k(\overline{\Delta^{(s)}_{r,3,1}}) \leqslant \frac{c_s}{n^s} \tag{7.24}$$

and

$$N_1^k\left\{x \in R^k : \left| \frac{\varphi_r(x)}{\sqrt{\lambda_k}} \right| > a_s\sqrt{\log n}\right\} \leqslant \frac{c_s}{n^s} , \tag{7.25}$$

then the assertion follows in a direct way by (7.3) and Lemma (7.20).

(7.25) follows immediately from the well-known convolution formula for normal distributions and from (7.5).

By Lemma (7.20)

$$N_1^k(\overline{\Delta^{(s)}_{r,3,1}}) \leqslant N_1^k(\overline{\Gamma^{(s)}_r}) + N_1^k(\Gamma^{(s)}_r \cap \overline{\Delta^{(s)}_{r,3,1}}) \leqslant$$

$$\leqslant \frac{c_s}{n^s} + N_1^k\Bigg\{x \in R^k :$$

$$\Bigg| \sum_{i=1}^{k} \frac{x_i^3}{\sqrt{r_i - r_{i-1}}} \cdot 1_{\{y \in R : |y| \leqslant a_s\sqrt{\log n}\}}(x_i) \Bigg| > a_s\sqrt{\gamma_r \log^5 n}\Bigg\} .$$

Now (7.24) follows from (7.6) with $t = \frac{a_s}{\sqrt{\log^3 n}}$.

(7.26) **Lemma.** *Let* $m, q \in N$ *be fixed. Let* $\{i_1, \ldots, i_m\} \subset \{1, \ldots, k(n)\}$ *and* $j_i \leqslant q$ *for* $i = 1, \ldots, m$.

$$\int\limits_{\Theta_{r(n)}^{(s)}} |x_{i_1}|^{j_1} \ldots |x_{i_n}|^{j_m} \, d\mathrm{N}_{r(n)}(x) \leqslant \frac{c_{s,m,q}}{n^s}.$$

Proof. The lemmas (7.20), (7.21) and (7.23) imply that

$$\int\limits_{\Theta_r^{(s)}} |x_{i_1}|^{j_1} \ldots |x_{i_m}|^{j_m} \, d\mathrm{N}_r(x) \leqslant$$

$$\leqslant \frac{c_s}{n^s} + \sum_{i_\nu \in \{i_1, \ldots, i_m\}}' \int\limits_{\{x \in R^k : |x_{i_\nu}| \geqslant n^2\}} |x_{i_1}|^{j_1} \ldots |x_{i_m}|^{j_m} \, d\mathrm{N}_r(x).$$

Using Lemma (7.22) with $\hat{r}(n) = (0, r_{i_1}, \ldots, r_{i_m}, n)$ we obtain for each $i_\nu \in \{i_1, \ldots, i_m\}$

$$\int\limits_{\{x \in R^k : |x_{i_\nu}| \geqslant n^2\}} |x_{i_1}|^{j_1} \ldots |x_{i_m}|^{j_m} \, d\mathrm{N}_r(x) =$$

$$= \int\limits_{\{w \in R^m : |\psi_{\hat{r},\nu}^{-1}(w)| \geqslant n^2\}} |^{j_1} \ldots |\psi_{\hat{r},m}^{-1}|^{j_m} \, d\mathrm{N}_1^m \leqslant$$

$$\leqslant \sum_{\nu=1}^{m} \int\limits_{\{w \in R^m : |x_\nu| \geqslant n\}} |\psi_{\hat{r},1}^{-1}|^{j_1} \ldots |\psi_{\hat{r},m}^{-1}|^{j_m} \, d\mathrm{N}_1^m.$$

Using some simple estimate for $\int\limits_{(-n,n)} |x|^j \, d\mathrm{N}_1(x)$ the assertion follows now by some direct calculations.

With the help of Lemma (7.22) we compute that

$$\int R^2_{r(n),1}\, d\mathrm{N}_{r(n)} = \frac{2}{3}\,\gamma_{r(n)} + \frac{1}{n - r_{k(n),n}} - 2\,\frac{k(n)}{n} -$$

$$(7.27) \qquad - \frac{5}{3n} \sum_{i=0}^{k(n)} (\lambda_{i+1,n} - \lambda_{i,n})^2 - \frac{2}{n} \sum_{i=1}^{k(n)-1} \lambda_{i,n} -$$

$$- \frac{10}{3n} \sum_{i=1}^{k(n)} (\lambda_{i,n} - \lambda_{i-1,n})(1 - \lambda_{i,n}),$$

and

$$(7.28) \qquad \int R_{r(n),2}\, d\mathrm{N}_{r(n)} = -\frac{1}{4}\,\gamma_{r(n)} - \frac{1}{2(1 - r_{k(n),n})} + \frac{k(n)}{n} + \frac{3}{4n}.$$

Note added in proof. A result similar to that in our Application (6.2) is given by G. Tusnády, using a direct method, in the paper "On testing density functions", Periodica Math. Hung., 5 (1974).

REFERENCES

[1] R.R. Bahadur, A note on quantiles in large samples, *Ann. Math. Statist.*, 37 (1966), 577-580.

[2] P.J. Bickel – M. Rosenblatt, On some global measures of the deviation of density function estimates, *Ann. Statist.*, 1 (1973), 1071-1095.

[3] H.A. David, *Order Statistics*, Wiley, New York, 1970.

[4] W. Feller, *An Introduction to Probability Theory and Its Application*, Vol. I, Wiley, New York, 1966.

[5] T.S. Ferguson, *Mathematical Statistics*, Academic Press, New York, 1967.

[6] M. Loève, *Probability Theory*, Van Nostrand, New York, 1955.

[7] D.O. Loftsgaarden – C.P. Quesenberry, A nonparametric estimate of a multivariate density function, *Ann. Math. Statist.*, 36 (1965), 1049-1051.

[8] F. Mosteller, On some useful ineffecient statistics, *Ann. Math. Statist.*, 17 (1946), 377-408.

[9] R.-D. Reiss, On the accuracy of the normal approximation for quantiles, *Ann. Prob.*, 2 (1974), 741-744.

[10] R.-D. Reiss, Asymptotic expansions for quantiles, Preprints in Statistics No. 6, University of Cologne, 1974.

[11] P. Révész, Testing of density functions, *Periodica Math. Hung.*, 1 (1971), 35-44.

[12] H. Richter, *Wahrscheinlichkeitstheorie,* Springer-Verlag, Berlin, 1966.

[13] M.M. Siddiqui, Distribution of quantiles in samples from a bivariate population, *J. Res. N.B.S.*, 64 B (1960), 145-150.

[14] N.V. Smirnov, Über die Verteilung des allgemeinen Gliedes in der Variationsreihe, *Metron,* 12 (1935), 59-81.

[15] N.V. Smirnov, Sur la dépendance des members d'un series de variation, *Bull. Math. Univ. Moscow,* 1 (1937-38), 1-12.

[16] N.V. Smirnov, Limit distributions for the terms of a variational series, *Trudy Math. Inst. Steklov,* 25 (1949), (English transl.: *Amer. Math. Soc. Transl.*, (1), 11 (1962), 82-143).

[17] N.V. Smirnov, Some remarks on the limit laws for order statistics, *Theory Prob. and its Applications,* 12 (1967), 337-339.

[18] H.R. van der Vaart, A simple derivation of the limiting distribution function of a sample quantile with increasing sample size, *Statist. Neerlandica,* 15 (1961), 239-242.

[19] J. van Ryzin, On a histogram method of density estimation, Technical Report, No. 226, University of Wisconsin, 1970.

[20] R. von Mises, *La distribution de la plus grande de n valeurs*, *Rev. Math. Union Interbalkanique,* 1 (1936), 141-160 (reproduced in Selected Papers of Richard von Mises, *Amer. Math. Soc.*, 2 (1964), 271-294.

[21] A.M. Walker, A note on the asymptotic distribution of sample quantiles, *J. Roy. Statist. Soc.*, 30 (1968), 570-575.

[22] L. Weiss, The asymptotic joint distribution of an increasing number of sample quantiles, *Ann. Inst. Statist. Math.*, 21 (1969), 257-263.

[23] L. Weiss, Statistical procedures based on a gradually increasing number of order statistics, *Commun. Statist.*, 2 (1973), 95-114.

COLLOQUIA MATHEMATICA SOCIETATIS JÁNOS BOLYAI
11. LIMIT THEOREMS OF PROBABILITY THEORY, KESZTHELY (HUNGARY), 1974.

ON THE CONVERGENCE OF THE EXPECTATION OF THE SAMPLE QUANTILE

K. SARKADI

It is well-known since long time that under fairly general conditions the expectation of the sample quantile tends to the corresponding quantile of the theoretical distribution, if the sample size increases. The most known such condition is that the distribution should be continuous and its first moment should exist. For this and other cases, dealt with in the literature, we refer to David [1].

In this paper we show that the mentioned convergence holds under weaker conditions. No supposition on continuity is necessary. It is sufficient that at least one order statistic with finite expectation should exist. Of course, this condition is necessary in the same time.

Let us define the quantile function $Q(x)$ of an arbitrary distribution $F(x)$ by

$$(1) \qquad Q(x) = \inf [y: F(y+0) \geqslant x] .$$

It is well known and simple to check that if U is uniformly distributed over the interval $(0, 1)$:

$$P(U < x) = x \qquad (0 \leqslant x \leqslant 1)$$

then $X = Q(U)$ has the distribution

$$P(X < x) = F(x) .$$

For this reason, if $X_{y:n}$ is the r'th order statistic in a sample of n from the distribution $F(x)$ its expectation can be expressed as follows

$$(2) \qquad \mathsf{E}(X_{r:n}) = \mathsf{E}[Q(U_{r:n})] = n\binom{n-1}{r-1}\int_0^1 Q(x)x^{r-1}(1-x)^{n-r}dx$$

where $U_{r:n}$ is the corresponding order statistic from the distribution of U.

Let us take a sample of size n from the distribution $F(x)$ and denote the empirical distribution function by $F_n(x)$. Replacing $F(x)$ by $F_n(x)$ in formula (1) we obtain the definition of the empirical quantile $Q_n(x)$. We have

$$Q_n(x) = X_{r:n}$$

where the integer r is determined by the inequality

$$(3) \qquad nx \leqslant r < nx + 1 .$$

We prove the following

Theorem. *If* $\mathsf{E}(X_{R:N})$ *exists for some* R, N *then*

$$\lim_{n\to\infty} \mathsf{E}[Q_n(y)] = \frac{Q(y) + Q(y+0)}{2} \qquad (0 < y < 1) .$$

Proof. First we want to prove that

$$(4) \qquad \lim_{n\to\infty} \mathsf{E}[Q_n(y) \mid Q_n(y) \leqslant Q(y)] = Q(y) .$$

For this purpose let us choose a number $z < Q(y)$ and write this conditional expectation in the following form

$$\mathsf{E}[Q_n(y) \mid Q_n(y) \leqslant Q(y)] =$$

$$(5) \qquad = \mathsf{P}[Q_n(y) \leqslant z \mid Q_n(y) \leqslant Q(y)]\mathsf{E}[Q_n(y) \mid Q_n(y) \leqslant z] +$$

$$+ \mathsf{P}[z < Q_n(y) \leqslant Q(y) \mid Q_n(y) \leqslant Q(y)]\mathsf{E}[Q_n(y) \mid z < Q_n(y) \leqslant Q(y)] .$$

Now we prove that the first term of the above sum tends to 0.

In fact, using the definition of $Q_n(y)$:

$$\lim_{n \to \infty} \mathsf{P}[Q_n(y) \leqslant z \mid Q_n(y) \leqslant Q(y)] =$$

$$= \lim_{n \to \infty} \mathsf{P}\{F_n(z+0) \geqslant y \mid F_n[Q(y)+0] \geqslant y\} =$$

$$= \lim_{n \to \infty} \frac{\mathsf{P}[F_n(z+0) \geqslant y]}{\mathsf{P}\{F_n[Q(y)+0] \geqslant y\}}$$

where we have taken the monotonicity of the empirical distribution function into account.

$F_n(z+0)$ and $F_n[Q(y)+0]$ are binomially distributed and we have for their expectations $F(z+0) < y$ and $F[Q(y)+0] \geqslant y$, respectively. Applying the central limit theorem we conclude that the above limit is equal to 0. Therefore, for proving that the first term in the left hand side of (5) tends to 0, it is sufficient to show that $\mathsf{E}[Q_n(y) \mid Q(y) \leqslant z]$ is bounded.

Now we see from formula (2) that increasing N (with R unaltered) preserves the existence of $\mathsf{E}(X_{R:N})$. Therefore, with the appropriate increase of the value of N, we can suppose, without loss of generality, that $\frac{R}{N} < F(z+0)$.

We suppose $n > N$. If $Q_n(y) = X_{r:n}$ then (cf. (3))

$$F(z+0) < y \leqslant \frac{r}{n} .$$

Multiplying the last two inequalities by N and n, respectively, we obtain

$$F(z+0) < \frac{r-R}{n-N}.$$

Let us truncate the distributions of $U_{r:n}$ and $U_{R:N}$ from above in the point $F(z+0)$ and denote the corresponding conditional density functions by $g_1(x)$ and $g_2(x)$ respectively. $\frac{g_1(x)}{g_2(x)}$ is proportional to $x^{r-R}(1-x)^{n-N-r+R}$ hence, it is monotone increasing in the interval $\left(0, \frac{r-R}{n-N}\right)$ or in the interval $(0, F(z+0))$. Let x_0 be such that $g_1(x_0) = g_2(x_0)$; it follows

$$\int_0^{F(z+0)} [Q(x) - Q(x_0)][g_1(x) - g_2(x)]dx > 0$$

which implies that

$$\mathsf{E}(X_{r:n} \mid X_{r:n} \leqslant z) > \mathsf{E}(X_{R:N} \mid X_{R:N} \leqslant z),$$

i.e. the left hand side is bounded and the first term in the left hand side of (5) vanishes in the limit.

Therefore, for sufficiently large n

$$z \leqslant \mathsf{E}[Q_n(y) \mid Q_n(y) \leqslant Q(y)] \leqslant Q(y).$$

If z tends to $Q(y)$ we obtain (4). Obviously the converse inequality

$$\lim_{n\to\infty} \mathsf{E}[Q_n(y) \mid Q_n(y) \geqslant Q(y+0)] = Q(y+0) \tag{6}$$

follows similarly.

Since

$$\mathsf{E}[Q_n(y) \mid Q_n(y) \leqslant Q(y)] \leqslant$$
$$\leqslant \mathsf{E}[Q_n(y)] \leqslant \mathsf{E}[Q_n(y) \mid Q_n(y) \geqslant Q(y+0)].$$

(4) and (6) prove the theorem for the case $Q(y) = Q(y+0)$.

If, on the other hand, $Q(y) < Q(y+0)$, then, using the asymptotic distribution of $U_{r:n}$ we obtain that

$$\lim_{n\to\infty} \mathsf{P}[Q_n(y) \leqslant Q(y)] = \lim_{n\to\infty} \mathsf{P}[Q_n(y) \geqslant Q(y+0)] = \frac{1}{2}.$$

Using (4), (6) and the rule of total probability we obtain the assertion of the theorem again.

Note. Our theorem can be easily generalized in the following way:

Let $r = r_n$ where $r_1, r_2, \ldots$ is some sequence with

$$\lim_{n\to\infty} \frac{r_n}{n} = y.$$

If $\mathsf{E}(X_{R:N})$ exists and $r_n = ny + o(\sqrt{n})$ then, clearly, our Theorem can be extended for this case, i.e.

$$\lim_{n\to\infty} \mathsf{E}(X_{r_n:n}) = \frac{Q(y) + Q(y+0)}{2}.$$

If, however, the convergence of $\frac{r_n}{n}$ is slower and $Q(y) < Q(y+0)$ then we can not say more than

$$\limsup_{n\to\infty} \mathsf{E}(X_{r:n}) \leqslant Q(y+0),$$

$$\liminf_{n\to\infty} \mathsf{E}(X_{r:n}) \geqslant Q(y).$$

The author wishes to thank J. Komlós and G. Tusnády for their helpful comments.

REFERENCE

[1] H. A. David, *Order Statistics,* Wiley, New York, 1970.

COLLOQUIA MATHEMATICA SOCIETATIS JÁNOS BOLYAI
11. LIMIT THEOREMS OF PROBABILITY THEORY, KESZTHELY (HUNGARY), 1974.

SHOCKS IN A TWO COMPONENT PARALLELED SYSTEM

DOMOKOS SZÁSZ

The system we investigate can be illustrated by a house which is supplied by two different elevators working independently of each other. The functioning of each elevator forms an alternating renewal process with "up-time" (work time) distributions F_1 and F_2 and "down-time" (repair time) distributions G_1 and G_2 resp. $G_i = G_i^\epsilon$ $(i = 1, 2)$ depends on the parameter $\epsilon > 0$ in such a way that $G_i^\epsilon \Rightarrow \delta_0$ $(\epsilon \to 0;\ i = 1, 2)$, where δ_0 is the unit distribution. Denote by $\tau = \tau^\epsilon$ the time of the first shock of the system, i.e. of the first moment when both elevators are out of order. Now the problem is to determine the asymptotic distribution of τ^ϵ under suitable normalization when $\epsilon \to 0$.

The reason of formulating the problem as above is that if F_i, G_i $(i = 1, 2)$ are arbitrary but fixed then to determine the exact distribution of τ is hopeless. However, in the practice repairs are much shorter than working times, and this is why an asymptotic result is expected to serve with a useful approximation.

For convenience we formulate the problem more generally. We say that our *system is shocked* in time t if in t one of the elevators breaks down while the other one is being repaired. Denote by $0 < \tau_1^\epsilon < \tau_2^\epsilon < \ldots$ the sequence of shocks ($\tau_1^\epsilon = \tau^\epsilon$) and with W^ϵ the point process $0 < w_1^\epsilon < w_2^\epsilon < \ldots$, where $w_k^\epsilon = \epsilon \tau_k^\epsilon$ ($k \geqslant 1$).

Theorem. *Suppose that*

(i) F_i *has a density bounded on finite intervals, and for a suitable* $n_0 \geqslant 1$ *the* n_0*-th power of the characteristic function of* F_i *is integrable* ($i = 1, 2$);

(ii) $\int x dF_i(x) = \lambda_i$ ($0 < \lambda_i < \infty$; $i = 1, 2$);

(iii) $\int x dG_i^\epsilon(x) = \mu_i \epsilon$ ($0 < \epsilon \leqslant 1$) *and the family of measures* $\{x dG_i^\epsilon(x)\colon 0 < \epsilon \leqslant 1\}$ *is weakly compact* ($i = 1, 2$);

(iv) *for every* ϵ ($0 < \epsilon \leqslant 1$) *there exists a distribution function* $M^\epsilon(x)$ *such that*

$$\frac{1 - G_i^\epsilon(x+y)}{1 - G_i^\epsilon(y)} \leqslant 1 - M^\epsilon(x) \qquad (G_i^\epsilon(y) < 1;\ i = 1, 2)$$

and $\lim_{\epsilon \to 0} \int x dM^\epsilon(x) = 0$;

(v) *for* $N^\epsilon(x) = \min_{i=1,2} \inf_{\epsilon' \leqslant \epsilon} G^\epsilon(x)$ *we have*

$$\lim_{\epsilon \to 0} \int x dN^\epsilon(x) = 0 .$$

Then W^ϵ *tends to the Poisson process with parameter* $(\mu_1 + \mu_2)\lambda^{-2}$, *as* $\epsilon \to 0$, *in the sense of the weak convergence of finite dimensional distributions and of the weak convergence in space* $D[0, \infty)$ (cf. Lindwall [1]).

In particular, it follows from the theorem that the limit distribution of $\epsilon\tau^\epsilon$ is exponential with parameter $(\mu_1 + \mu_2)\lambda^{-2}$.

This theorem is only slightly more general than the one proved in [2], and its proof goes the same way.

REFERENCES

[1] T. Lindwall, Weak convergence of probability measures and random functions in the space, *Z. Wahrscheinlichkeitstheorie verw. Geb.*, 22 (1973), 1-7.

[2] D. Szász, On the two lift problem, Preprint No. 11/1975 of the *Math. Inst. Hung. Acad. Sci.*, Budapest.

COLLOQUIA MATHEMATICA SOCIETATIS JÁNOS BOLYAI
11. LIMIT THEOREMS OF PROBABILITY THEORY, KESZTHELY (HUNGARY), 1974.

SOME RESULTS AND PROBLEMS IN THE LIMIT THEORY OF RANDOM SUMS (INDEPENDENT CASE)

DOMOKOS SZÁSZ

1. For sums of a non-random number of independent random variables the limit distribution problem (also called central limit problem) seems to be solved in the sense that we know quite natural necessary and sufficient conditions for the existence of a limit distribution (in the case of uniformly asymptotically negligible summands see the classical work of Gnedenko – Kolmogorov [4] and in the general case the more recent work of Zolotarev [17]).

In the case when the random indices are independent of the summands, Gnedenko – Fahim [3] gave sufficient conditions for the convergence of random sums of identically distributed summands and Freyer – Szász [14] obtained necessary conditions under additional assumptions. These results made it reasonable to work out a general limit theory for random sums. In a series of papers, the author of the present note has tried to do so (for a summary and references see [13]); but even in the case of identically distributed summands, where we have more information, we have – in general – no easily applicable results, mainly because of analytic difficulties.

In this note we restrict ourselves to identically distributed summands and we will outline the basic results and collect the main problems arising in this case.

2. For every $n (= 1, 2, \dots)$ let $\{\xi_{nk}\}$ be a sequence of independent identically distributed (i.i.d.) random variables and ν_n be a random index, independent of the sequence $\{\xi_{nk}\}_k$. Suppose that

$$P \lim_{n \to \infty} \nu_n = \infty$$

($P \lim$ is the limit in probability) and write

$$S_k^{(n)} = \xi_{n1} + \dots + \xi_{nk} .$$

In 1969, Gnedenko and Fahim gave the following sufficient conditions

Theorem 1 (Gnedenko – Fahim [3]). *If there exists a sequence* $\{k_n\}$ *of positive integers* ($\lim_{n \to \infty} k_n = \infty$) *and distribution functions* $\Phi(x)$ *and* $A(x)$ *such that for* $n \to \infty$

(A) $$\mathsf{P}\{S_{k_n}^{(n)} < x\} \Rightarrow \Phi(x)$$

(B) $$\mathsf{P}\left\{\frac{\nu_n}{k_n} < x\right\} \Rightarrow A(x) ,$$

then

(C) $$\mathsf{P}\{S_{\nu_n}^{(n)} < x\} \Rightarrow \Psi(x)$$

($\Rightarrow$ *means the weak convergence).*

The distribution function $\Psi(x)$ *is determined by the characteristic function*

(1) $$\psi(t) = \int_{-\infty}^{+\infty} e^{ixt}\, d\Psi(x) = \int_0^{\infty} [\varphi(t)]^y\, dA(y) ,$$

where

$$\varphi(t) = \int_{-\infty}^{+\infty} e^{ixt}\, d\Phi(x) .$$

The intuitive background of this theorem is quite clear. Since the summands are i.i.d., the stochastic processes

$$\chi_n(y) = S^{(n)}_{[k_n y]} \qquad (y \geqslant 0)$$

are nearly the same in distribution as the process that has stationary, independent increments and is determined by the characteristic function

$$\mathsf{E} \exp(it\chi(u)) = [\varphi(t)]^y .$$

Thus

$$S^{(n)}_{\nu_n} \overset{d}{=} S^{(n)}_{k_n \frac{\nu_n}{k_n}} \overset{d}{=} \chi_n\left(\frac{\nu_n}{k_n}\right) \overset{d}{\sim} \chi(\tau) ,$$

where $\overset{d}{=}$ and $\overset{d}{\sim}$ mean equality and asymptotic equality in distribution, and τ is a random variable independent of the process $\{\chi(t);\ t \geqslant 0\}$ and it has distribution A. The way we obtained $\chi(\tau)$ is often called subordination (see [1], XVII. 4. (e)); obviously, the characteristic function of $\chi(\tau)$ coincides with (1).

3. The first necessary conditions for the existence of a limit distribution of $S^{(n)}_{\nu_n}$ was obtained in 1971.

Theorem 2. (Szász – Freyer [14]). *If Conditions* A *and* C *hold and* $\Phi \neq \delta_0$, *then* B *is satisfied* (δ_a *concentrates mass* 1 *in the point* a).

In order to formulate another similar statement, we need a new Condition D; possibly, this condition is always satisfied, but until now we have not succeeded in proving or disproving this.

Condition (D). The identity

$$a(\varphi(t)) \equiv a(\varphi^*(t))$$

where $\varphi(t)$ and $\varphi^*(t)$ are infinitely divisible characteristic functions and

$$(2) \qquad a(z) = \int_0^\infty z^y \, dA(y) \qquad (0 < |z| < 1)$$

$(A \neq \delta_0)$ implies that $\varphi(t) \equiv \varphi^*(t)$.

Theorem 3. (Szász – Freyer [14]). *If Conditions* B, C *and* D *hold and* $A \neq \delta_0$, *then* A *also holds.*

Problem 1. Does Condition D really always hold or it does not?

Under special additional assumptions the answer has turned out to be in the affirmative [14]. Actually each of the following conditions guarantees D:

(a) $a(z)$ has an inverse in the unit circle (for example A is exponential);

(b) φ and φ^* are characteristic functions of symmetric r.v.'s;

(c) φ and φ^* are characteristic functions of nonnegative r.v.'s.

Nevertheless Tortrat conjectures that the answer is no [15].

A. Vetier and the author have recently obtained the following less trivial

Proposition 1. *If* A *has a finite (non zero) expectation and* φ, φ^* *are infinitely divisible characteristic functions then*

$$a(\varphi(t)) \equiv a(\varphi^*(t))$$

implies that

$$\varphi(t) = \varphi^*(t)$$

in some neighbourhood of the origin.

Proof. Note that

1. $a(z)$ is continous in the closed unit circle;

2. $a(z)$ is regular in the open unit circle except for the origin;

3. If A has a finite expectation, then

$$\lim_{\substack{z \to 1 \\ |z|<1}} a'(z) = \int_0^\infty y\, dA(y) = \mu .$$

If φ and φ^* are both degenerate then by the uniqueness theorem of characteristic functions $\varphi(t) = \tilde{\varphi}(t)$ identically. If this is not the case then suppose that $|\varphi(t)| < 1$ in some neighbourhood of the origin. If the assertion of the proposition does not hold, then there exists a sequence $\{t_k\}$ such that

$$\lim_{k \to \infty} t_k = 0 \quad \text{and} \quad \varphi(t_k) \neq \varphi^*(t_k) \qquad (k = 1, 2, \ldots) .$$

But at the same time

$$0 = a(\varphi^*(t_k)) - a(\varphi(t_k)) = \int_{\varphi(t_k)}^{\varphi^*(t_k)} a'(z)\, dz =$$

$$= \int_0^1 a'(\varphi(t_k) + sh_k)h_k\, ds ,$$

where $h_k = \varphi^*(t_k) - \varphi(t_k) \neq 0$. In view of property 3

$$a'(z) = \mu + o(1) \qquad (z \to 1,\ |z| < 1) .$$

Thus, substituting this in our preceding equation, we obtain

$$0 = \mu h_k + o(h_k) \qquad (k \to \infty)$$

and this is impossible.

An obvious application of Proposition 1 can be obtained if we assume in addition that φ and φ^* are analytic. Then $\varphi(t) \equiv \varphi^*(t)$ necessarily.

Unfortunately, we can not hope that our method works when A has infinite expectation, because then property 3 fails (cf. Szász [11]).

4. In 1972 we obtained the following theorem, which has many interesting consequences.

Theorem 4 [12]. *If Condition C is satisfied, then there exists a sequence* $\{k_n\}$ *such that the sequences* $\{S_{k_n}^{(n)}\}$ *and* $\left\{\frac{\nu_n}{k_n}\right\}$ *are stochastically bounded.*

This result immediately raises a question, interesting in itself, but it would also be necessary to know the answer when investigating random sums with centering.

Problem 2. Weaken the assumption of Theorem 4 in such a way that instead of Condition C we only require the stochastical boundedness of the sequence $\{S_{\nu_n}^{(n)}\}$:

The two proofs I know for Theorem 4 fail to work in this case.

5. We turn to the consequences of Theorem 4. First let us remark that Theorems 2 and 3 are also consequences of Theorem 4. To go further for an arbitrary characteristic function $\psi(t)$ we introduce $\mathscr{H}_\psi$ as the set of all solutions (a, φ) of the equation

$$\psi(t) = a(\varphi(t)) \tag{3}$$

where $a(z)$ has form (2) and $\varphi(t)$ is an infinitely divisible characteristic function. Since if $(a(z), \varphi(t)) \in \mathscr{H}_\psi$ then for every $s > 0$

$$(a(z^{\frac{1}{s}}), \varphi^s(t)) \in \mathscr{H}_\psi\,, \tag{4}$$

we consider those elements of $\mathscr{H}_\psi$ that can be obtained from each other by the transformation under (4) as identical. After this identification let $s(\psi) = \text{card}\, \mathscr{H}_\psi$. $s(\psi)$ plays an important role in the consequences of Theorem 4. Let $\mathscr{K}$ be the class of all distributions for the characteristic functions of which $s(\psi) \geqslant 1$ holds.

Corollary 1. *The class of all limit distributions in the scheme described in point 2 coincides with* $\mathscr{K}$.

Obviously $\mathscr{K}$ is wider than $\mathscr{I}$ – the class of all infinitely divisible distributions – but it does not contain every distribution. For example if

$\psi = \dfrac{\delta_a + \delta_{-a}}{2}$ and $a > 0$ then $s(\psi) = 0$. It would be quite interesting to have a simpler description of the class $\mathscr{K}$ than ours but this does not seem very hopeful, so we do not formulate a problem on this.

Corollary 2. *If* $s(\psi) = 1$ *then Condition C holds if and only if there exists a sequence* $\{k_n\}$ *such that Conditions* A *and* B *are satisfied.*

Thus the information $s(\psi) = 1$ is very important, because in this case we have a final result, and in checking A we can use the classical conditions. As to the class of such distributions, however, our knowledge is ϵ. A trivial example is $\Psi = \delta_a$ $(a \neq 0)$. The most interesting result has been proved by Pečinkin.

Proposition 2 (Pečinkin [9]). *If* Ψ *is standard normal and we restrict ourselves to symmetrically distributed summands, i.e.* φ *is real, then* φ *is also normal and* A *is degenerate.*

Proof. Denote by Δ the least point of increase of A, i.e. $\Delta = \sup\{x : A(x) = 0\}$. First suppose that $\Delta = 0$. By the Lévy – Khintchine representation

$$\log \varphi(t) = 2 \int_0^\infty \frac{\cos tx - 1}{x^2} M(dx) ,$$

where M is a canonical measure on $[0, \infty)$ (cf. [1], Chapter XVII). Now a simple transformation yields that

$$\log \varphi(t) = - 2t^2 \int_0^\infty \frac{1 - \cos tx}{t^2 x^2} M(dx) .$$

But

$$\frac{1 - \cos tx}{t^2 x^2} \leqslant \min\left(R, \frac{2}{x^2}\right) \qquad (t \geqslant 1)$$

where $R = \max\limits_{u \geqslant 0} \dfrac{1 - \cos u}{u^2}$. Noting that the right hand side of this inequality is M-integrable, we obtain

$$\lim_{t\to\infty} - \frac{\log \varphi(t)}{t^2} = M(\{0\}) = m .$$

We supposed

$$e^{-\frac{t^2}{2}} = \int_0^\infty [\varphi(t)]^y \, dA(y) = \int_0^\infty e^{-t^2 y \frac{\log \varphi(t)}{-t^2}} \, dA(y) ,$$

and for large t's this is not less than

$$\int_0^\infty e^{-t^2 y(m+1)} \geqslant A(\delta) e^{-t^2 \delta (m+1)} .$$

Now if δ is so small that $\frac{1}{2} > 2\delta(m+1)$, then

$$e^{-\frac{t^2}{2}} \geqslant A(\delta) e^{-t^2 \delta (m+1)}$$

can not be true for all large enough t. Thus $\Delta = 0$ is impossible.

If $\Delta > 0$, then

$$e^{-\frac{t^2}{2}} = [\varphi(t)]^\Delta \int_0^\infty [\varphi(t)]^y \, dA(y - \Delta) .$$

Here both factors are characteristic functions and, by Cramér's theorem, they must be normal. We can also suppose that they have zero expectations. But our proof for the case $\Delta = 0$ implies that the second factor can only be degenerate. Then

$$\varphi(t) = e^{-\frac{t^2}{2\Delta}} ,$$

and necessarily $A = \delta_\Delta$.

Another interesting theorem in this direction has been obtained by Klonecki [8]. *Among the distributions* A *with an entire characteristic function and compound Poisson distributions* Φ *of finite order equation* (3) *has at most one solution.* Recall that those distributions are called compound Poisson distributions of finite order whose characteristic functions have the form

$$\varphi(t) = \exp\left\{\sum_{k=1}^{N} c_k (e^{ikt} - 1)\right\},$$

where N is a natural number and $c_k \geqslant 0$ $(k = 1, \ldots, N-1)$, $c_N > 0$.

Problem 3. Omit in Pečinkin's theorem the assumption on the symmetry of the distribution of summands.

If this is possible, then its consequence is that the random sums i.i.d. summands can tend to a normal limit only if the random indices are asymptotically non-random, i.e. when suitably normed they converge in probability to a constant.

Problem 4. Find sufficient conditions for $s(\psi) = 1$.

Corollary 3. *If for the distribution* Ψ $s(\psi) < \infty$, *then* C *is satisfied with* Ψ *as the limit if and only if*

(E) *there exists a sequence* $\{k_n\}$, *a partition of the indices into a finite number of subsequences* $N_1, \ldots, N_j$ $(j \leqslant s(\psi))$, *and elements* $(a_i, \varphi_i) \in$ $\in$ ψ $(1 \leqslant i \leqslant j)$ *such that*

$$\mathsf{P}\{S_{k_n}^{(n)} < x\} \Rightarrow \Phi_i(x) \qquad (n \to \infty,\ n \in N_i)$$

and

$$\mathsf{P}\left\{\frac{\nu_n}{k_n} < x\right\} \Rightarrow A_i(x) \qquad (n \to \infty,\ n \in N_i)\,.$$

Thus in this case we again have necessary and sufficient conditions though they are more complicated than in the case $s(\psi) = 1$.

Problem 5. Give an example when $1 < s(\psi) < \infty$!

Problem 6. Obtain sufficient conditions for $s(\psi) < \infty$!

Unfortunately $s(\psi) < \infty$ is not always satisfied. For example, it follows from a result of Zolotarev on subordinated processes [16] that if Φ is strictly stable with exponent $\alpha \leqslant 2$ and A is also strictly stable with exponent β ($\beta < 1$ necessarily) then Ψ is strictly stable with exponent $\alpha\beta$ (see also [1], X., 7.c).

Thus, if Ψ is strictly stable with an exponent $\gamma < 2$ then equation (3) has uncountably many different solutions.

This remark shows that – even if the analytical problems were solved – Theorem 4 is not strong enough to give effective necessary and sufficient conditions in general, because if $s(\psi) = \infty$, then there is a gap between our necessary and sufficient conditions. In fact Theorem 4 gives only

Corollary 4.

(a) *A sufficient condition for* C *is condition* E *with an arbitrary but finite* j *in it.*

(b) *A necessary condition for* C *is condition* E *with* $j = \infty$.

Note, however, that, without the requirement of some effectiveness, we can formulate a general necessary and sufficient condition as follows:

Corollary 5.

$$\mathsf{P}\{S_{\nu_n}^{(n)} < x\} \Rightarrow \Psi(x) \qquad (n \to \infty)$$

if and only if there exists a sequence of positive integers k_n ($\lim_{n\to\infty} k_n = \infty$) *such that for every subsequence* N' *of integers there exist a further subsequence* N'' ($\subset N'$) *and distribution functions* Φ *and* A *such that* $a(\varphi(t)) = \psi(t)$ *and*

$$\mathsf{P}\{S_{k_n}^{(n)} < x\} \Rightarrow \Phi(x) \qquad (n \to \infty,\ n \in N')$$

and

$$\mathsf{P}\left\{\frac{\nu_n}{k_n} < x\right\} \Rightarrow A(x) \qquad (n \to \infty,\ n \in N'') .$$

Problem 7. Fill the gap between sufficient and necessary conditions for C in general!

6. In Section 2 we have shown that mixtures of type (1) or, what is the same, the distributions of the class $\mathscr{K}$ can be obtained by subordination. But this class also arises in many applications, e.g. in queueing and reliability theory (see [2]), and some properties of these distributions have already been investigated from various aspects. In this final section we pick out some interesting results without aiming at completeness.

As it is obvious from the definition via subordination, if A is infinitely divisible then so is Ψ. Gnedenko asked the question whether the converse statement was true or not. The simplest example showing that the answer is *no* was found by Steutel [10]. Indeed, he has proved that if Φ is the exponential distribution, then for arbitrary A the mixture Ψ is infinitely divisible (cf. also [15]). Later Gnedenko's question was posed in a stricter sense by Grandell and Matthes: *Suppose that* Φ *is an infinitely divisible distribution on the nonnegative integers. Does it happen that* Ψ *is infinitely divisible and* A *is not so*?

(If the answer were in the affirmative, then a doubly stochastic Poisson process could be infinitely divisible only if its generic random measure were infinitely divisible!)

As to the continuity of the distributions Ψ, Huff has proved that

in case Φ is continuous, Ψ is continuous if and only if, A has no jump at the origin [5];

in case Φ is discontinuous, Ψ is continuous if and only if the corresponding process $\chi(t)$ (see point 2 above) has a nonzero trend and A is continuous [6].

The closedness of the class $\mathscr{K}$ under some operations – also in a more general setting – and moment inequalities have been investigated by Keilson – Steutel [7].

Note added in proof. The author has been communicated by Prof. J. Grandell that the question posed by Prof. Matthes and himself has recently been answered by O. Kallenberg in the negative. The counterexample will be published in the forthcoming book of O. Kallenberg: *Random measures,* Akademie – Verlag, Berlin.

REFERENCES

[1] W. Feller, *Introduction to probability theory and its applications,* Vol. II, Wiley, New York, 1971.

[2] B.V. Gnedenko, Limit theorems for sums of a random number of positive independent random variables, *Proc. Sixth Berkeley Symposium,* 1970, 537-549.

[3] B.V. Gnedenko – H. Fahim, On a transfer theorem, *Doklady Akad. Nauk SSSR,* 187 (1969), 15-17.

[4] B.V. Gnedenko – A.N. Kolmogorov, *Limit distributions for sums of independent random variables,* Cambridge, Mass. Addison – Wesley, 1954.

[5] B.W. Huff, Comments on the continuity of distribution obtained by superposition, *Proc. Amer. Math. Soc.,* 27 (1971), 141-146.

[6] B.W. Huff, Further comments on the continuity of distribution functions obtained by superposition, *Proc. Amer. Math. Soc.,* 35 (1972), 561-564.

[7] J. Keilson – F.W. Steutel, Mixtures of distributions, moment inequalities and measures of exponentiality and normality, *Ann. Prob.,* 2 (1974), 112-130.

[8] W. Klonecki, Mixtures and characteristic functions, *Proc. Nat. Acad. Sci. USA,* 65 (1970), 831-836.

[9] A.V. Pečinkin, On the convergence of random sums of random variables to the normal law, *Theory Probability Appl,* 18 (1973), 380-382.

[10] F.W. Steutel, Note on completely monotone densities, *Ann. Math. Statist.,* 40 (1969), 1130-1131.

[11] D. Szász, On the behaviour of power series in a boundary point of the circle of convergence, (in Hungarian), *Matematikai Lapok,* 10 (1969), 347-350.

[12] D. Szász, On the limiting distribution classes for sums of a random number of independent identically distributed random varibles, *Theory Probability Appl.,* 17 (1972), 424-439.

[13] D. Szász, Limit theorems for the sums of a random number of random variables, *Transactions Sixth Prague Conf. on Information Theory,* 1971, 833-838.

[14] D. Szász – B. Freyer, A problem of summation theory with random indices, *Litovski Mat. Sbornik,* 11 (1971), 181-187.

[15] A. Tortrat, Mélanges de lois et lois indéfiniment divisibles, *Proc. Fourth. Conf. Probability Theory,* Brasov, 1973, 227-244.

[16] V.M. Zolotarev, Distribution of the superposition of infinitely divisible processes, *Theory Probability Appl.,* 3 (1958), 185-188.

[17] V.M. Zolotarev, Théoremes limites généraux pour les sommes des variables indépendentes, Comptes Rendus Acad. Sci. Paris, 270 (1970), 899-902.

COLLOQUIA MATHEMATICA SOCIETATIS JÁNOS BOLYAI
11. LIMIT THEOREMS OF PROBABILITY THEORY, KESZTHELY (HUNGARY), 1974.

ON THE POLYNOMIALS OF INDEPENDENT RANDOM VARIABLES

G.J. SZÉKELY

INTRODUCTION

Let $\{\xi_i\}_{i=1}^{\infty}$ be a sequence of independent identically distributed (real) random variables and let $\{g(x_1, x_2, \ldots, x_n)\}_{n=1}^{\infty}$ be a sequence of arbitrary Borel measurable functions $(g(x_1, x_2, \ldots, x_n)\colon R_n \to R_1)$. A typical questıon of probability theory concerns the possibility of finding a simple (e.g. linear) transformations $T_n\colon R_1 \to R_1$ such that the limit distribution

$$\lim_{n \to \infty} \mathsf{P}(T_n g(\xi_1, \xi_2, \ldots, \xi_n) < x) = F(x)$$

exists at all continuity points of $F(x)$, and such that $F(x)$ is a nondegenerate distribution (has more than one point of increase).

In the following we discuss the limit distributions of the polynomials $A_n = \sum_{i=0}^{n} \xi_1 \xi_2 \ldots \xi_i$ and we also deal with the asymptotic behavior of the elementary symmetric polynomials of $\xi_1, \xi_2, \ldots, \xi_n$.

1. THE LIMIT DISTRIBUTION OF A_n

Theorem 1. *Suppose that* $\xi_i > 0$ *and* $\mathsf{E}(|\log \xi_i|) < \infty$.

(a) *Then* $\lim_{n \to \infty} A_n = A < \infty$ *exists with probability one if and only if* $E = \mathsf{E}(\log \xi_i) < 0$.

(b) *If* $E \geq 0$ *and* $0 < \mathsf{D}^2(\log \xi_i) < \infty$ *then* $\mathsf{P}\left(\frac{\log A_n - nE}{\sqrt{n}} < x\right)$ *tends to a nondegenerate distribution.*

Proof.

(a) Let $E < 0$. By the strong law of large numbers if n is sufficiently large $(n > n_0)$ then with probability one

$$\xi_1 \xi_2 \ldots \xi_n = \exp\left\{\sum_{i=1}^{n} \log \xi_i\right\} < \exp\{(E + \epsilon)n\}$$

for arbitrary $\epsilon > 0$. Let $E + \epsilon < 0$. Then

$$\sum_{n=0}^{\infty} \xi_1 \xi_2 \ldots \xi_n <$$

$$< \sum_{n=0}^{n_0} \xi_1 \xi_2 \ldots \xi_n + \sum_{n=n_0+1}^{\infty} \exp\{(E + \epsilon)n\} < \infty .$$

Similar argument shows that if $E > 0$ then $\lim_{n \to \infty} A_n = +\infty$ with probability one.

If $E = \mathsf{E}(\log \xi_i) = 0$, then by virtue of Theorem 8.3.3 of [1], the random walk $S_n = \sum_{i=1}^{n} \log \xi_i$ is recurrent i.e. there exists at least one $x \in R_1$ such that for every $\epsilon > 0$ we have

$$\mathsf{P}(|S_n - x| < \epsilon \text{ infinitely often}) = 1 .$$

This theorem implies that $\lim_{n \to \infty} A_n = +\infty$ with probability one.

(b) Let $E = 0$ and $0 < \mathsf{D}^2(\log \xi_i) < +\infty$. Easy to see that

$$\exp\Big\{\max_{0\le j\le n}\sum_{i=1}^{j}\log\xi_i\Big\}\le$$

$$\le A_n\le(n+1)\exp\Big\{\max_{0\le j\le n}\sum_{i=1}^{j}\log\xi_i\Big\}$$

By a well-known theorem of Erdős and Kac ([8]) the distribution of $\frac{1}{\sqrt{n}}\max_{0\le j\le n}\sum_{i=1}^{j}\log\xi_i$ tends to a reflected normal distribution, therefore the same is true for $\frac{1}{\sqrt{n}}\log A_n$.

Finally in the case $E>0$

$$A_n=\xi_1\xi_2\dots\xi_n(1+\xi_n^{-1}+\xi_n^{-1}\xi_{n-1}^{-1}+\dots+\xi_n^{-1}\xi_{n-1}^{-1}\dots\xi_1^{-1}$$

where $\mathsf{E}(\log\xi_i^{-1})<0$ therefore by (a) of our Theorem 1

$$\lim_{n\to\infty}(1+\xi_n^{-1}+\xi_n^{-1}\xi_{n-1}^{-1}+\dots+\xi_n^{-1}\xi_{n-1}^{-1}\dots\xi_1^{-1})<\infty$$

with probability one, thus $\frac{\log A_n-nE}{\sqrt{n}}$ tends to a normal distribution.

Remarks. The sum $A_n^*=1+\sum_{i=0}^{n-1}\xi_n\xi_{n-1}\dots\xi_{n-i}$ $(n=0,1,\dots)$ (which has the same distribution as A_n) satisfies the equation $A_n^*=$ $=\xi_nA_{n-1}^*+1$ for $n\ge 1$, $A_0\equiv 1$.

Let $\{(w_n,Z_n)\}_{n=1}^{\infty}$ be a sequence of independent identically distributed random pairs. The sequence $\{Y_n\}_{n=0}^{\infty}$ defined by the stochastic difference equation

$$Y_n=w_nY_{n-1}+Z_n\qquad\text{for}\qquad n\ge 1$$

is a generalization of A_n^* and it is investigated in [2], [3]. For random vectors Y_n and Z_n and random matrices w_n the above difference equation has been treated in [4].

In connection with $Z_n\equiv 1$ and $\mathsf{P}(w_n=0)=1-\mathsf{P}(w_n=1)=p$ $(0<p<1)$ see [5], where the geometric distribution is obtained as the limit law of Y_n.

If the i.i.d. random variables ξ_i are rectangulary distributed on $[0, 1]$ then $\mathsf{E}(\log \xi_i) < 0$, therefore $A = \sum_{n=0}^{\infty} \xi_1 \xi_2 \ldots \xi_n < \infty$ exists with probability one. The Laplace – Stieltjes transformation of A can be found in [6].

The random variable $A(\alpha) = \sum_{n=1}^{\infty} \prod_{j=1}^{n} \xi_j^{\frac{1}{\alpha}}$ for $\alpha > 0$ is investigated in [7], Theorem 4.7.7. Among others it is proved that $F_\alpha(x) = \mathsf{P}(A(\alpha) < x)$ form a convolution semigroup of distribution functions: $F_\alpha * F_\beta = F_{\alpha+\beta}$ for $\alpha, \beta > 0$ and $\mathsf{P}(A(\alpha) < x \mid A(\alpha) \leqslant 1) = x^\alpha$ $(x \in [0, 1])$ i.e. given $A(\alpha) \leqslant 1$, $A(\alpha)$ has the same distribution as the first term $\xi_1^{\frac{1}{\alpha}}$ of the series which defines $A(\alpha)$.

2. THE ASYMPTOTIC BEHAVIOUR OF THE ELEMENTARY SYMMETRIC POLYNOMIALS OF INDEPENDENT RANDOM VARIABLES

A theorem of Hoeffding [9] implies that if $\xi_1, \xi_2, \ldots, \xi_n$ are i.i.d. random variables, $h(x_1, x_2, \ldots, x_k)$ is a given Borel-measurable function of k variables (k is a fix number, $k \leqslant n$) for which $\mathsf{E}(h(\xi_1, \xi_2, \ldots, \xi_k)^2) < \infty$ and

$$S_n^{(k)} = \frac{1}{n(n-1)\ldots(n-k+1)} \sum_{(\alpha_1, \alpha_2, \ldots, \alpha_k)} h(\xi_{\alpha_1}, \ldots, \xi_{\alpha_k})$$

where $(\alpha_1, \alpha_2, \ldots, \alpha_k)$ runs over the possible permutations of k different integer numbers with the restriction $1 \leqslant \alpha_i \leqslant n$ $(i = 1, 2, \ldots, k)$, then the distribution of $\sqrt{n}(S_n^{(k)} - \mu)$ where $\mu = \mathsf{E}(h(\xi_1, \xi_2, \ldots, \xi_k))$ tends to a normal distribution as $n \to \infty$.

The asymptotic behaviour of $S_n^{(k)}$ becomes more interesting and at the same time more complicated if $k \to +\infty$. In the following we prove some simple facts for the case $h(x_1, x_2, \ldots, x_k) = x_1 x_2 \ldots x_k$ when $k \to \infty$.

Let

$$T_n^{(k)} = \sqrt[k]{S_n^{(k)}} = \sqrt[k]{(k!)^{-1}\binom{n}{k}^{-1} \sum_{(\alpha_1,\dots,\alpha_k)} \xi_{\alpha_1}\dots\xi_{\alpha_k}}\,.$$

We conjecture that if $\lim_{n\to\infty} \frac{k}{n} = c$ $(0 \leqslant c \leqslant 1)$ then $\lim_{n\to\infty} T_n^{(k)} = T^{(c)}$ exists with probability one for a wide class of random variables $\{\xi_i\}$. If $\xi_i \geqslant 0$ and $T^{(c)}$ exists then by a well-known inequality ([10], p. 51) $T^{(c)}$ is a decreasing function of c. If $k = o(\sqrt{n})$ and $0 \leqslant \xi_i \leqslant L < +\infty$ then

$$\lim_{n\to\infty} T_n^{(k)} = \lim_{n\to\infty} \sqrt[k]{\frac{(\xi_1 + \dots + \xi_n)^k + o(n^k)}{n^k + o(n^k)}} = \mathsf{E}(\xi_i)$$

with probability one.

On the other hand if $k \sim n$, $0 < a \leqslant \xi_i \leqslant b < \infty$ and $\mathscr{H}(.,.,\dots)$ denotes the harmonic mean of the numbers in the brackets then

$$T_n^{(k)} = \sqrt[k]{\frac{\xi_1\xi_2\dots\xi_n}{\mathscr{H}(\xi_1\xi_2\dots\xi_{n-k},\dots)}} = \frac{\left(\sqrt[n]{\xi_1\xi_2\dots\xi_n}\right)^{\frac{k}{n}}}{\sqrt[k]{\mathscr{H}(\xi_1\xi_2\dots\xi_{n-k},\dots)}} \to$$

$$\to \exp\{\mathsf{E}(\log \xi_1)\} = T^{(1)}$$

with probability one because $a^{n-k} \leqslant \mathscr{H}(.,.,\dots) \leqslant b^{n-k}$ and using $k \sim n$ $\lim_{n\to\infty} a^{\frac{n-k}{k}} = \lim_{n\to\infty} b^{\frac{n-k}{k}} = 1$.

Theorem 2. *If* $\mathsf{P}(\xi_i = 1) = 1 - \mathsf{P}(\xi_i = 0) = p$, *where* $p \neq c$, *then* $T^{(c)}$ *exists, and* $T^{(0)} = p$, $T^{(c)} = 0$ *if* $c > p$ *and*

$$T^{(c)} = \exp\left\{-\frac{H(p, 1-c, c-p)}{c}\right\} \quad \text{if} \quad 0 < c < p\,,$$

where $H(x_1, x_2, \dots, x_n) = -\sum_{i=1}^{n} x_i \log |x_i|$.

Proof. Let $0 < c < p$. By the strong law of large numbers and by the Stirling formula

$$T_n^{(k)} = \sqrt[k]{\frac{\binom{pn+o(n)}{k}}{\binom{n}{k}}} =$$

$$\equiv \sqrt[cn+o(n)]{\frac{(p+o(1))^{pn}[(1-c)+o(1)]^{(1-c)n}}{[(p-c)+o(1)]^{(p-c)n}}}\,(1+o(1)) \to$$

$$\to \frac{p^{\frac{p}{c}}(1-c)^{\frac{1-c}{c}}}{(p-c)^{\frac{p-c}{c}}}$$

with probability one as $n \to \infty$.

The remaining cases can be handled similarly.

Remark.

$$\lim_{c \to +0} T^{(c)} = \lim_{c \to +0} \frac{(1-c)^{\frac{1}{c}}(p-c)}{\left(1-\frac{c}{p}\right)^{\frac{p}{c}}(1-c)} = p = T^{(0)}$$

and

$$\lim_{c \to p-0} T^{(c)} = p(1-p)^{\frac{1-p}{p}} = \exp\left\{-\frac{H(p,1-p)}{p}\right\}.$$

In the near future I shall publish a theorem about more general random variables.

REFERENCES

[1] K.L. Chung, *A course in probability theory,* Acad. Press, New York-- London, 1974.

[2] W. Verwaat, On records, maxima and a stochastic difference equa-- tion, *Annals of Probability,* (to appear).

[3] F. Solomon, Random walks in a random environment, *Annals of probability,* (to appear).

[4] H. Kesten, Random difference equations and renewal theory for products of random matrices (preprint).

[5] A.S. Paulson,– V.R.R. Uppulum, A characterization of the geometric distribution and a bivariate geometric distribution, *Sankhyā*, 34 (1972).

[6] G.J. Székely, On limit distributions, *Annales Univ. Sci. Budapest,* 16 (1973), 65-67.

[7] W. Verwaat, *Succes epochs in Bernoulli trials,* Math. Centrum, Amsterdam, 1972.

[8] P. Erdős,– M. Kac, On certain limit theorems of the theory of probability, *Bull. Amer. Math. Soc.,* 52 (1946), 292-302.

[9] W. Hoeffding, A class of statistics with asymptotically normal distribution, *Ann. Math. Stat.,* 19 (1948), 293-325.

[10] G.H. Hardy – J.E. Littlewood – G. Pólya, *Inequalities,* Cambridge Univ. Press, Cambridge, 1952.

COLLOQUIA MATHEMATICA SOCIETATIS JÁNOS BOLYAI
11. LIMIT THEOREMS OF PROBABILITY THEORY, KESZTHELY (HUNGARY), 1974.

S_p-SYSTEMS AND THEIR GENERALIZATIONS

A. SZÉP

Among the several ways of vweakening of the concept of independence S_p-systems seem to be the most useful setting for extending the three series theorem. In the present paper we deal with a further generalization of the S_p-property.

Consider a finite measure space $\{X, \mathscr{S}, \mu\}$.

Definition 1. A set $F \subset L_p \ (X, \mathscr{S}, \mu)$ is said to be an S_p-system if

$$(1) \qquad \int_X \Big| \sum_{k=1}^{n} c_k X_k \Big|^p \, d\mu \leqslant K_p \Big(\sum_{k=1}^{n} c_k^2 \Big)^{\frac{p}{2}}$$

for arbitrary $X_1, X_2, \ldots, X_n \in F$ and $c_1, c_2, \ldots, c_n$. Here K_p is a universal constant depending possibly at most on p.

Definition 2. Let $\varphi(u)$ be an N-function in the sense of Orlicz ([1], p. 16) and denote $L_\varphi(X, \mathscr{S}, \mu)$ the Orlicz-space determined by φ. A set $F \subset L_\varphi(X, \mathscr{S}, \mu)$ is said to be an S_φ-system if

(2) $$\int_X \varphi\left(\sum_{k=1}^{n} c_k X_k\right) d\mu \leq K_\varphi \varphi\left(\left(\sum_{k=1}^{n} c_k^2\right)^{\frac{1}{2}}\right)$$

for arbitrary $X_1, X_2, \ldots, X_n \in F$ and $c_1, c_2, \ldots, c_n$.

Here K_φ does not depend on $X_1, X_2, \ldots, X_n$, $c_1, c_2, \ldots, c_n$.

Definition 3. A sequence $\{X_k\}_{k=1}^{\infty}$ of measurable functions is said to be a convergence system if $\sum_k c_k^2 < +\infty$ implies the convergence of the partial sums of the function series

$$\sum_k c_k X_k$$

almost everywhere.

S_p-systems have been introduced by S. Banach. Historically the first known examples (for $p > 2$) were certain lacunary subsystems of the trigonometric system and, on the other hand, sequences of independent random variables as well. The properties of S_p-systems are summarized in [2] and [3].

S_φ-systems seem to be very natural generalization of the concept. Keeping fixed the underlying measure space we denote by S_p, S_φ, CS the categories of S_p-systems, S_φ-systems and convergence-systems, respectively.

It is known [3] that $p > 2$ implies $S_p \subset CS$. Now we are going to investigate the corresponding inclusion for S_φ. We prove the following

Theorem. *Let $\varphi(u)$ be an N-function satisfying the Δ_2-condition [1] and such that for a positive function $\rho(s)$ the conditions*

(A) $$\sum_{s=1}^{\infty} \frac{\varphi\left(\frac{\alpha}{2^{\frac{s}{2}}}\right)}{\varphi\left(\frac{\alpha\rho(s)}{2^{\frac{s}{2}}}\right)} = O(1) \qquad (\alpha \to 0)$$

(B) $$\sum_{s=1}^{\infty} \varphi^{-1}\left(\frac{2^s}{\alpha^2}\varphi\left(\frac{\alpha\rho(s)}{2^{\frac{s}{2}}}\right)\right) = o(1) \qquad (\alpha \to 0)$$

hold. Then

$$S_\varphi \subset CS .$$

In the proof we shall make use of the following elementary lemma of Erdős [4]:

Lemma. *Let* $a_1, a_2, \dots, a_n$ *be arbitrary real numbers,* $a_1^2 + a_2^2 + \dots + a_n^2 = \epsilon$. *Then there exist an index* l, $1 \leqslant l \leqslant n$ *and a decomposition* $a_l = a_l' + a_l''$ *so that*

$$a_1^2 + a_2^2 + \dots + a_l'^2 = a_l''^2 + a_{l+1}^2 + \dots + a_n^2 \leqslant \frac{\epsilon}{2}$$

and

$$|a_l'|, |a_l''| \leqslant |a_l| .$$

Proof of the Theorem. Let $\{X_s\}_{s=1}^\infty \in S_\varphi$, $\sum a_s^2 < +\infty$, $s_n = \sum_{s=1}^{n} a_s X_s$. By (2) and the Δ_2-condition the sequence s_n converges to an $f \in L_\varphi$ a.e. Now choose the sequence m_k so that

$$\sum_{k=1}^{\infty} \varphi\Big(\sum_{s=m_k+1}^{\infty} a_s^2\Big) < +\infty .$$

Then by (2) and Beppo Levi's theorem the subsequence s_{m_k} converges a.e. Define

$$P_k = \sum_{s=m_k+1}^{m_{k+1}} a_s X_s .$$

We shall show that

$$\lim_{n\to\infty} \max_{m_k+1 \leqslant q \leqslant m_{k+1}} \Big|\sum_{s=m_k+1}^{q} a_s X_s\Big| = 0$$

a.e.

Applying the Lemma, we divide each P_k into two "quadratically equal" parts, i.e.

$$P_k = P_{k1}^{(1)} + P_{k1}^{(2)}$$

where

$$P_{k1}^{(1)} = \sum_{s=m_k+1}^{l-1} a_s X_s + a_l' X_l$$

$$P_{k1}^{(2)} = \sum_{s=l+1}^{m_k+1} a_s X_s + a_l'' X_l$$

$$a_l = a_l' + a_l'' ,$$

$$a_{m_k+1}^2 + \ldots + a_{l-1}^2 + a_l'^2 = a_l''^2 + a_{l+1}^2 + \ldots + a_{m_{k+1}}^2 ,$$

$$|a_l'|, |a_l''| \leqslant |a_l| .$$

Then we repeat this procedure with $P_{k1}^{(1)}$ and $P_{k1}^{(2)}$ instead of P_k attaining $P_{k2}^{(1)}, P_{k2}^{(2)}, P_{k2}^{(3)}, P_{k2}^{(4)}$ and so on.

So we get the blocks

$$P_{ks}^{(i)} \qquad (i = 1, 2, \ldots, 2^s;\ s = 1, 2, \ldots, \nu_k)$$

where the smallest blocks for $s = \nu_k$ contain at most two terms, i.e. they are linear combinations of two X-s. So we have

$$P_k = \sum_{i=1}^{2^s} P_{ks}^{(i)} \qquad (s = 1, 2, \ldots, \nu_k)$$

and if

$$\epsilon_k = \sum_{s=m_k+1}^{m_{k+1}} a_s^2$$

then the quadratic sum $\epsilon_{ks}^{(i)}$ of the coefficients a_s in $P_{ks}^{(i)}$ does not exceed $\frac{\epsilon_k}{2^s}$. Put

$$E_{ks}^{(i)} = \left\{ x\colon\ \varphi(P_{ks}^{(i)}) > \frac{2^s \varphi\left(\dfrac{\sqrt{\epsilon_k}\,\rho(s)}{2^{\frac{s}{2}}}\right)}{\epsilon_k} \right\}.$$

By (2)

$$\mu(E_{ks}^{(i)}) \frac{2^s \varphi\left(\dfrac{\sqrt{\epsilon_k}\,\rho(s)}{2^{\frac{s}{2}}}\right)}{\epsilon_k} \leqslant \int_{E_{ks}^{(i)}} \varphi(P_{ks}^{(i)})\, d\mu \leqslant \int_X \varphi(P_{ks}^{(i)})\, d\mu =$$

$$\leqslant K_\varphi \varphi(\sqrt{e_{ks}^{(i)}}) \leqslant K_\varphi \varphi\left(\sqrt{\frac{\epsilon_k}{2^s}}\right),$$

hence

$$\mu(E_{ks}^{(i)}) \leqslant K_\varphi \frac{\varphi\left(\dfrac{\sqrt{\epsilon_k}}{2^{\frac{s}{2}}}\right)}{\varphi\left(\dfrac{\sqrt{\epsilon_k}\,\rho(s)}{2^{\frac{s}{2}}}\right)} \frac{\epsilon_k}{2^s}.$$

Let

$$E_k = \bigcup_{s=1}^{\nu_k} \bigcup_{i=1}^{2^s} E_{ks}^{(i)}.$$

Then

$$\mu(E_k) \leqslant K_\varphi \epsilon_k \sum_{s=1}^{\infty} \frac{\varphi\left(\dfrac{\sqrt{\epsilon_k}}{2^{\frac{s}{2}}}\right)}{\varphi\left(\dfrac{\sqrt{\epsilon_k}\,\rho(s)}{2^{\frac{s}{2}}}\right)}.$$

By (A),

$$\sum_{k=1}^{\infty} \mu(E_k) < +\infty,$$

hence almost all points of X belonging to at most a finite number of the sets E_k. In other words, there exists a $k_0 = k_0(x)$ such that for $k \geqslant k_0$ the inequalities

$$(3) \qquad \varphi(P_{ks}^{(i)}) \leqslant \frac{2^s \varphi\left(\frac{\sqrt{\epsilon_k \rho(s)}}{2^{\frac{s}{2}}}\right)}{\epsilon_k}$$

hold a.e.

Let $k \geqslant k_0$ and $m_k + 1 \leqslant q \leqslant m_{k+1}$ fixed. Then the representation

$$\sum_{s=m_k+1}^{q} a_s X_s = \sum_{s=1}^{\nu_k} \eta_s P_{ks}^{(i_s)} + a'_q X_q$$

follows from the definition of the $P_{ks}^{(i)}$-s, $|a'_q| \leqslant |a_q|$, $1 \leqslant i_s \leqslant 2^s$, $\eta = 0$ or 1. Let k such that (3) holds. Then

$$(4) \qquad \left| \sum_{s=m_k+1}^{q} a_s X_s \right| \leqslant \sum_{s=1}^{\nu_k} \varphi^{-1} \left(\frac{2^s \varphi\left(\frac{\sqrt{\epsilon_k \rho(s)}}{2^{\frac{s}{2}}}\right)}{\epsilon_k} \right) + |a'_q X_q| .$$

For $k \to \infty$, $\epsilon_k \to 0$, hence by (B) the first term on the right side of (4) tends to 0 as $k \to \infty$. For the second one, we note that conditions (B) implies

$$\varphi(u) = o(u^2) \quad \text{for} \quad u \to 0 .$$

Hence by (2),

$$\int_X \varphi(a_s X_s)\, d_\mu \leqslant K_\varphi \varphi(|a_s|) .$$

Corollary 1. *Applying the theorem with* $\rho(s) = \sqrt{s}$ *for the functions* u^p $(p > 2)$ *we get* $S_p \subset CS$ *for* $p > 2$ (cf. [3]).

Corollary 2. *Applying the theorem with* $\rho(s) = s^{\frac{1}{2} + \delta}$ $(\delta > 0)$ *we* *get the inclusion* $S_\varphi \subset CS$ *for* $\varphi(u) = \dfrac{u^2}{\log^p \dfrac{1}{u}}$ $(p > 3)$.

Remark. Note that conditions (A), (B) restrict the N-function φ for $u > 0$ small, while the Δ_2-condition is a restriction for u large.

REFERENCES

[1] M.A. Krasnoselskij – Ya.B. Rutitski, *Convex functions and Orlicz-spaces* (in Russian), Moscow, 1958.

[2] S. Kaczmarz – H. Steinhaus, *Theorie der Orthogonalreihen,* Warszawa – Lwów, 1935.

[3] V.F. Gapoškin, Lacunary series and independent functions (in Russian), *Uspehi Mat. Nauk.*, 21 (1966), 2-82.

[4] P. Erdős, On the convergence of trigonometric series, *Journ. of Math. and Phys.*, 22 (1943), 37-39.

COLLOQUIA MATHEMATICA SOCIETATIS JÁNOS BOLYAI
11. LIMIT THEOREMS OF PROBABILITY THEORY, KESZTHELY (HUNGARY), 1974.

PROBABILITY LIMIT THEOREMS FOR TRIGONOMETRIC SERIES

S. TAKAHASHI

1. INTRODUCTION

We shall be concerned here with probability limit theorems for trigonometric series

$$\sum_{m=1}^{\infty} a_m \cos 2\pi m(t + \alpha_m) .$$

Since the trigonometric system is not independent, so we decompose the series into "almost independent" summands. In this direction it seems to be reasonable to take the sequence

$$\Big\{ \sum_{m=n_k+1}^{n_{k+1}} a_m \cos 2\pi m(t + \alpha_m) \Big\} \quad \Big(\frac{n_{k+1}}{n_k} > q > 1 \Big) .$$

as summands.

In fact, R. Salem and A. Zygmund have proved the

Theorem A ([13], II., p. 203). *Let* $S_N(t) = \sum_{m=1}^{N} a_m \cos 2\pi n_m (t + \alpha_m)$

$\left(\frac{n_{m+1}}{n_m} > q > 1\right)$ *where* $\{a_m\}$ *and* $\{\alpha_m\}$ *are any sequences of real numbers for which*

$$A_N^2 = \frac{1}{2}\sum_{m=1}^{N} a_m^2 \to +\infty \quad \textit{and} \quad a_N = o(A_N), \quad \textit{as} \quad N \to +\infty .$$

Then, for any set $E \subset [0, 1]$ *of positive measure and any* x,

$$\lim_{N\to\infty} \frac{1}{|E|} \left|\left\{t;\ t \in E,\ \frac{S_N(t)}{A_N} \leqslant x\right\}\right| = \frac{1}{\sqrt{2\pi}} \int_{-\infty}^{x} e^{-\frac{u^2}{2}} du .$$

Further, it is known that the sequence of functions

$$\{a_m \cos 2\pi n_m (t + \alpha_m)\}, \quad \frac{n_{m+1}}{n_m} > q > 1 ,$$

is not independent, but exhibits properties of independent random variables. Many attempts have been made to weaken the lacunarity condition.

2. A VERSION OF THE CENTRAL LIMIT THEOREM

We set

$$S_N(t) = \sum_{m=1}^{N} a_m \cos 2\pi m(t + \alpha_m),\ A_N^2 = \frac{1}{2}\sum_{m=1}^{N} a_m^2 ,$$

$$\Delta_k(t) = S_{n_k}(t) - S_{n_{k-1}}(t) \qquad (k = 2, 3, \ldots),$$

$$\Delta_0 = 0, \quad \Delta_1 = S_{n_1}(t)$$

where $\{n_k\}$ is any sequence of positive integers satisfying

$$(2.1) \qquad \frac{n_{k+1}}{n_k} > q > 1 \qquad (k = 1, 2, \ldots).$$

Then our theorem can be stated as follows:

Theorem 1 ([4]). *Suppose*

$$(2.2) \qquad A_k \to +\infty \quad \textit{and} \quad \max_t |\Delta_k(t)| = o(A_{n_k}), \quad \textit{as} \quad k \to +\infty ,$$

and there exists a function $g(t)$ *such that*

$$\text{(2.3)} \qquad \lim_{k\to\infty} \int_0^1 \left| \frac{1}{A_{n_k}^2} \sum_{m=1}^{k} \{\Delta_m^2(t) + 2\Delta_m(t)\Delta_{m-1}(t)\} - g(t) \right| dt = 0 \,,$$

then the function $g(t)$ *is non-negative and, for any set* E *of positive measure and any real number* $x \neq 0$,

$$\text{(2.4)} \qquad \lim_{N\to\infty} \frac{1}{|E|} \left| \left\{ t;\ t\in E,\ \frac{S_N(t)}{A_N} \leqslant x \right\} \right| = G_E(x,g) \,,$$

where

$$G_E(x,g) = \frac{1}{\sqrt{2\pi}\,|E|} \int_E \int_{-\infty}^{\frac{x}{\sqrt{g(t)}}} e^{-\frac{u^2}{2}}\, du\, dt$$

and $\frac{x}{0}$ *denotes* $+\infty$ *or* $-\infty$ *according as* $x > 0$ *or* $x < 0$.

If $g(t)$ in (2.3) is a constant, then $G_E(\cdot, g)$ is an ordinary normal distribution function. The condition (2.3) is, in some sense, that of Lindeberg for sums of independent random variables* and for those sums $g(t)$ is constant by the $0 - 1$ law. In our case for any $g(t)$, $g(t) \geqslant 0$ and $\int_0^1 g(t)\, dt = 1$, there exists a trigonometric series for which (2.4) holds with this $g(t)$.

Also, there exists a series such that $\lim_{k\to\infty} \frac{1}{A_{n_k}^2} \sum_{m=1}^{k} \Delta_m(t)\Delta_{m-1}(t)$ exists and does not vanish identically. This shows that $\{\Delta_k(t)\}$ is "almost one-dependent".

*If $\{x_k\}$ is independent with mean-value zero and $\mathrm{E}(x_k^2) < +\infty$, then Lindeberg's condition is $\max_{k\leqslant N} \frac{|x_k|}{V_N} \to 0$, in probability and $\mathrm{E}\left(\left|\frac{1}{V_N^2} \sum_{k=1}^{N} x_k^2 - 1\right|\right) \to 0$, as $N \to +\infty$, where $V_N^2 = \sum_{k=1}^{N} \mathrm{E}(x_k^2)$.

In Theorem A, we can take $\{\Delta_k(t)\}$ so that $\Delta_{2k}(t) = 0$ and $\Delta_{2k+1}(t)$ consists of only one term for each k and in this case $g(t)$ becomes a constant.

Further it is easily seen that the characteristic function of $G_E(\cdot, g)$ is $\frac{1}{|E|} \int_E e^{-\frac{\lambda^2 g(t)}{2}} dt$.

3. PROOF OF THEOREM 1

(i) Without loss of generality, we may assume that the constant q in (2.1) is greater than 6 (cf. [4], p. 386).

(ii) By (2.2), we can take a sequence of integers $\{p(k)\}$ such that $p(0) = 0$, $p(k+1) - p(k) \to \infty$, as $k \to \infty$ and if we put

$$T_k(t) = \sum_{m=p(k)+2}^{p(k+1)} \Delta_m(t) \quad \text{and} \quad D_k = A_{n_{p(k+1)}},$$

then

$$(3.1) \quad \begin{aligned} &\epsilon_N = \frac{1}{D_N} \max_{k \leq N} \Big(\sum_{m=p(k)+2}^{p(k+1)} \max_t |\Delta_m(t)| \Big) \to 0, \\ &\int_0^1 \Big(\sum_{k=1}^{N} \Delta_{p(k)+1} \Big)^2 dt = \sum_{k=1}^{N} \int_0^1 \Delta^2_{p(k)+1} dt = o(D_N^2), \\ &\qquad \text{as} \quad N \to +\infty. \end{aligned}$$

Lemma 1. *We have*

$$\lim_{N \to \infty} \int_0^1 \Big| \frac{1}{D_N^2} \sum_{k=1}^{N} T_k^2(t) - g(t) \Big| dt = 0.$$

Proof. We have

$$\Big| \sum_{k=1}^{N} T_k^2 - \sum_{m=1}^{p(N+1)} \{\Delta_m^2 + 2\Delta_m \Delta_{m-1}\} \Big| \leq$$

$$\leqslant 2 \sum_{k=1}^{N} |\Delta_{p(k)+1}| \sum_{j=0}^{2} |\Delta_{p(k)+j}| +$$

$$+ 2 \Big| \sum_{k=1}^{N} \sum_{m=p(k)+4}^{p(k+1)} \Delta_m \sum_{j=p(k)+2}^{m-2} \Delta_j \Big| .$$

Since $\Delta_m \sum^{M-2}_{\cdot} \Delta_j$ and $\Delta_n \sum^{n-2}_{\cdot} \Delta_j$ are orthogonal if $|n-m| \geqslant 2$, we have

$$\int_0^1 \Big| \sum_{k=1}^{N} T_k^2 - \sum_{m=1}^{p(N+1)} (\Delta_m^2 + 2\Delta_m \Delta_{m-1}) \Big| \, dt \leqslant$$

$$\leqslant 2 \Big\{ \sum_{k=1}^{N} \int_0^1 \Delta^2_{p(k)+1} \, dt \sum_{k=1}^{N} \Big(\int_0^1 \sum_{j=0}^{2} |\Delta_{p(k)+j}| \Big)^2 dt \Big\}^{\frac{1}{2}} +$$

$$+ 4 \Big\{ \sum_{k=1}^{N} \sum_{m=p(k)+4}^{p(k+1)} \int_0^1 \Big(\Delta_m \sum_{j=p(k)+2}^{m-2} \Delta_j \Big)^2 dt \Big\}^{\frac{1}{2}} ,$$

and by (3.1) the above integrals are $o(D_N^2)$, as $N \to +\infty$.

We also see that $g(t)$ is non-negative.

The sequence $\{T_k(t)\}$ is multiplicatively orthogonal and it is enough for the proof to show that, for any real λ,

$$\lim_{N \to \infty} \int_E e^{\frac{i\lambda}{D_N} \sum_{k=1}^{N} T_k} dt = \int_E e^{-\frac{\lambda^2 g(t)}{2}} dt . \tag{3.2}$$

But to prove the equality (3.2) is difficult because we do not know whether $\exp \Big\{ \frac{\lambda^2}{D_N^2} \sum_{k=1}^{N} T_k^2(t) \Big\}$ is integrable or not.

(iii) Let us put, for $k = 1, 2, \ldots, N$ and $M > 1$,

$$P_{k,N} = P_{k,N}(t, M) = \prod_{m=1}^{k} \Big\{ 1 - \frac{T_m^2(t)}{MD_N^2} \Big\} \quad \text{and} \quad P_{0,N} = 1 .$$

Then by (3.1) we may assume that $\epsilon_N \leqslant \frac{1}{2}$ and we have, easily

$$\exp\left\{-\frac{(1+\epsilon_N^2)}{MD_N^2}\sum_{k=1}^{N} T_k^2\right\} \leqslant P_{N,N}(t,M) \leqslant$$

$$\leqslant \exp\left\{-\frac{1}{MD_N^2}\sum_{k=1}^{N} T_k^2\right\},$$

(3.3)

$$\left|\frac{2}{D_N^2}\sum_{k=1}^{N} T_k^2 P_{k-1,N}^2 - M(1-P_{N,N}^2)\right| \leqslant \epsilon_N^2,$$

$$M\,|\,P_{N,N}^{\alpha} - e^{-\frac{\alpha g}{M}}\,| \leqslant \frac{\alpha\epsilon_N^2}{D_N^2}\sum_{k=1}^{N} T_k^2 + \alpha\left|\frac{1}{D_N^2}\sum_{k=1}^{N} T_k^2 - g\right| \quad (\alpha > 0).$$

Lemma 2. *For any* $M > 1$ *and any real* λ, *we have*

$$\lim_{N\to\infty}\int_0^1 \left|\frac{2}{D_N^2}\sum_{k=1}^{N} T_k^2 P_{k-1,N}^2 + M(e^{-\frac{2g}{M}} - 1)\right| dt = 0\,.$$

Proof. The integrand is not greater than

$$\left|\frac{2}{D_N^2}\sum_{k=1}^{N} T_k^2 P_{k-1,N}^2 - M(1-P_{N,N}^2)\right| + M\,|\,P_{N,N}^2 - e^{-\frac{2g}{M}}\,|\,.$$

By Lemma 1 and (3.3), we can prove the lemma.

Lemma 3. *We have*

$$\int_0^1 \left|\exp\left(\frac{i\lambda}{D_N}\sum_{n=1}^{N} T_k\right) - \exp\left\{\frac{i\lambda}{D_N}\sum_{k=1}^{N} T_k(t) P_{k-1,N}(t,M)\right\}\right| dt =$$

$$= |\lambda|\,(o_N(1) + o_M(1))\,,$$

where $o_N(1) \to 0$ *(or* $o_M(1) \to 0$*), uniformly in* M *(or* N*), as* N *(or* M*)* $\to +\infty$.

Proof. By (i), we estimate the frequencies of terms of trigonometric polynomials $T_k(t)\{1 - P_{k-1,N}(t,M)\}$ and we can see that $T_k(t)\,\{1 - P_{k-1,N}(t,M)\}$ $(k = 1, 2, \ldots, N)$ is an orthogonal system. Hence, the integral is not greater than

$$|\lambda| \int_0^1 \left| \frac{1}{D_N} \sum_{k=1}^{N} T_k(t) \{1 - P_{k-1,N}(t, M)\} \right| dt \leqslant$$

$$\leqslant |\lambda| \left[\int_0^1 \frac{1}{D_N^2} \sum_{k=1}^{N} T_k^2(t) \{1 - P_{k-1,N}(t, M)\}^2 dt \right]^{\frac{1}{2}}.$$

The integrand of the above integral is not greater than

$$\frac{1}{D_N^2} \sum_{k=1}^{N} T_k^2(t) \{1 - P_{k-1,N}(t, M)\} =$$

$$= \frac{1}{D_N^2} \sum_{k=1}^{N} T_k^2(t) - M\{1 - P_{N,N}(t, M)\} =$$

$$\leqslant \frac{1}{D_N^2} \left| \sum_{k=1}^{N} T_k^2 - g \right| + M |P_{N,N} - e^{-\frac{g}{M}}| + |g - M(1 - e^{-\frac{g}{M}})|.$$

Since $g \in L_1$, by Lemma 1 and (3.3) we can complete the proof.

Lemma 4. *If we put*

$$Q_{k,N}(t) = Q_{k,N}(t, \lambda, M) =$$

$$= \prod_{m=1}^{k} \left\{1 + \frac{i\lambda}{D_N} T_m(t) P_{m-1,N}(t, M)\right\},$$

then $Q_{N,N}(t, \lambda, M) \to 1$ *in weak-star* (L_∞) *as* $N \to +\infty$, *that is, for any* $f \in L_1$,

$$\int_0^1 f(t) Q_{N,N}(t, \lambda, M)\, dt \to \int_0^1 f(t)\, dt, \qquad \text{as} \qquad N \to +\infty.$$

Proof. Since $|Q_{N,N}| \leqslant \exp\left\{\frac{1}{2D_N^2} \sum_{k=1}^{N} T_k^2 P_{k-1,N}^2\right\} \leqslant e^{\frac{\lambda^2 M}{2}}$, it is sufficient to show that, for any measurable set E,

$$\int_E Q_{N,N}(t, \lambda, M)\, dt \to |E|, \qquad \text{as} \qquad N \to +\infty.$$

We write, for $Q_{N,N}(t)$ and the indicator function $I_E(t)$ of E,

$$Q_{N,N}(t, \lambda, M) \sim c_0 + \sum_{m=1}^{\infty} c_m \cos 2\pi m(t + \varphi_m)$$

$$I_E(t) \sim |E| + \sum_{m=1}^{\infty} d_m \cos 2\pi m(t + \psi_m),$$

m_k (or m'_k) = the largest (or smallest) frequency of

$T_k(t) P_{k-1,N}(t, M) Q_{k-1,N}(t, \lambda, M)$,

where, of course, c_m depends on (N, λ, M) m_k and m'_k on N. Using (i) we estimate m_k and m'_k, then we can see that

$$1 < m'_k < m_k < m'_{k+1} \qquad (k = 1, 2, \ldots).$$

Since $Q_{N,N} = 1 + \frac{i\lambda}{D_N} \sum_{k=1}^{N} T_k P_{k-1,N} Q_{k-1,N}$, we have $c_0 = 1$ and

$$\frac{i\lambda}{D_N} \sum_{m=1}^{k} T_m(t) P_{m-1,N}(t) Q_{m-1,N}(t) =$$

$$= \sum_{m=1}^{m_k} c_m \cos 2\pi m(t + \varphi_m).$$

Hence, we have,

$$\Big| \int_E Q_{N,N} dt - |E| \Big| = \frac{1}{2} \Big| \sum_{m=1}^{N} c_m d_m \cos 2\pi m(\varphi_m - \psi_m) \Big| \leqslant$$

$$\leqslant \frac{1}{2} \Big| \sum_{m=1}^{m_{N'}} c_m d_m \cos 2\pi m(\varphi_m - \psi_m) \Big| +$$

$$+ \frac{1}{2} \Big(\sum_{m=1}^{\infty} |c_m|^2 \Big)^{\frac{1}{2}} \Big(\sum_{m \geqslant N'} d_m^2 \Big)^{\frac{1}{2}} \leqslant$$

$$\leqslant \frac{|\lambda|}{D_N} \Big| \int_E \sum_{k=1}^{N'} T_k P_{k-1,N} Q_{k-1,N} dt \Big| +$$

$$+ \Big(\int_0^1 |Q_{N,N}|^2 dt \Big)^{\frac{1}{2}} \Big(\sum_{m \geqslant N'} d_m^2 \Big)^{\frac{1}{2}}.$$

If we take $N' = \Big[\frac{1}{\sqrt{\epsilon_N}} \Big]$, then by (3.1) we can prove the lemma because

$|Q_{k-1,N}(t, \lambda, M)|^2 \leqslant e^{\lambda^2 M}$ for $k = 1, 2, \ldots, N$.

Lemma 5. *For any measurable set* E, *we have*

$$\lim_{N\to\infty} \int_E \exp\left\{\frac{i\lambda}{D_N} \sum_{k=1}^{N} T_k(t)P_{k-1,N}(t,M)\right\} dt =$$

$$= \int_E \exp\left\{\frac{\lambda^2 M}{4}\left(e^{-\frac{2g}{M}} - 1\right)\right\} dt .$$

Proof. Since $\frac{1}{D_N} \mid T_k(t)P_{k-1,N}(t,M)\mid < \epsilon_N \to 0$ as $N \to +\infty$, we have, uniformly in t,

$$\exp\left(\frac{i\lambda}{D_N} \sum_{k=1}^{N} T_k P_{k-1,N}\right) =$$

$$= Q_{N,N} \exp\left\{-\frac{\lambda^2}{2D_N^2} \sum_{k=1}^{N} T_k^2 P_{k-1,N}^2\right\} + o(1)$$

as $N \to +\infty$. On the other hand, by Lemma 4 and Lemma 2

$$\left|\int_E Q_{N,N} \exp\left\{-\frac{\lambda^2}{2D_N^2} \sum_{k=1}^{N} T_k^2 P_{k-1,N}^2\right\} -\right.$$

$$\left.- \int_E \exp\left\{\frac{\lambda^2}{2D_N^2}\left(e^{-\frac{2g}{M}} - 1\right)\right\} dt\right| =$$

$$= \left|\int_E Q_{N,N}\left[\exp\left(-\frac{\lambda^2}{2D_N^2} \sum_{k=1}^{N} T_k^2 P_{k-1,N}^2\right) -\right.\right.$$

$$\left.\left.- \exp\left\{\frac{\lambda^2 M}{4}\left(e^{-\frac{2g}{M}} - 1\right)\right\}\right] dt\right| + o(1) =$$

$$= \lambda^2 e^{\frac{\lambda^2 M}{2}} \int_E \left|\frac{2}{D_N^2} \sum_{k=1}^{N} T_k^2 P_{k-1,N}^2 + M\left(e^{-\frac{2g}{M}} - 1\right)\right| dt + o(1) =$$

$$= o(1) \text{ as } N \to +\infty .$$

Since

$$\int_E \exp\left\{\frac{\lambda^2 M}{4}\left(e^{-\frac{2g(t)}{M}} - 1\right)\right\} dt \to \int_E e^{-\frac{\lambda^2 g(t)}{2}} dt ,$$

as $M \to +\infty$, we can prove (3.2) by Lemma 3 and Lemma 5.

4. LACUNARY TRIGONOMETRIC SUMS

In this section we set

$$S_N(t) = \sum_{m=1}^{N} a_m \cos 2\pi n_m (t + \alpha_m) \quad \text{and} \quad A_N^2 = \frac{1}{2} \sum_{m=1}^{N} a_m^2 ,$$

where $\{n_m\}$ is a sequence of positive integers and

$$A_N \to +\infty, \quad \text{as} \quad N \to +\infty . \tag{4.1}$$

Theorem 2 ([5]). *If* $\{n_m\}$ *and* $\{a_m\}$ *satisfy the conditions*

$$\frac{n_{m+1}}{n_m} \geqslant 1 + cm^{-\alpha} \qquad (m = 1, 2, \ldots), \tag{4.2}$$

where $c > 0$ *and* $0 \leqslant \alpha \leqslant \frac{1}{2}$ *and*

$$a_m = o(A_m m^{-\alpha}), \quad \text{as} \quad m \to +\infty , \tag{4.3}$$

then we have, for any $\{\alpha_m\}$, *any set* E *of positive measure and any real number* x,

$$\lim_{N\to\infty} \frac{1}{|E|} \left|\left\{t;\ t \in E, \frac{S_N(t)}{A_N} \leqslant x\right\}\right| = \frac{1}{\sqrt{2\pi}} \int_{-\infty}^{x} e^{-\frac{u^2}{2}} du . \tag{4.4}$$

If $\alpha = 0$, then Theorem 2 is Theorem A in §1.

Proof. Let us put, for $k = 0, 1, 2, \ldots$,

$$p(k) = \max\{m;\ n_m \leqslant 2^k\} ,$$

$$\Delta_k(t) = S_{p(k+1)}(t) - S_{p(k)}(t) \quad \text{and} \quad B_k = A_{p(k+1)} .$$

Then it is seen that

$$(4.5) \quad \begin{aligned} & p(k+1) - p(k) = O(p^\alpha(k)) , \\ & \frac{p(k+1)}{p(k)} \to 1, \quad \text{as} \quad k \to +\infty . \end{aligned}$$

Therefore, by (4.3) and (4.5),

$$b_k = \max\{|a_m|;\ p(k) < m \leqslant p(k+1)\} = o(B_k p^{-\alpha}(k)),$$

(4.6)
$$\sum_{m=p(k)+1}^{p(k+1)} |a_m| \leqslant b_k\{p(k+1) - p(k)\} = o(B_k), \quad \text{as} \quad k \to +\infty.$$

Hence, by Theorem 1 it is sufficient to prove the

Lemma 6. *We have*

(i) $$\int_0^1 \left|\frac{1}{B_N^2} \sum_{m=1}^{N} \Delta_m^2(t) - 1\right|^2 dt = o(1),$$

(ii) $$\int_0^1 \left|\frac{2}{B_N^2} \sum_{m=1}^{N} \Delta_m(t)\Delta_{m-1}(t)\right|^2 dt = o(1), \qquad as \qquad N \to +\infty.$$

To prove Lemma 6 we need the following

Lemma 7. *For any given* k, j, q *and* h *satisfying*

$$p(j) + 1 < h \leqslant p(j+1) < p(k) + 1 < q \leqslant p(k+1),$$

the number of solutions (n_r, n_i) *of the equations**

$$n_q - n_r = n_h \pm n_i,$$

where $p(j) < i < h$ *and* $p(k) < r < q$, *is at most* $C2^{j-k}p^{\alpha}(k)$, *where* C *is a positive constant independent of* k, j, q *and* h.

Proof. If $k < j + 3$, the lemma is evident by (4.5). Let us assume that $k \geqslant j + 3$. We have $n_h \pm n_i < 2^{j+2}$ and if m denotes the smallest number of r's of solutions (n_r, n_i), then

(4.7) (the number of solutions) $\leqslant q - m$ and

$$n_m > n_q - 2^{j+2} \geqslant n_q(1 - 2^{j+2-k}) \geqslant \frac{n_q}{1 + 8 \cdot 2^{j-k}}.$$

Hence, we have by (4.2)

$$1 + 8 \cdot 2^{j-k} \geqslant \frac{n_q}{n_m} \geqslant \prod_{s=m}^{q-1} (1 + cs^{-\alpha}) > 1 + cp^{-\alpha}(k+1)(q-m).$$

*The equations $n_q + n_r = n_h \pm n_i$ has no solution.

By (4.5) and (4.7) we can prove the lemma.

In the same way we can prove the following

Lemma 7′. *For any given* k, j, q *and* h *such that* $j \leqslant k-2$, $p(j+1) < h \leqslant p(j+2)$ *and* $p(k+1) < q \leqslant p(k+2)$, *the number of solutions of the equations*

$$n_q - n_r = n_h \pm n_i\,,$$

where $p(j) < i \leqslant p(j+1)$ *and* $p(k) < r \leqslant p(k+1)$, *is at most* $C2^{j-k}p^{\alpha}(k)$ *where* C *is a positive constant independent of* k, j, q *and* h.

Proof of Lemma 6. Let us put, for $k = 1, 2, \ldots,$

$$U_k(t) = \Delta_k^2(t) - \|\Delta_k\|_2^2 - \frac{1}{2}\sum_{m=p(k)+1}^{p(k+1)}{}' a_m^2 \cos 4\pi n_m (t + \alpha_m)\,.$$

Then we have, by (4.6)

$$|U_k(t)| \leqslant \Big(\sum_{m=p(k)+1}^{p(k+1)} |a_m|\Big)^2 + 2\|\Delta_k\|_2^2 = o(B_k^2)\,,$$

$$\Big\|B_k^{-2}\sum_{m=1}^{k}\Delta_m^2 - 1\Big\|_2 = \Big\|B_k^{-2}\sum_{m=1}^{k} U_m\Big\|_2 + o(1),$$

as $\quad k \to +\infty\,.$

Therefore, for the proof of (i) it is enough to show that

$$\sum_{k=2}^{N}\sum_{j=1}^{k-1}\Big|\int_0^1 U_k(t)U_j(t)\,dt\Big| = o(B_N^4), \qquad \text{as} \qquad N \to +\infty\,. \tag{4.8}$$

By Lemma 6 (4.5) and (4.6), we have, for $k > j$,

$$\Big|\int_0^1 U_k(t)U_j(t)\,dt\Big| \leqslant$$

$$\leqslant C2^{j-k}p^{\alpha}(k)\sum_{q=p(k)+1}^{p(k+1)}{}' |a_q|\,b_k \sum_{h=p(j)+1}^{p(j+1)} |a_h|\,b_j =$$

$$= o(2^{j-k}\|\Delta_k\|_2\|\Delta_j\|_2\, p^{-\frac{\alpha}{2}}(j)\,p^{\frac{\alpha}{2}}(k)B_N^2), \qquad \text{as} \qquad N \to +\infty\,.$$

Since $\frac{p(j+1)}{p(j)} \to 1$, as $j \to +\infty$, we have, for all k,

$$\sum_{j=1}^{k-1} 2^{j-k} p^{-\alpha}(j) \leqslant C' p^{-\alpha}(k), \quad \text{for some} \quad C' > 0 .$$

Hence, we have

$$\sum_{k=2}^{N} \sum_{j=2}^{k-1} \| \Delta_k \|_2 \| \Delta_j \|_2 2^{j-k} p^{\frac{\alpha}{2}}(k) p^{-\frac{\alpha}{2}}(j) \leqslant$$

$$\leqslant C' \sum_{k=2}^{N} \| \Delta_k \|_2 \Big(\sum_{j=1}^{k-1} 2^{j-k} \| \Delta_j \|_2^2 \Big)^{\frac{1}{2}} \leqslant$$

$$\leqslant C' \Big(\sum_{k=1}^{N} \| \Delta_k \|_2^2 \Big)^{\frac{1}{2}} \Big(\sum_{k=2}^{N} \sum_{j=1}^{k-1} 2^{j-k} \| \Delta_j \|_2^2 \Big)^{\frac{1}{2}} = O(B_N^2) ,$$

$$\text{as} \quad N \to +\infty .$$

By the above relations, we can prove (4.8). Further, using Lemma 7′ we can prove (ii) in the same way.

Using the same method we can prove the following

Theorem 2′. *If* $\{n_m\}$ *and* $\{a_m\}$ *satisfy the conditions*

$$\frac{n_{m+1}}{n_m} > 1 + c_m m^{-\alpha} \qquad (m = 1, 2, \ldots) ,$$

where $\lim_{m \to \infty} c_m = +\infty$ *and* $0 < \alpha \leqslant \frac{1}{2}$, *and*

(4.9) $\qquad a_m = O(A_m m^{-\alpha})$, *as* $\quad m \to +\infty$,

then we have (4.4).

When $a_m = 1$, $\alpha = \frac{1}{2}$ and $E = [0, 1]$, this theorem was proved by P. Erdős [1]. The above two theorems show that the lacunarity condition of $\{n_m\}$ and the growth order of $\left\{\frac{a_m}{A_m}\right\}$ are closely related each other. In fact, we can prove the following

Theorem 3 [7]. *In Theorem* 2 *the condition* (4.3) *can not be replaced by the condition* (4.9) *for every* α, $0 \leqslant \alpha \leqslant \frac{1}{2}$.

For $\alpha = \frac{1}{2}$ this was first proved by P. Erdős ([1] and [2]).

5. LACUNARY TRIGONOMETRIC SERIES

As a byproduct of Theorem 2, we can prove the following

Theorem 4 ([6], [8]). *Consider the trigonometric series*

$$\sum_m a_m \cos 2\pi n_m (t + \alpha_m), \tag{5.1}$$

where $\frac{n_{m+1}}{n_m} > 1 + cm^{-\alpha}$, *for some* $c > 0$ *and* $0 \leqslant \alpha \leqslant \frac{1}{2}$. *If*

$$A_N^2 = \frac{1}{2} \sum_{m=1}^{N} a_m^2 \to +\infty \qquad \text{and} \qquad a_N = O(A_N N^{-\alpha}),$$

$$\text{as} \qquad N \to +\infty,$$

then, for any $\{\alpha_m\}$, *the series* (5.1) *diverges a.e. and is not a Fourier series of any integrable function.*

For $\alpha = 0$, this theorem was proved by A. Zygmund ([13], I, p. 203).

Proof. Let us put

$$S_N(t) = \sum_{m=1}^{N} a_m \cos 2\pi n_m (t + \alpha_m),$$

$$T_N(t) = \sum_{m=1}^{N} \frac{a_m}{A_m} \cos 2\pi n_m (t + \alpha_m), \quad \text{and}$$

$$B_N^2 = \frac{1}{2} \sum_{m=1}^{N} \left(\frac{a_m}{A_m}\right)^2.$$

Then by the Abel-transformation we can see that

(i) If $\{S_N(t)\}$ converges on E, then $\{T_N(t)\}$ converges on E.

(ii) If (5.1) is a Fourier series, then $\{S_N(t)\}$ is L_ρ-bounded,

$0 \leqslant \rho < 1$ ([13], I, p. 267). Since in this case we have $\| S_N \|_1 \leqslant \leqslant \| S_N \|_2^{\frac{2-2\rho}{2-\rho}} \| S_N \|_\rho^{\frac{\rho}{2-\rho}} \leqslant C A_N^{\frac{2-2\rho}{2-\rho}}$, $\{T_N(x)\}$ converges in L_1.

On the other hand we have

$$B_N \to \infty \qquad \text{and} \qquad \frac{a_N}{A_N} = o(B_N N^{-\alpha}), \qquad \text{as} \qquad N \to +\infty .$$

Therefore, by Theorem 2 $\{\frac{T_N(x)}{B_N}\}$ is asymptotically normal on any set of positive measure. This contradicts to both of (i) and (ii).

6. LAW OF THE ITERATED LOGARITHM FOR LACUNARY TRIGONOMETRIC SERIES

We consider the trigonometric sums

$$S_N(t) = \sum_{m=1}^{N} a_m \cos 2\pi n_m (t + \alpha_m) ,$$

where $\{n_m\}$ is a sequence of positive integers and a_m are real numbers satisfying the conditions:

$$\frac{n_{m+1}}{n_m} \geqslant 1 + c m^{-\alpha}, \qquad \text{for some} \qquad c > 0 \qquad \text{and} \qquad 0 \leqslant \alpha \leqslant \frac{1}{2}$$

$$A_N^2 = \frac{1}{2} \sum_{m=1}^{N} a_m^2 \to + \infty, \qquad \text{as} \qquad N \to + \infty .$$

When $\alpha = 0$, M. Weiss [12] proved that if

$$a_N = o\left(\frac{A_N}{\sqrt{\log \log A_N}}\right), \qquad \text{as} \qquad N \to + \infty ,$$

then, for any sequence of real numbers $\{\alpha_m\}$,

$$\overline{\lim_N} \frac{S_N(t)}{\sqrt{2 A_N^2 \log \log A_N}} = 1 , \qquad \text{a.e.}$$

For $\alpha > 0$, we can prove the following

Theorem 5 ([10]). *Suppose, for some* $\beta > \frac{1}{2}$

(6.1) $$a_N = O(A_N (\log A_N)^{-\beta} N^{-\alpha}), \quad \text{as} \quad N \to +\infty,$$

then we have, for any $\{\alpha_m\}$,

$$\overline{\lim_N} \frac{S_N(t)}{\sqrt{2A_N^2 \log\log A_N}} \leqslant 1, \quad \text{a.e.}$$

Theorem 6 ([11]). *Suppose*

(6.2) $$a_N = O(A_N \omega_N^{-1} N^{-\alpha}), \quad \text{as} \quad N \to +\infty,$$

where $\omega_N = (\log N)^\beta (\log A_N)^4 + (\log A_N)^8$ *and* $\beta > \frac{1}{2}$, *then we have, for any* $\{\alpha_m\}$,

$$\overline{\lim_N} \frac{S_N(t)}{\sqrt{2A_N^2 \log\log A_N}} \geqslant 1, \quad \text{a.e.}$$

For the proof of these theorems we approximate $S_N(t)$ by sums of "multiplicatively orthogonal" trigonometric polynomials. But in these cases the polynomials are not necessarily uniformly bounded when they are normalized. Under (6.1) we apply the method of [9] to these polynomials. Under (6.2) we can see that the polynomials are "almost strongly multiplicative system" and use the method of P. Révész [3].

If $\alpha < \frac{1}{2}$ and $\{a_n\}$ is non-increasing, then both of (6.1) and (6.2) are satisfied and we can obtain

$$\overline{\lim_N} \frac{S_N(t)}{\sqrt{2A_N^2 \log\log A_N}} = 1, \quad \text{a.e.}$$

REFERENCES

[1] P. Erdős, On trigonometric sums with gaps, *Magyar Tud. Akad. Kutató Int. Közl.*, 7 (1962), 37-42.

[2] A. Földes, Further statistical properties of the Walsh functions, *Studia Sci. Math. Hungarica,* 7 (1972), 147-153.

[3] P. Révész, The law of the iterated logarithm for multiplicative systems, *Indiana Univ. Math. Journ.*, 21 (1972), 557-564.

[4] S. Takahashi, A version of the central limit theorem for trigonometric series, *Tôhoku Math. Journ.*, 16 (1964), 384-398.

[5] S. Takahashi, On lacunary trigonometric series, *Proc. Japan Acad.*, 41 (1965), 503-506.

[6] S. Takahashi, On lacunary Fourier series, *Tôhoku Math. Journ.*, 19 (1967), 78-85.

[7] S. Takahashi, On lacunary trigonometric series II, *Proc. Japan Acad.*, 44 (1968), 766-770.

[8] S. Takahashi, On trigonometric Fourier coefficients, *Tôhoku Math. Journ.*, 21 (1969), 406-418.

[9] S. Takahashi, Notes on the law of the iterated logarithm, *Studia Sci. Math. Hungarica,* 7 (1972), 21-24.

[10] S. Takahashi, On the law of the iterated logarithm for lacunary trigonometric series, *Tôhoku Math. Journ.*, 24 (1972), 319-329.

[11] S. Takahashi, On the law of the iterated logarithm II, (to appear).

[12] M. Weiss, On the law of the iterated logarithm for lacunary trigonometric series, *Trans. Amer. Math. Soc.*, 91 (1959), 444-469.

[13] A. Zygmund, *Trigonometric seriees,* I, II, Cambridge Univ. Press, 1959.

COLLOQUIA MATHEMATICA SOCIETATIS JÁNOS BOLYAI
11. LIMIT THEOREMS OF PROBABILITY THEORY, KESZTHELY (HUNGARY), 1974.

REGULAR SPEED OF CONVERGENCE FOR THE MAXIMUM OF A RANDOM WALK

N. VERAVERBEKE – J.L. TEUGELS

1. INTRODUCTION AND RESULTS

Let $X_1, X_2, \ldots, X_n, \ldots$ be a sequence of independent identically distributed random variables, with distribution function $F(x)$. Let $S_0 = 0$, $S_n = X_1 + \ldots + X_n$ $(n \geqslant 1)$, $M_n = \max(0, S_1, \ldots, S_n)$ $(n \geqslant 1)$ and $M_\infty = \lim_{n \to \infty} M_n = \sup(0, S_1, S_2, \ldots)$. As is well-known [6] $M_\infty < \infty$ a.s. if and only if

$$B = \sum_{n=1}^{\infty} \frac{1}{n} \mathsf{P}(S_n > 0) < \infty .$$

We are interested in the asymptotic behavior as $n \to \infty$ of either $G_n(x) = \mathsf{P}(M_n \leqslant x)$ if $B = \infty$ or $G_n(x) - G(x)$ if $B < \infty$ where $G(x) = \mathsf{P}(M_\infty \leqslant x)$. Our basic assumptions will be connected with regular variation in contrast with possible exponential behavior which was considered by us in [7]. In that paper we proved the following

Theorem A. *Let* X_1 *satisfy the following conditions:*

(i) $-\infty \leqslant \mathsf{E}(X_1) < 0$,

(ii) $\theta(s) = \mathsf{E}(e^{sX})$ *converges for* $\operatorname{Re} s \in [0, a)$ *for some* $a > 0$,

(iii) $\theta(s)$ *attains a minimum at* τ $(0 < \tau < a)$ *where* $\theta'(\tau) = 0$ *and* $\theta(\tau) = \gamma < 1$,

(iv) *if* X_1 *is lattice valued, then* $\mathsf{P}(X_1 = 0) > 0$.

Then for all $x \geqslant 0$

$$G_n(x) - G(x) \sim cH(x) n^{-\frac{3}{2}} \gamma^n \quad \text{as} \quad n \to \infty$$

where c *is a known constant and* $H(x)$ *depends solely on* x.

The proof of this theorem as well as explicit expressions for c and $H(x)$ are given in [7].

In this paper we prove the following two theorems.

Theorem B. *Assume* $B < \infty$, $0 \leqslant \alpha < 1$ *and that* $L(n)$ *is a slowly varying sequence on* $N = \{1, 2, \ldots\}$. *Then the following relations are equivalent:*

(i) $\displaystyle\sum_{n+1}^{\infty} \frac{1}{k} \mathsf{P}(S_k > 0) \sim n^{-\alpha} L(n)$ *as* $n \to \infty$,

(ii) $G_n(x) - G(x) \sim G(x) n^{-\alpha} L(n)$ *as* $n \to \infty$ *for all* $x \geqslant 0$.

Theorem C. *Assume* $B = \infty$, $0 < \alpha < 1$. *If*

$$\frac{1}{n} \sum_{k=0}^{n} \mathsf{P}(S_k > 0) \to \alpha \tag{1}$$

then for all finite $x \geqslant 0$

$$G_n(x) \sim \frac{1}{\Gamma(1-\alpha)} K(x) n^{-\alpha} M(n) \tag{2}$$

where $K(0) = 1$, $K(x)$ *is a finite renewal function and* $M(n)$ *is a slowly varying sequence.*

2. REMARKS AND AUXILIARY RESULTS

2.1. Theorem C improves an earlier result of Bingham [1] and Emery [2] who independently from each other showed that (2) was valid at all continuity points of $K(x)$. Our proof is simpler and avoids this shortcoming.

That condition (1) is related to regular variation is most clearly seen from a result of Rogozin [5] who showed that if (1) holds then

$$\sum_{n=0}^{\infty} s^n G_n(x) \sim \frac{(1 + U(1,x))(1-s)^{\alpha-1}}{L\left(\frac{1}{1-s}\right)}$$

where $U(s, x)$ is defined below and

$$L\left(\frac{1}{1-s}\right) = \exp\left\{\sum_{n=1}^{\infty} n^{-1} s^n [\mathsf{P}(S_n > 0) - \alpha]\right\}$$

is slowly varying at infinity as $s \to 1$. In our theorem $M(n) \sim \frac{1}{L(n)}$.

2.2. A further remark is connected with $K(x)$. Let

$$N_1 = \inf\{n > 0 \colon S_n > 0\}$$

$$Z_1 = S_{N_1}$$

be the first ladder point and first ladder height of the random walk $\{S_n\}$. Let $Z(x)$ be the distribution function of the proper random variable Z_1 (since $B = \infty$). Then [4] $K(x)$ is the renewal function generated by $Z(x)$, i.e. $K(x) = \sum_{n=1}^{\infty} Z^{(n)}(x)$.

2.3. The condition (i) of Theorem B is rather natural since

$$B - \sum_{k=1}^{n} \frac{1}{k} \mathsf{P}(S_k > 0) = \sum_{k=n+1}^{\infty} \frac{1}{k} \mathsf{P}(S_k > 0)$$

tends to zero as $n \to \infty$. In [8] it is shown that (i) is equivalent to

$$\mathsf{P}(n < N_1 < \infty) \sim e^{-B} n^{-\alpha} L(n) \qquad (n \to \infty).$$

A similar interpretation is possible for condition (1) in Theorem C. Indeed, if $B = \infty$ and $\sum_{n=1}^{\infty} \frac{1}{n} \mathsf{P}(S_n < 0) = \infty$, we have from [8] that (1) is equivalent to

$$\mathsf{P}(N_1 > n) \sim n^{-\alpha} L_1(n) \qquad (n \to \infty)$$

for some slowly varying sequence $L_1(n)$.

2.4. Before proceeding to the proofs of Theorems B and C we introduce some notations.

Let

$$v_0 = 1, \; u_0(x) \equiv 0;$$

$$v_n = G_n(0) = \mathsf{P}(S_1 \leqslant 0, \ldots, S_n \leqslant 0) \;\; (n \geqslant 1);$$

$$u_n(x) = \mathsf{P}(S_1 > 0, \, S_2 > 0, \ldots, S_{n-1} > 0, \; 0 < S_n \leqslant x) \;\; (n \geqslant 1).$$

Then [4]

$$G_0(x) = U_0(x) = \begin{cases} 0 & \text{for} \quad x < 0 \\ 1 & \text{for} \quad x \geqslant 0 \end{cases}$$

and

$$G_n(x) = v_n + \sum_{k=1}^{n} u_k(x) v_{n-k} \, .$$

The corresponding generating functions $(|s| \leqslant 1)$

$$V(s) = \sum_{n=0}^{\infty} v_n s^n$$

and

$$U(s, x) = \sum_{n=1}^{\infty} u_n(x) s^n$$

can be used to write down a Spitzer – Baxter identity for the sequence $\{G_n(x)\}$

(3) $$\sum_{n=0}^{\infty} G_n(x)s^n = V(s)[1 + U(s,x)]$$

where

$$V(s) = \frac{e^{-B(s)}}{1-s}$$

and

$$B(s) = \sum_{k=1}^{\infty} \frac{1}{k} \mathsf{P}(S_k > 0)s^k .$$

A few facts follow now easily. First $B = B(1)$ and if $B < \infty$

(4) $$G(x) = e^{-B}[1 + U(1,x)] .$$

Now $U(1,x) = \sum_{n=1}^{\infty} u_n(x) < \infty$ for all finite $x > 0$ [4]; moreover

$$\lim_{s \uparrow 1} \frac{U(1,x) - U(s,x)}{1-s} = \sum_{n=1}^{\infty} nu_n(x) < \infty .$$

Indeed for $\sigma > 0$, $0 < s < 1$ we have [4]

$$1 + \int_{+0}^{\infty} e^{-\sigma x}\, dU(s,x) = \exp\left\{ \sum_{n=1}^{\infty} \frac{1}{n} s^n \int_{+0}^{\infty} e^{-\sigma x}\, dF^{(n)}(x) \right\} .$$

Differentiation with respect to s leads to

$$\sum_{n=1}^{\infty} nu_n(x) = \sum_{n=1}^{\infty} F^{(n)}(x) + \sum_{n=1}^{\infty} F^{(n)} * U(1,x)$$

where $*$ denotes convolution. Since $U(1,x) < \infty$ so is $\sum_{n=1}^{\infty} nu_n(x) < \infty$ for all finite $x \geq 0$.

2.5. We finally mention the useful Karamata theorem for generating functions [3]. Let $L(n)$ be slowly varying at infinity and $0 \leq \gamma < \infty$. If $f_n \geq 0$ and $F(s) = \sum_{n=0}^{\infty} f_n s^n$ $(0 \leq s < 1)$ then

$$F(s) \sim (1-s)^{-\gamma} L\left(\frac{1}{1-s}\right) \quad \text{as} \quad s \uparrow 1$$

if and only if

$$\sum_{k=0}^{n} f_k \sim \frac{1}{\Gamma(1+\gamma)} n^{\gamma} L(n) \quad \text{as} \quad n \to \infty .$$

If in addition $\{f_n\}$ is monotone and $0 < \gamma < \infty$ then this is equivalent to

$$f_n \sim \frac{1}{\Gamma(\gamma)} n^{\gamma - 1} L(n) \quad \text{as} \quad n \to \infty .$$

3. PROOF OF THEOREM B

The condition (i) leads equivalently to a relation

$$B(1) - B(s) = (1-s) \sum_{k=0}^{\infty} s^k \sum_{n=k+1}^{\infty} \frac{1}{n} \mathsf{P}(S_n > 0) \sim$$

$$\sim \Gamma(1-\alpha)(1-s)^{\alpha} L\left(\frac{1}{1-s}\right) \quad \text{as} \quad s \uparrow 1$$

in view of Karamata's theorem. This in turn is equivalent to

$$e^{-B(s)} - e^{-B(1)} \sim e^{-B} \Gamma(1-\alpha)(1-s)^{\alpha} L\left(\frac{1}{1-s}\right) \quad \text{as} \quad s \uparrow 1 .$$

This is extremely helpful in estimating the right hand side of the expression

$$(1-s) \sum_{n=0}^{\infty} s^n [G_n(x) - G(x)] =$$

$$= [1 + U(1,x)][e^{-B(s)} - e^{-B(1)}] - e^{-B(s)}[U(1,x) - U(s,x)]$$

which follows from (3) and (4).

Using the results of 2.4 we obtain for $s \uparrow 1$

$$\sum_{n=0}^{\infty} s^n [G_n(x) - G(x)] \sim$$

$$\sim [1 + U(1,x)] e^{-B} \Gamma(1-\alpha)(1-s)^{\alpha-1} L\left(\frac{1}{1-s}\right)$$

which by Karamata's theorem and the monotonicity of $G_n(x) - G(x)$ in n is equivalent with

$$G_n(x) - G(x) \sim G(x) n^{-\alpha} L(n) \quad \text{as} \quad n \to \infty .$$

This proves the theorem for $x > 0$.

For $x = 0$ we use $G(0) = v_\infty = e^{-B}$ to obtain

$$\sum_{n=0}^{\infty} s^n [G_n(0) - G(0)] \sim e^{-B} \frac{B(1) - B(s)}{1-s} \quad \text{as} \quad s \uparrow 1$$

from which the result follows as before. This finishes the proof.

4. PROOF OF THEOREM C

As before we obtain for $x > 0$

$$\sum_{n=0}^{\infty} s^n G_n(x) = [1 + U(s,x)] \exp\left\{ \sum_{n=1}^{\infty} \frac{1}{n} s^n \mathrm{P}[S_n \leqslant 0] \right\} .$$

By Rogozin's result (1) implies simply that

$$\sum_{n=0}^{\infty} s^n G_n(x) \sim [1 + U(1,x)](1-s)^{\alpha-1} L^{-1}\left(\frac{1}{1-s}\right) \quad \text{as} \quad s \uparrow 1 .$$

Prabhu [4] has shown that $1 + U(1,x) = K(x)$ so that the monotonicity of $G_n(x)$ in n allows us to apply Karamata's theorem again.

The case $x = 0$ is dealt with similarly.

REFERENCES

[1] N.H. Bingham, Limit theorems in fluctuation theory, *Advances in Appl. Probability*, 5 (1973), 554-569.

[2] D.J. Emery, Limiting behaviour of the distributions of the maxima of partial sums of certain random walks, *J. Appl. Probability,* 9 (1972), 572-579.

[3] W. Feller, *An introduction to probability theory and its applications,* Vol., II, Wiley, New York, 1966.

[4] N.U. Prabhu, *Stochastic Processes,* Macmillan, New York, 1965.

[5] B.A. Rogozin, The distribution of the first ladder moment and height and fluctuation of a random walk, *Theor. Probability Appl.,* 16 (1971), 575-595.

[6] F. Spitzer, A combinatorial lemma and its application to probability theory, *Trans. Amer. Math. Soc.,* 82 (1956), 323-339.

[7] N. Veraverbeke – J.L. Teugels, The exponential rate of convergence of the distribution of the maximum of a random walk, *J. Appl. Probability,* (to appear).

[8] N. Veraverbeke, Doctoral dissertation, Katholieke Universiteit, Leuven, 1974.

COLLOQUIA MATHEMATICA SOCIETATIS JÁNOS BOLYAI
11. LIMIT THEOREMS OF PROBABILITY THEORY, KESZTHELY (HUNGARY), 1974.

AN INVARIANCE PRINCIPLE FOR A NON-RANDOMIZED THINNING OF A RENEWAL PROCESS

H. WALK

1. INTRODUCTION

An ordinary renewal process (see e.g. [5]) is defined as the sequence of partial sums belonging to a sequence of independent identically distributed random variables T_k $(k \in N)$ on a probability space $(\Omega, \mathfrak{A}, \mathrm{P})$ with $\mathrm{P}[0 \leqslant T_1 < \infty] = 1$, $\mathrm{P}[T_1 = 0] < 1$. The counting process belonging to it is defined as the family $\{N_t;\ t \in R_+\}$ of random variables $N_t = \sup\{k \in N\colon T_1 + \ldots + T_k \leqslant t\}$ denoting the random number of renewals in the time interval $[0, t]$. In the special case when the random variable T_1 has an exponential distribution with parameter λ the counting process is a Poisson process Π^λ with parameter λ.

There are two well-known cases in which a limit relation exists between general (ordinary) renewal processes, more exactly their counting processes, and Poisson processes. – One case concerns the superposition of renewal processes, see e.g. Störmer [16]. – The other case concerns a randomized thinning of a single renewal process. For $\mathrm{E}T_1 < \infty$ Rényi [15] has investigated the situation when the single renewals are independently deleted with probability $1-p$ $(0<p<1)$; if one changes the time scale by the factor $\frac{1}{p}$ and lets $p \to 0$, then the counting process approaches a Poisson process with parameter $\frac{1}{\mathsf{E}T_1}$. This case has been generalized, see e.g. Nawrotzki [12], Beljaev [2]. – Invariance principles for the two cases are due to Kennedy [9], Jagers [7], Jagers and Lindvall [8].

In the following we treat a non-randomized thinning of a renewal process.

We start with a sequence $\{T_k;\ k \in N\}$ of random variables as above, its renewal process and its counting process $\{N_t;\ t \in R_+\}$. Let M_n ($n \in N$, at first fixed) be Borel sets in R_+ with Lebesgue measure $|M_n| = \infty$. We record only the renewals contained in the set M_n. Denote

$$\nu_n(t) = \max\{x \in R_+ : |M_n \cap [0,x]| = t\} \qquad (t \in R_+)$$

and by Z_t^n the random number of renewals in $M_n \cap [0, \nu_n(t)]$. We assume that for all $a,\ t \in R_+$

$$|M_n \cap [\nu_n(z), \nu_n(z)+a]| \to 0 \qquad (n \to \infty)$$

uniformly in $z \in [0,t]$. Let $Z^n = \{Z_t^n;\ t \in R_+\}$.

A special case is given by $M_n = \bigcup_{j=0}^{\infty} I_{nj}$ with half-open intervals $I_{nj} \subset [j, j+1)$ where $\sum_{j=0}^{\infty} |I_{nj}| = \infty$, $\lim_{n\to\infty} |I_{nj}| = 0$ uniformly in $j \in \{0,1,\ldots\}$, e.g. $|I_{nj}| = \frac{1}{n}$.

In contrary to Rényi's case of randomized thinning, generally the counting processes Z^n do not correspond to renewal processes. Of course, if the initial counting process is a Poisson process, then Z^n is a Poisson process, too.

We shall show in the form of an invariance principle: If T_1 possesses a density and a finite expectation, then – for $n \to \infty$ – Z^n approaches a Poisson process with parameter $\frac{1}{\mathsf{E}T_1}$.

We can describe the situation intuitively in the following way. There are taken snapshots, e.g. of length of time $\frac{1}{n}$, during time intervals of length 1; the snapshots are then composed to a film. Under the above assumption the film shows – for large n – approximately the realization of a Poisson process.

The result will be generalized to the case of a compound renewal model*. A corollary concerning the supremum functional yields an application to risk theory.

Let us remark that for ordinary resp. compound renewal models invariance principles in connection with the Wiener process have been given by Lamperti [10], Billingsley ([3], Theorem 17.3, which has been generalized by several authors), Iglehart [6].

2. AN INVARIANCE PRINCIPLE CONCERNING THE POISSON PROCESS

In this and the following chapter, there is taken as basis the configuration described in Chapter 1 and further it is assumed that T_1 has a density and that $\mathsf{E}T_1 < \infty$. Let $\lambda = \frac{1}{\mathsf{E}T_1}$.

At first the result is stated in a simple version.

Theorem 1. *The finite dimensional distributions of* Z^n *converge weakly to those of* Π^λ, *as* $n \to \infty$.

Let us formulate another version of the result. Let $D[0, \infty)$ be the linear space of real-valued functions on R_+ which are right-continuous and have left-hand limits. $D[0, \infty)$ provided with the Skorokhod – Stone J_1-topology is metrizable and separable (Stone [17], Whitt [21], Lindvall [11]). Convergence $y_n \to y$ in this topology means that there

*The author thanks Professor W. Bühler for pointing out this possibility of generalization.

exists a sequence of homeomorphisms λ_n of R_+ onto itself with $\lambda_n(t) \to t$ and $y_n(\lambda_n(t)) \to y(t)$ uniformly on compact sets in R_+. Endowing $D[0, \infty)$ with this topology and with the Borel field induced by it, we have the following invariance principle.

Theorem 1′. *The distribution of* Z^n *converges weakly to the distribution of* Π^λ, *as* $n \to \infty$.

From results of Whitt [21], Straf [19], Lindvall [11] one knows for counting processes that in the case of a Poisson process as limiting process weak convergence of all finite dimensional distributions is equivalent to weak convergence of the distributions on $D[0, \infty)$ with its Borel field mentioned above. Therefore Theorems 1 and 1′ are equivalent, and it suffices to prove Theorem 1.

We need the following

Lemma. *Let* $S_k^n = \inf\{t \in R_+ : Z_t^n \geqslant k\}$ $(k, n \in N)$ *with* $\inf \phi = \infty$. *For fixed* $t \in R_+$ *there holds*

$$\mathsf{E} Z_t^n \to \lambda t \qquad (n \to \infty),$$

and – for suitably chosen versions of conditional expectations –

$$\mathsf{E}(Z_t^n \mid S_1^n = x) \to 1 + \lambda \cdot (t - x) \qquad (n \to \infty)$$

uniformly in $x \in [0, t]$,

$$\mathsf{E}(Z_t^n - Z_{S_k^n}^n \mid S_k^n = y) \to \lambda \cdot (t - y) \qquad (n \to \infty)$$

uniformly in $y \in [0, t]$,

$$\mathsf{E}(Z_t^n - Z_{S_k^n}^n \mid S_k^n = y,\ S_{k+1}^n = z) \to 1 + \lambda \cdot (t - z) \qquad (n \to \infty)$$

uniformly in $(y, z) \in [0, t] \times [0, t]$.

Proof of the Lemma. In order to avoid an overburdening of the presentation we restrict ourselves to prove the last assertion and that under the assumption

$$v_n(t) = \inf\{x \in R_+ : |M_n \cap [0, x]| = t\} \qquad (t \in R_+).$$

Because T_1 possesses a density, there exists for the renewal process $(T_1, T_1 + T_2, \ldots)$ a renewal density $u \colon R_+ \to R_+$, defined as a measurable function by

$$\mathsf{E}N_a = \int_{[0,a]} u(s)ds \qquad (a \in R_+) .$$

Noticing the independence of $\{T_1, T_2, \ldots\}$, then as a version of $\mathsf{E}(Z_t^n - Z_{S_k^n}^n \mid S_k^n, S_{k+1}^n)$ on the restricted domain $[0, t] \times [0, t]$ we get the function

$$(y, z) \to 1 + \int_{W(n,z,t)} u(s)ds$$

with

$$W(n, z, t) = \{u \in R_+ : u + v_n(z) \in M_n \cap (v_n(z), v_n(t)]\}$$

$$(z \in [0, t]) .$$

We further notice for

$$W_a(n, z) = \{u \in R_+ : u + v_n(z) \in M_n \cap (v_n(z), v_n(z) + a)\}$$

with $a \in R_+$, $z \in [0, t]$ the inclusion relation

$$W(n, z, t) \subset W_a(n, z) \cup (W(n, z, t) \cap [a, \infty))$$

and for its Lebesgue measure that

$$| W_a(n, z) | \to 0 \qquad (n \to \infty) \qquad \text{uniformly in} \qquad z \in [0, t] .$$

According to C. Stone ([18], p. 271), there exists a decomposition $u = u_1 + u_2$ with measurable functions $u_{1,2} \colon R_+ \to R_+$ such that

$$\int_{R_+} u_1(s)ds < \infty, \qquad u_2(s) \to \lambda \qquad (s \to \infty) .$$

We obtain (cf. the regularity proof of various summability methods)

$$\int_{W(n,z,t)} u_1(s)ds \to 0 \qquad (n \to \infty) ,$$

$$\left| \int_{W(n,z,t)} u_2(s)ds - \lambda \cdot (t-z) \right| \leq \int_{W(n,z,t)} |u_2(s) - \lambda| ds \to 0$$

$$(n \to \infty),$$

both limit relations uniformly in $z \in [0, t]$, and thus Lemma is proved.

Proof of Theorem 1. Let S be a countable and dense subset of R_+. For every $k \in N$ and every k-tuple $t_1 < t_2 < \ldots < t_k$ with $t_i \in S$ the sequence of the distributions of the random vectors $(Z^n_{t_1}, \ldots, Z^n_{t_k})$ is tight, because for every $\epsilon > 0$ there holds

$$\begin{aligned} \mathsf{P}[Z^n_{t_i} \leq K \quad (i = 1, \ldots, k)] &\geq 1 - k\mathsf{P}[Z^n_{t_k} > K] \geq \\ &\geq 1 - \frac{k}{K} \mathsf{E} Z^n_{t_k} \geq \\ &\geq 1 - \epsilon \end{aligned}$$

for $K \in R_+$ sufficiently large and $n \in N$. At the last inequality we have used the Lemma. Using Prokhorov's theorem on tight families of probability measures – here for the case R^k – (see [3], p. 37), Cantor's diagonal method and Kolmogorov's consistency theorem, we obtain the following compactness result. For every subsequence $(Z^{n'})$ of (Z^n) there exist a subsequence $(Z^{n''})$ and a stochastic process $\bar{Z}$ with index space S, state space $N_0 = \{0, 1, \ldots\}$ and non-decreasing realizations, such that the finite dimensional distributions of $Z^{n''}_{|S}$ (restriction of $Z^{n''}$ to S) converge weakly to those of $\bar{Z}$.

The theorem is proved if we can show that the finite dimensional distributions of $Z^{n''}$ converge weakly to those of Π^λ. For the sake of simplicity from now on we use the symbol n instead of n''.

Applying a standard argument we define a stochastic process $Z = \{Z_t;\ t \in R_+\}$ with state space N_0 and non-decreasing right-continuous realizations by

$$Z_t(\omega) = \lim_{\substack{s \to t+0 \\ s \in S}} \bar{Z}_s(\omega) \qquad (\omega \in \Omega,\ t \in R_+).$$

For all $s, t \in S$ with $s > t$ we have

$$\mathsf{P}[\bar{Z}_s - \bar{Z}_t \geqslant 1] = \lim \mathsf{P}[Z^n_s - Z^n_t \geqslant 1] \leqslant$$

$$\leqslant \lim \mathsf{E}(Z^n_s - Z^n_t) = \lambda \cdot (s-t) \,,$$

the last equation holds because of the Lemma. Therefore, with probability one, $Z_t = \bar{Z}_t$ for all $t \in S$, and every $t \in R_+$ is, with probability one, a continuity point of Z.

We define random variables S^n_k $(k \in N)$, S^n with values in $R_+ \cup \{\infty\}$ by

$$S^n_k = \inf\{t \in R_+ : Z^n_t \geqslant k\} \,,$$

$$S_k = \inf\{t \in R_+ : Z_t \geqslant k\} \,.$$

Because of the continuity property of Z just mentioned, every j-tuple $(j \in N)$ of random variables S_k has a continuous distribution function. We then obtain that the finite-dimensional distributions of $(S^n_1, S^n_2, \ldots)$ converge to those of $(S_1, S_2, \ldots)$ in the following sense: For all $j \in N$, $k_i \in N$, $a_i \in R_+$ $(i = 1, \ldots, j)$ there holds

$$\mathsf{P}[S^n_{k_i} \leqslant a_i \quad (i = 1, \ldots, j)] \to \mathsf{P}[S_{k_i} \leqslant a_i \quad (i = 1, \ldots, j)] \,.$$

Of course, an analogous convergence assertion holds for finite sums of bounded intervals in R^j_+ instead of intervals $\prod_{i=1}^{j} (-\infty, a_i]$. From this and from the fact that – because of the independence of $\{T_1, T_2, \ldots\}$ – $(S^n_1, S^n_2, \ldots)$ is a Markovian sequence, we obtain by an elementary consideration that also $(S_1, S_2, \ldots)$ is a Markovian sequence. Furthermore it follows immediately from the above convergence relation that the finite dimensional distributions of Z^n converge weakly to those of Z, even in the above stronger sense.

Finally we show that Z is a Poisson process Π^λ. For this purpose we show by induction that with probability one $S_k < \infty$, $k \in N$, and that the random variables

$$X_k = \begin{cases} S_k - S_{k-1}, & \text{if } S_k < \infty \\ \infty & \text{if } S_k = \infty \end{cases} \qquad (S_0 = 0)$$

are independent, each with exponential distribution with parameter λ.

We use the so-called result of the first step and write for $t \in R_+$

$$\mathsf{E}Z_t^n = \int_{[0,t]} \mathsf{E}(Z_t^n \mid S_1^n = x)\mathsf{P}_{S_1^n}(dx)\,.$$

By the Lemma, the left side converges to λt and the integrand on the right side converges to $1 + \lambda \cdot (t - x)$ uniformly in $x \in [0, t]$. Thus we get

$$\lambda t = \int_{[0,t]} [1 + \lambda \cdot (t - x)]\mathsf{P}_{S_1}(dx), \qquad t \in R_+\,,$$

and therefore, by solving a simple integral equation for the distribution function of S_1, the above assertion for $S_1 = X_1$.

Now we assume that the above assertion holds for S_i, X_i $(i = 1, \ldots, k)$. Let $t \in (0, \infty)$ and let $A \subset [0, t]$ be an interval of positive length. Then $\mathsf{P}[S_k \in A] > 0$ and $\mathsf{P}[S_k^n \in A] > 0$ for n sufficiently large. With $w = (y, z) \in A \times [0, t]$ we have

$$\mathsf{E}(Z_t^n - Z_{S_k^n}^n \mid S_k^n \in A) =$$
$$= \frac{1}{\mathsf{P}(S_k^n \in A)} \int_{A \times [0,t]} \mathsf{E}(Z_t^n - Z_{S_k^n}^n \mid S_k^n = y,\ S_{k+1}^n = z) \times$$
$$\times \mathsf{P}_{(S_k^n, S_{k+1}^n)}(dw)\,.$$

The left side is

$$\frac{1}{\mathsf{P}(S_k^n \in A)} \int_A \mathsf{E}(Z_t^n - Z_{S_k^n}^n \mid S_k^n = y)\mathsf{P}_{S_k^n}(dy)$$

and converges, by the Lemma, to

$$\frac{1}{\mathsf{P}(S_k \in A)} \int_A \lambda \cdot (t - y)\mathsf{P}_{S_k}(dy)\,.$$

The right side converges, by the Lemma, to

$$\frac{1}{\mathsf{P}(S_k \in A)} \int_{A \times [0,t]} [1 + \lambda \cdot (t - z)] \mathsf{P}_{(S_k, S_{k+1})}(dw) =$$

$$= \frac{1}{\mathsf{P}(S_k \in A)} \times$$

$$\times \int_A \Big\{ \int_{[0,t-y]} [1 + \lambda \cdot (t - y - x)] \mathsf{P}_{X_{k+1} | S_k}(y, dx) \Big\} \mathsf{P}_{S_k}(dy) .$$

Noticing that S_k has a positive density, we get

$$\lambda \cdot (t - y) = \int_{[0,t-y]} [1 + \lambda \cdot (t - y - x)] \mathsf{P}_{X_{k+1} | S_k}(y, dx)$$

for Lebesgue-almost all $y \in [0, t]$. It is possible to choose $\mathsf{P}_{X_{k+1} | S_k}$ in such a way that the relation holds for all $y, t \in R_+$ with $t \geqslant y$. We then obtain, by a consideration as before, that $P_{X_{k+1} | S_k}$ is given by the exponential distribution with parameter λ. This together with the fact that $(S_1, S_2, \ldots)$ is a Markovian sequence, yields the above assertion for S_i, X_i $(i = 1, \ldots, k + 1)$.

Remark to Theorems 1 and 1′.

(a) Trivial counterexamples show that it is not possible to omit the continuity assumption on the distribution of T_1.

(b) With $\Pi^\lambda = \{\Pi_t^\lambda;\ t \in R_+\}$ obviously the following strengthening of the assertion in Theorem 1 is valid: For all $j \in N$, $t_i, b_i \in R_+$ $(i = 1, \ldots, j)$ there holds

$$\mathsf{P}[Z_{t_i}^n \leqslant b_i \ (i = 1, \ldots, j)] \to \mathsf{P}[\Pi_{t_i}^\lambda \leqslant b_i \ (i = 1, \ldots, j)] ,$$

as $n \to \infty$.

(c) In the special case $M_n = \bigcup_{j=0}^{\infty} I_{nj}$ mentioned in Chapter 1, a proof analogous to that of Theorem 1 shows that it is possible to assume only that T_1 (with $\mathsf{E}T_1 < \infty$) has a continuous distribution function and that one of the sums $T_1 + \ldots + T_k$ has a distribution function with an absolutely continuous component.

(d) The first part of the proof shows that in the case $\mathsf{E}T_1 = \infty$ one has convergence in distribution (and in probability) to a process identical zero.

Now we apply the invariance principle given by Theorem 1′ to the supremum functional. For the Poisson process Π^λ an explicit expression for

$$\mathsf{P}[\sup_{0\leqslant t\leqslant T}(\Pi_t^\lambda - ct)\leqslant x] = \sigma(x,T) \qquad (x, T\in R_+),$$

with $c\in(0,\infty)$ fixed, has been given by Pyke ([13], Theorem 1), who also treated the limiting case $T=\infty$.

Corollary. *For all* $x\in R_+$, $c\in(0,\infty)$, $T\in R_+$ *there holds*

$$\mathsf{P}[\sup_{0\leqslant t\leqslant T}(Z_t^n - ct)\leqslant x]\to\sigma(x,T) \qquad (n\to\infty).$$

Proof. A result of Lindvall ([11], p. 119) together with a remark of Billingsley ([3], p. 138) yield that the measurable function $h\colon D[0,\infty)\to R$ with

$$h(z) = \sup_{0\leqslant t\leqslant T}(z(t)-ct)$$

is continuous almost everywhere relative to the distribution of Π^λ on the space $D[0,\infty)$ with its Borel field induced by the Skorokhod – Stone J_1-topology. Using Theorem 1 we get convergence in distribution of $h\circ Z_n$ to $h\circ\Pi^\lambda$ by virtue of the continuous mapping theorem in Billingsley [3] (pp. 30-31).

Noticing that $\sigma(\cdot,T)$ is continuous in $(0,\infty)$ we obtain the result for $0<x<\infty$. We now consider the case $x=0$, $0<T<\infty$. The result follows from the obvious inequality

$$\overline{\lim}\,\mathsf{P}[\sup_{0\leqslant t\leqslant T}(Z_t^n - ct)\leqslant 0]\leqslant\sigma(0,T)$$

and the corresponding inequality with $\underline{\lim}$ and $\geqslant$ for the right side. The latter is given by the fact that for $\delta\in\left(0,\min\left\{\frac{1}{c},T\right\}\right)$ there holds

$$P[\sup_{0 \leqslant t \leqslant T} (Z_t^n - ct) \leqslant 0] \geqslant$$

$$\geqslant P[\sup_{\delta \leqslant t \leqslant T} (Z_t^n - ct) \leqslant 0] + P[\sup_{0 \leqslant t < \delta} (Z_t^n - ct) \leqslant 0] - 1$$

with

$$P[\sup_{\delta \leqslant t \leqslant T} (Z_t^n - ct) \leqslant 0] \to P[\sup_{\delta \leqslant t \leqslant T} (\Pi_t^\lambda - ct) \leqslant 0] \qquad (n \to \infty),$$

$$P[\sup_{0 \leqslant t < \delta} (Z_t^n - ct) \leqslant 0] \geqslant P[Z_\delta^n = 0] \to e^{-\lambda\delta} \qquad (n \to \infty).$$

The last limit relation follows from the above Remark which also yields the assertion in the case $x = T = 0$.

Whether the Corollary holds for $T = \infty$, remains open. Obviously there holds

$$\overline{\lim}\, P[\sup_{0 \leqslant t < \infty} (Z_t^n - ct) \leqslant x] \leqslant P[\sup_{0 \leqslant t < \infty} (\Pi_t^\lambda - ct) \leqslant x]$$

for $x \in R_+$, $c \in (0, \infty)$.

3. A GENERALIZATION AND AN APPLICATION

Beside the random variables T_k let us define real-valued random variables Y_j, $j \in N$, on $(\Omega, \mathfrak{A}, P)$ which are identically distributed, with independence of $\{T_k, Y_j;\ k, j \in N\}$. Let $\{\bar{Y}_j;\ j \in N\}$ be a replica of $\{Y_j;\ j \in N\}$ and independent of Π^λ. For $n \in N$, $t \in R_+$ we put

$$V_t^n = Y_1 + \ldots + Y_{Z_t^n}, \qquad V^n = \{V_t^n;\ t \in R_+\},$$

$$V_t = \bar{Y}_1 + \ldots + \bar{Y}_{\Pi_t^\lambda}, \qquad V = \{V_t;\ t \in R_+\}.$$

The random variables Y_j can be interpreted as random losses occuring at the single renewals; V_t^n then denotes the total loss for the time interval $[0, t]$. In the special case $Y_j \equiv 1$ for all $j \in N$ the stochastic processes V^n and the so-called compound Poisson process V coincide with the counting processes Z^n resp. Π^λ. As above we take as basis the space $D[0, \infty)$ with the Skorokhod – Stone J_1-topology and the Borel field induced by it.

Using a device of Pyke [14] and a result of Dudley [4] on the connection between convergence in distribution and almost sure convergence one can derive from Theorem 1′ the following generalization in a straightforward manner.

Theorem 2′. *The distribution of* V^n *converges weakly to the distribution of* V, *as* $n \to \infty$.

As in Chapter 2 one now obtains a generalization of the Corollary given there, in so far as Z^n and Π^λ are replaced by V^n resp. V and $x \in R$ is a continuity point of the distribution function of $\sup_{0 \leq t \leq T} (V_t - ct)$ with $c \in R$, $T \in R_+$. For explicit expressions or at least numerical approximations of these distribution functions see beside Pyke ([13], Theorem 2) e.g. Takács [20], Beekman and Bowers [1] with references.

The Corollary and its generalization just mentioned can be applied in risk theory. A very simple example shall illustrate this applicability.

We assume that apple-blossom occurs periodically and continues for one week. Let the time unit be one year and $n = 52$. Let I_{nj} with $|I_{nj}| = \frac{1}{n}$ be the time interval of apple-blossom in the jth year. Hail occurs according to a renewal process. We record hail at the time of apple-blossom. We assume that a farmer has regular income by his apple-trees. His profits therefore increase in an approximately linear manner, say with rate $\frac{c}{n}$. Furthermore he has an initial capital x. By hail at the time of apple-blossom he suffers a financial loss of size one. Ruin does not occur as long as total loss minus total profit is less than or equal x. We are interested in the probability of ruin for the time interval $[0, nT]$. On the transformed time scale obtained by the thinning procedure we have approximately the time interval $[0, T]$ and a rate of increase c. The probability of ruin is then approximately $1 - \sigma(x, T)$. In the case of non-constant financial losses one has to use a generalization of the Corollary. – This situation also appears at sale of seasonal goods if disturbances occur according to a renewal process.

REFERENCES

[1] J.A. Beekman – N.L. Bowers, Jr., An approximation to the finite time ruin function, II, *Skand. Aktuartidskr.*, 55 (1972), 128-137.

[2] Yu. K. Beljaev, Limit theorems for dissipative flows, *Theory Prob. Appl.*, 8 (1963), 165-173.

[3] P. Billingsley, *Convergence of probability measures,* New York, Wiley, 1968.

[4] R.M. Dudley, Distances of probability measures and random variables, *Ann. Math. Statist.*, 39 (1968), 1563-1572.

[5] W. Feller, *An introduction to probability theory and its applications,* II, New York, Wiley, 1971.

[6] D.L. Iglehart, Diffusion approximations in collective risk theory, *J. Appl. Prob.*, 6 (1969), 285-292.

[7] P. Jagers, On the weak convergence of superpositions of point processes, *Z. Wahrscheinlichkeitstheorie verw. Geb.*, 22 (1972), 1-7.

[8] P. Jagers – T. Lindvall, Thinning and rare events in point processes, *Z. Wahrscheinlichkeitstheorie verw. Geb.*, 28 (1974), 89-98.

[9] D.P. Kennedy, Weak convergence for the superposition and thinning of point processes, Technical Report No. 11, Department of Operations Research, Stanford University (1970).

[10] J. Lamperti, An invariance principle in renewal theory, *Ann. Math. Statist.*, 33 (1962), 685-696.

[11] T. Lindvall, Weak convergence of probability measures and random functions in the function space $D[0, \infty)$, *J. Appl. Prob.*, 10 (1973), 109-121.

[12] K. Nawrotzki, Ein Grenzwertsatz für homogene zufällige Punktfolgen (Verallgemeinerung eines Satzes von A. Rényi), *Math. Nachr.*, 24 (1962), 201-217.

[13] R. Pyke, The supremum and infimum of the Poisson process, *Ann. Math. Statist.*, 30 (1959), 568-576.

[14] R. Pyke, Applications of almost surely convergent constructions of weakly convergent processes, *Probability and information theory,* 187-200, Berlin, Springer, 1969.

[15] A. Rényi, A characterization of the Poisson process, *Magyar Tud. Akad. Mat. Kutató Int. Közl.*, 1 (1956), 519-527 (in Hungarian).

[16] H. Störmer, Zur Überlagerung von Erneuerungsprozessen, *Z. Wahrscheinlichkeitstheorie verw. Geb.*, 13 (1969), 9-24.

[17] C. Stone, Weak convergence of stochastic processes defined on semi-infinite time intervals, *Proc. Amer. Math. Soc.*, 14 (1963), 694-696.

[18] G. Stone, On absolutely continuous components and renewal theory, *Ann. Math. Statist.*, 37 (1966), 271-275.

[19] M. Straf, Weak convergence of stochastic processes with several parameters, *Proc. 6th Berk. Symp. Stat. Prob.*, 2 (1972), 187-221.

[20] L. Takács, *Combinatorial methods in the theory of stochastic processes,* New York, Wiley, 1967.

[21] W. Whitt, Weak convergence of probability measures on the function space $D[0, \infty)$, Technical report, Department of Administrative Sciences, Yale University (1970).